# SUCCESS IN MATHS

## pupil's book

**Rob Kearsley Bullen**
**Andrew Edmondson**
**Tony Ward**

Longman

# CONTENTS

# Brush Up Your Number 1

## Addition and Subtraction of Whole Numbers

### Learn About It

There are lots of different ways of adding whole numbers. Here are three ways to work out **346 + 183**.

> Split 183 into 3, 80 and 100.

Add 3
346 + 3  = 349
Add 80
349 + 80  = 429
Add 100
429 + 100 = 529

> Add the hundreds, tens and units separately.

300 + 100 = 400
40 + 80 = 120
6 + 3 =  9
529

> Then add to find the answers.

> Set it out in columns.

```
  346
+ 183
  529
  1
```

> 1 carried from the 10s column

### Try It Out

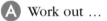 Work out …

**1** 247 + 145      **2** 261 + 172      **3** 358 + 722

**4** 149 + 4576      **5** 2583 + 176      **6** 2345 + 3671

### Learn More About It

You can also subtract in different ways. Here are three ways to work out **347 – 275**.

> Split 275 into 5, 70 and 200.

Subtract 5
347 – 5 =  342
Subtract 70
342 – 70 = 272
Subtract 200
272 – 200 = 72

> Count on from 275.

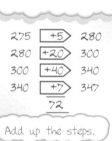

275 | +5 ⟩ 280
280 | +20 ⟩ 300
300 | +40 ⟩ 340
340 | +7 ⟩ 347
72

> Add up the steps.

> Set it out in columns.

```
  2 1
  3̶4̶7̶   1 borrowed
- 275
   72
```

### Try It Out

**B** Work out …

**1** 456 – 234      **2** 362 – 143      **3** 671 – 490

**4** 234 – 153      **5** 2456 – 1937      **6** 1226 – 875

## Practice

A shop puts money from sales into the bank and takes out money for costs. Copy and complete this table. For each starting balance, write the new balance after sales or costs.

| | Money in the bank | | | New bank balance |
|---|---|---|---|---|
| | £10 000 | Sales | £2500 | £12 500 |
| 1 | £25 345 | Sales | £3720 | |
| 2 | £13 500 | Costs | £3500 | |
| 3 | £7 245 | Sales | £2754 | |
| 4 | £3 670 | Sales | £2872 | |
| 5 | £12 624 | Costs | £5436 | |
| 6 | £13 400 | Costs | £2356 | |
| 7 | £16 250 | Sales | £4255 | |
| 8 | £34 576 | Costs | £16 285 | |
| 9 | £125 360 | Sales | £58 243 | |
| 10 | £234 576 | Costs | £108 628 | |

In each question below, there are three calculations. Two have the same answer and one is different. Write down the answer to the odd one out in each set.

1 (a) 275 + 377    (b) 1002 – 350    (c) 204 + 385
2 (a) 398 + 477    (b) 1597 – 703    (c) 2380 – 1486
3 (a) 365 + 498 + 221  (b) 23 682 – 22 348   (c) 16 374 + 8923 – 24 213
4 (a) 56 784 – 23 265  (b) 127 264 – 94 112  (c) 623 242 + 12 456 – 602 546

This map shows six towns and their populations.

1 What is the total population of Calm and Dodge?

2 What is the total population of Elda and Ford?

3 How much bigger is the population of Bedway than of Astor?

4 How much bigger is the population of Ford than of Dodge?

5 How much smaller is the population of Astor than of Ford?

6 How much bigger is the population of Elda than the total population of Calm and Dodge?

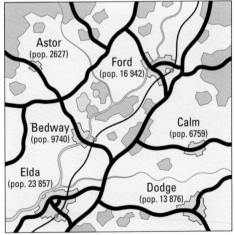

7 What is the difference between the total population of the three smallest towns and the total population of the three largest towns?

8 What is the total population of all six towns?

**Finished Early?**
➡ Go to page 376

# 1 Negative Numbers

In this chapter you will learn about …
1. working with negative numbers
2. adding and subtracting negative numbers
3. multiplying and dividing negative numbers

## T 1 Working with Negative Numbers

### Remember?

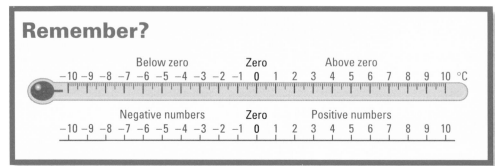

## Try It Out

**A** Draw a temperature scale from –10 °C to 10 °C.

**1** Find the difference between the temperatures in each pair.
(a) 9 °C and 6 °C     (b) –4 °C and 5 °C     (c) –3 °C and –7 °C

**2** Find the new temperature when …
(a) 5 °C falls by 9 °C     (b) –7 °C increases by 5 °C     (c) –3 °C falls by 4 °C

**3** (a) Write down the numbers shown by arrows A to F.

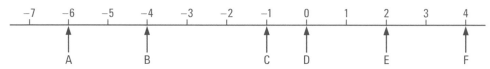

(b) Write down the numbers on the number line that are …
(i) more than zero     (ii) less than 2     (iii) less than –3.

**4** In each pair, how much bigger is the first number than the second?
(a) 2 and –3           (b) –4 and –7
(c) 4 and –5           (d) –1 and –6

## Learn About It

Sharna uses a number line to calculate 3 − 5.

She starts at 3 and moves 5 spaces left. The answer is -2 so she writes 3 − 5 = -2.

Paul calculates 3 − 5 a different way.

He can see the answer will be negative because 5 is bigger than 3.

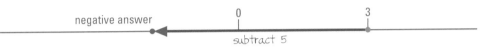

First he calculates the **difference** between 5 and 3:  5 − 3 = 2.

Then he makes the answer negative:  -2.

Paul writes 3 − 5 = -2.

Paul's method works for large numbers too.

He has to calculate -21 + 63.

### Word Check
**difference**  bigger number
 minus smaller number

The answer will be positive because 63 is bigger than 21.

He calculates the difference:  63 − 21 = 42.

Paul writes -21 + 63 = 42.

## Try It Out

**1** Calculate these.

    **(a)** 4 − 7         **(b)** -3 + 6         **(c)** -5 + 3

    **(d)** -5 + 5        **(e)** 0 − 3         **(f)** 2 − 4

**2** Calculate these.

    **(a)** 10 − 40      **(b)** -20 + 30      **(c)** -35 + 10

    **(d)** 50 − 75      **(e)** -14 + 37      **(f)** -100 + 300

## Learn More About It

Emma has to calculate –10 – 30.

She says 'I start at –10 and go down by 30. I'm at –40.'

She writes –10 – 30 = –40.

Emma checks her answer using a number line.

## Try It Out

Ⓒ **1** Calculate the following.

(a) –3 – 6        (b) –20 – 50        (c) –15 – 25

(d) –200 – 100        (e) –32 – 29        (f) –120 – 250

**2** Calculate the following. Check your answers using a number line.

(a) –15 + 25        (b) 20 – 80        (c) –14 – 17

(d) –30 + 12        (e) 57 – 100        (f) –24 – 25

(g) –60 + 39        (h) –460 + 900

## Practice

Ⓓ Calculate the following.

| **Example** | –7.41 + 2.53 |
|---|---|
| **Working** | The number line shows the answer is negative. |
| | 7.41 <br> – 2.53 <br> ―――― <br> 4.88      +2.53    –7.41     ?        0 |
| **Answer** | –4.88 |

**1**   0.5 – 0.7          **2**   –0.3 + 0.8

**3**   –2.3 – 4.8         **4**   0.27 – 0.59

**5**   –1.5 + 6.4         **6**   –0.32 + 0.58

**7**   12.8 – 24.6        **8**   –0.235 + 0.113

**9**   –0.03 – 0.06      **10**   0.08 – 0.1

**11**   –0.005 – 0.032    **12**   –0.629 + 0.384

**13**   48.2 – 65.1       **14**   –5394 – 2875

**15**   16 248 – 80 000    **16**   –429 000 + 294 300

Work out the following long calculations from left to right.

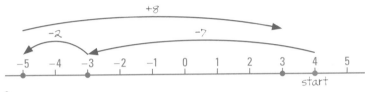

**Example** 4 − 7 − 2 + 8
**Working** 4 − 7 − 2 + 8  (*Work out the first two numbers.*)
= −3 − 2 + 8  (*Write down the answer. Repeat.*)
=  −5 + 8  (*Repeat.*)
=  3  (*Check using a number line.*)

**Answer** 3

**1** 4 − 8 + 3

**2** −2 + 7 − 3

**3** −3 − 2 − 1

**4** −2 + 5 −1 + 3

**5** −2 − 2 − 1 + 4 − 3

**6** −1 + 2 − 3 + 4 − 5 + 6 − 7

**7** −15 + 12 + 5

**8** −10 − 20 − 30

**9** 40 − 60 + 30 − 70 + 80

**10** −100 + 500 − 200 − 600 + 400

**11** 0.5 − 0.2 − 0.1 + 0.8

**12** −1.3 + 0.9 − 1.1 + 0.3 − 0.7

**Finished Early?**
Go to page 376

## Further Practice

Copy and complete the table, working out the output numbers. Put your working underneath the table.

| | Input numbers | | | Machine | Output numbers |
|---|---|---|---|---|---|
| Example | (a) 6 | (b) −8 | (c) −50 | − 10 | (a) −4 (b) −18 (c) −60 |
| 1 | (a) −4 | (b) −9 | (c) −70 | + 6 | |
| 2 | (a) 7 | (b) −10 | (c) −100 | − 15 | |
| 3 | (a) −500 | (b) −65 | (c) −1 | + 100 | |
| 4 | (a) 24 | (b) −6 | (c) −130 | − 72 | |
| 5 | (a) −0.3 | (b) 0.6 | (c) −1.5 | − 0.8 | |
| 6 | (a) −0.368 | (b) −0.149 | (c) −7 | + 0.253 | |
| 7 | (a) −200 | (b) 4800 | (c) −68 500 | − 7500 | |

**Finished Early?**
Go to page 376

# T ❷ Adding and Subtracting Negative Numbers

## Learn About It

Josh has to add together 3 and –5. He writes the negative number in brackets to make it clearer.

3 add –5
= 3 + (–5)

Adding a negative number is the same as subtracting the corresponding positive number.

= 3 – 5
= –2

When Josh subtracts a negative number, he does it like this:

4 – (–3)
= 4 + 3
= 7

Subtracting a negative number is the same as adding the corresponding positive number.

Use the same rules when the starting number is negative.

| **Example 1** Calculate (–6) + (–10) | **Example 2** Calculate (–4) – (–9) |
|---|---|
| **Working**  (–6) + (–10) | **Working**  (–4) – (–9) |
| = (–6) – 10 | = (–4) + 9 |
| = –16 | = 5 |
| **Answer**  –16 | **Answer**  5 |

## Try It Out

**G** Calculate these.

**1** (–2) + 4     **2** 3 – (–5)     **3** (–4) + (–3)

**4** 0 – (–3)     **5** (–6) + (–4)     **6** (–1) + (–2) + (–3)

**7** 6 – (–36)     **8** (–15) + (–15)     **9** 0 + (–2)

**10** (–2) – (–2) – (–2)     **11** 0 – (–18)     **12** (–5) – (–5) – 5

## Practice

**H** Calculate these.

**1** (–25) + (–17)     **2** 150 – (–200)

**3** (–126 )– 48     **4** 37 – (–25)

**5** (–120) + (–420)     **6** (–57) – (–57)

**7** 388 – (–58) + (–35)     **8** (–0.2) – (–0.7) + (–1.6)

**9** 53 000 – 28 500 – (–25 000)     **10** (–100) – 100 – (–100) – (–100) + (–100)

Each number machine has a letter.

E $\boxed{- (-63)}$&gt;   T $\boxed{+ (-5)}$&gt;   A $\boxed{- (-110)}$&gt;   O $\boxed{+ (-12)}$&gt;   N $\boxed{- 41}$&gt;

I $\boxed{+ 10}$&gt;   S $\boxed{+ (-250)}$&gt;   H $\boxed{+ 85}$&gt;   R $\boxed{- (-7)}$&gt;   D $\boxed{- 19}$&gt;

A word makes a set of calculations.

| | |
|---|---|
| **Example** | $6 \rightarrow$ **HI** |
| **Working** | $6$ $\boxed{+ 85}$&gt;—$\boxed{+ 10}$&gt; |
| | $= 6 + 85 + 10$ |
| | $= 91 + 10$ |
| **Answer** | 101 |

**1** $3 \rightarrow$ **IT**

**3** $0 \rightarrow$ **NET**

**5** $-4 \rightarrow$ **ROAR**

**7** $500 \rightarrow$ **SHRED**

**9** $312 \rightarrow$ **RETIRED**

**2** $12 \rightarrow$ **ROD**

**4** $50 \rightarrow$ **SHIRT**

**6** $-1 \rightarrow$ **DRAIN**

**8** $-50 \rightarrow$ **HOSE**

**10** $0 \rightarrow$ **ASTONISHED**

**Finished Early?**
➡ Go to page 377

# Further Practice

In each question below, there are three calculations. Two have the same answer and one is different. Write the answer to the odd one out in each set.

| | |
|---|---|
| **Example** | **(a)** $6 - (-4)$   **(b)** $-4 + (-6)$   **(c)** $(-6) + (-4)$ |
| **Working** | **(a)** $6 - (-4) = 6 + 4 = 10$ |
| | **(b)** $(-4) + (-6) = (-4) - 6 = -10$ |
| | **(c)** $(-6) + (-4) = (-6) - 4 = -10$ |
| **Answer** | **(a)** 10 |

**1 (a)** $5 + (-2)$   **(b)** $(-2) - (-5)$   **(c)** $(-5) - (-2)$

**2 (a)** $(-4) - 7$   **(b)** $(-7) + (-4)$   **(c)** $7 - 4$

**3 (a)** $20 + (-30)$   **(b)** $(-30) - 20$   **(c)** $10 + (-20)$

**4 (a)** $(-100) + (-200)$   **(b)** $(-100) - 200$   **(c)** $(-200) - (-100)$

**5 (a)** $(-56) + (-25)$   **(b)** $(-42) + (-36)$   **(c)** $15 + (-93)$

**6 (a)** $(-194) + (-63)$   **(b)** $252 - 145$   **(c)** $(-273) - (-16)$

**7 (a)** $0.7 + (-0.3)$   **(b)** $0.3 - (-0.7)$   **(c)** $(-0.3) - (-0.7)$

**8 (a)** $(-0.25) - (-0.25)$   **(b)** $0.75 - (-0.5)$   **(c)** $0.25 - (-1)$

**9 (a)** $(-52) - 34 + (-24)$   **(b)** $14 + (-26) - 56$   **(c)** $(-74) + (-32) + 38$

**10 (a)** $593 + (-231) - (-154)$   **(b)** $(-189) + 865 + (-160)$

**(c)** $1000 + (-231) - (-175)$

**Finished Early?**
➡ Go to page 377

# P ❸ Multiplying and Dividing Negative Numbers

## Remember?
- Always use the correct order of operations in calculations.
  Remember this as BoDMAS:
  **B**rackets first
  **P**owers
  **D**ivide and **M**ultiply (work from left to right)
  **A**dd and **S**ubtract (work from left to right)
- To square a number, multiply it by itself, e.g. the square of 7 is $7 \times 7 = 49$.
  Write the square of 7 like this: $7^2$. You say '7 squared'. So $7^2 = 7 \times 7 = 49$.

## Try It Out

**K** Calculate these.

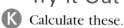

**1** $4 + 2 \times 3$       **2** $2 \times 6 \div 3$       **3** $9 \times 2 - 5$

**4** $2 + 6 \div 3 - 1$     **5** $3 \times (8 - 2)$        **6** $16 \div (4 \div 2)$

**7** $12 - (9 - 7)$         **8** $3 + (4 + 1) \times 6 - 2$  **9** $4^2$

**10** the square of 8       **11** nine squared             **12** $18 \div 2 + 4$

## Learn About It

Sam has to multiply the numbers 3 and –2 together.
She writes the calculation like this: $3 \times (-2)$.

Sam uses these rules to decide if the answer is
negative or positive:

3 is positive and –2 is negative, so Sam uses
the rule: $+ \times -$ gives $-$ .
The answer is negative.

| Same signs give + | Different signs give − |
|---|---|
| $+ \times +$ gives $+$ <br> $- \times -$ gives $+$ | $+ \times -$ gives $-$ <br> $- \times +$ gives $-$ |

Sam knows that $3 \times 2 = 6$.
So, $3 \times (-2) = -6$.

**1** Check this using your calculator. Don't forget the brackets.

**2** Calculate these.

   **(a)** $4 \times (-5)$       **(b)** $7 \times (-10)$       **(c)** $11 \times (-11)$

Sam multiplies 3 and –2 the other way around this time: $(-2) \times 3$. She uses the
rule: $- \times +$ gives $-$ and finds that the answer is negative.

Sam knows that $2 \times 3 = 6$ and so $(-2) \times 3 = -6$.
The answer is the same as for $3 \times (-2)$.

**3** Calculate these.
   **(a)** $(-4) \times 3$       **(b)** $(-10) \times 5$       **(c)** $(-12) \times 15$

Sam now has to multiply –4 and –5 together.
She writes the calculation like this: $(-4) \times (-5)$.
Sam uses the rule $- \times -$ gives $+$ and finds that the answer is positive.
She knows that $4 \times 5 = 20$ and so $(-4) \times (-5) = 20$.

**4** Calculate these.
   **(a)** $(-6) \times (-2)$       **(b)** $(-7) \times (-7)$       **(c)** $(-12) \times (-3)$

**5** $3^2$ means $3 \times 3$.
   So $(-3)^2$ means $(-3) \times (-3)$.
   **(a)** Work out $3^2$.      **(b)** Work out $(-3)^2$.
   What do you notice?

**6** Calculate these.
   **(a)** $(-5)^2$
   **(b)** $(-12)^2$
   **(c)** the square of –2

## Key Fact
Squaring a negative number gives a positive answer.

## Try It Out
Calculate these. First decide if the answer is positive or negative.

**1** $(-4) \times 3$     **2** $(-2) \times (-5)$     **3** $6 \times (-2)$
**4** $(-10) \times 7$     **5** $(-12) \times 9$     **6** $(-4)^2$
**7** $15 \times (-4)$     **8** $20 \times (-20)$     **9** $(-23) \times 14$
**10** $(-120) \times (-7)$     **11** the square of –10     **12** $(-6) - 3$

## Learn More About It
Use these rules to divide numbers. They are the same as for multiplying.

| Same signs give + | Different signs give − |
|---|---|
| $+ \div +$ gives $+$ <br> $- \div -$ gives $+$ | $+ \div -$ gives $-$ <br> $- \div +$ gives $-$ |

**Example**   $10 \div (-2)$
**Working**   The rule $+ \div -$ gives $-$ shows the answer is negative.
            $10 \div 2 = 5$
**Answer**    $-5$

# Try It Out

 Work out these calculations. First decide if the answer is positive or negative.

| | |
|---|---|
| **Example** | $\dfrac{-12}{-3}$ |
| **Working** | $\dfrac{-12}{-3}$ means the same as $(-12) \div (-3)$. |
| | The rule $- \div -$ gives $+$ shows the answer is positive. |
| | $12 \div 3 = 4$ |
| **Answer** | $4$ |

**1** $8 \div (-4)$  **2** $(-6) \div (-2)$  **3** $(-18) \div 3$  **4** $\dfrac{-15}{5}$

**5** $\dfrac{4}{-4}$  **6** $\dfrac{-14}{-7}$  **7** $(-40) \div 8$  **8** $(-68) \div (-2)$

**9** $\dfrac{135}{-5}$  **10** $312 \div (-13)$

# Practice

 Copy and complete the table, working out the output numbers.

 Put your working underneath the table.

| | Input numbers | | | Machine | Output numbers |
|---|---|---|---|---|---|
| Example | **(a)** 4 | **(b)** −12 | **(c)** −100 | × (−2) | **(a)** 8 **(b)** 24 **(c)** 200 |
| 1 | **(a)** −5 | **(b)** −30 | **(c)** −200 | × 3 | |
| 2 | **(a)** 8 | **(b)** −12 | **(c)** −50 | ÷ (−2) | |
| 3 | **(a)** 12 | **(b)** −46 | **(c)** 123 | ÷ (−5) | |
| 4 | **(a)** −0.5 | **(b)** −3.2 | **(c)** −0.07 | × 8 | |
| 5 | **(a)** −0.6 | **(b)** −1.8 | **(c)** −10 | ÷ 0.2 | |
| 6 | **(a)** −0.7 | **(b)** −2.5 | **(c)** −0.45 | × 0.2 | |
| 7 | **(a)** −10 | **(b)** 0.5 | **(c)** 0.75 | ÷ (−0.05) | |
| 8 | **(a)** −30 | **(b)** −8000 | **(c)** −29 000 | × 2000 | |
| 9 | **(a)** 4000 | **(b)** −1 000 000 | **(c)** 200 | ÷ (−500) | |

Calculate the following.

| | |
|---|---|
| **Example** | $3 + 4 \times (-2)$ |
| **Working** | $3 + 4 \times (-2)$ (*Multiply first.*) |
| | $= 3 + (-8)$ |
| | $= 3 - 8$ |
| | $= -5$ |
| **Answer** | $-5$ |

| | |
|---|---|
| **Example** | $(-2) \times (-12) \div (-3)$ |
| **Working** | $(-2) \times (-12) \div (-3)$ (*Work from left to right.*) |
| | $= 24 \div (-3)$ |
| | $= -8$ |
| **Answer** | $-8$ |

**1** $6 + (-3) \times 4$　　　**2** $(-14) \div 7 + 5$　　　**3** $12 \div (-3) \times 2$

**4** $1 - 4 \times (-2)$　　　**5** $5 \times (-4) \div 2$　　　**6** $(-3) + 6 \div (-2)$

**7** $(-8) \div (-2) + 3$　　**8** $(-12) - (-3) \times 2$　　**9** $(-3)^2 - 6$

**10** $10 - (-6)^2$　　　　**11** $(-4) \times 6 + 2$

> **Finished Early?**
> Go to page 377

# Further Practice

Work out which pairs of jigsaw pieces go together and write the pairs of letters.

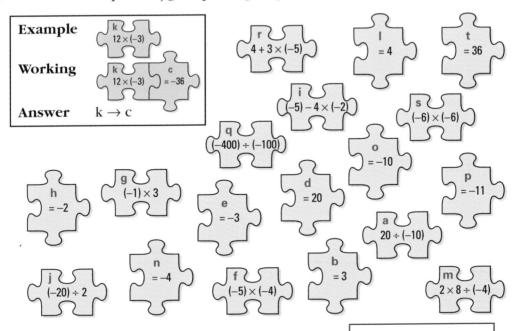

| | |
|---|---|
| **Example** | k $12 \times (-3)$ |
| **Working** | k $12 \times (-3)$　c $= -36$ |
| **Answer** | $k \rightarrow c$ |

r $4 + 3 \times (-5)$

l $= 4$

t $= 36$

i $(-5) - 4 \times (-2)$

s $(-6) \times (-6)$

q $(-400) \div (-100)$

o $= -10$

p $= -11$

h $= -2$

g $(-1) \times 3$

e $= -3$

d $= 20$

a $20 \div (-10)$

j $(-20) \div 2$

n $= -4$

f $(-5) \times (-4)$

b $= 3$

m $2 \times 8 \div (-4)$

> **Finished Early?**
> Go to page 377

# 2 Line Graphs

In this chapter you will learn about ...
1. reading graphs
2. drawing graphs

## 1 Reading Graphs

### Remember?

In a line graph, points are joined by straight lines.

The scales on the axes are important; they do not have to start from 0.

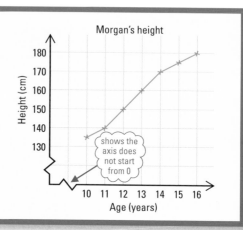

Morgan's height

shows the axis does not start from 0

## Try It Out

A When Kate was in hospital, her temperature was recorded every hour on a graph.

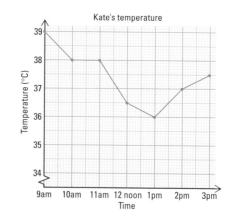

Kate's temperature

1 What was Kate's temperature at 11am?
2 What was Kate's temperature at 2pm?
3 What was Kate's highest temperature?
4 What was Kate's lowest temperature?
5 When was Kate's temperature 38 °C?
6 When was Kate's temperature 36.5 °C?
7 How much did Kate's temperature fall between 11am and 12 noon?
8 How much did Kate's temperature rise between 1pm and 3pm?

Andy was also in hospital and his temperature was taken every hour.

Graph paper

**1** Draw a line graph to show the following information.

| Time | 9am | 10am | 11am | 12 noon | 1pm | 2pm | 3pm | 4pm |
|---|---|---|---|---|---|---|---|---|
| Temperature (°C) | 36 | 35 | 37 | 38 | 38 | 39 | 38 | 37.5 |

**2** When was Andy's temperature lowest?

**3** What was Andy's highest temperature?

**4** When was Andy's temperature 37 °C?

## Learn About It

Jason weighed himself on his birthday every year and drew a graph.

You can see that when Jason was 9 he weighed 25 kg.

When Jason was $9\frac{1}{2}$ he probably did not weigh exactly $27\frac{1}{2}$ kg. This is an **estimate** of his weight.

The line on the graph is steepest when Jason's weight increased most quickly. His fastest increase in weight was between the ages of 12 and 13.

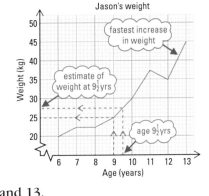

## Try It Out

The graph shows the sales of a company, Techno Toys, for six months.

**1** What were the sales in July? (Note that the sales axis is in thousands.)

**2** In which two months were the sales figures the same?

**3** When were the sales £40 000?

**4** Between which two months did the sales increase the most?

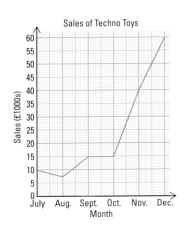

## Key Fact

The steeper the line, the faster the increase or decrease.

## Word Check

**estimate** a guess at a value, based on what you know

## Practice

**D 1** The graph shows how the price of one share in Techno Toys changes in a week.

(a) What was the share price on Sunday?

(b) What was the share price on Monday?

(c) When was the share price 125p?

(d) What was the highest share price?

(e) When was the biggest increase in the share price?

(f) When was the biggest decrease in the share price?

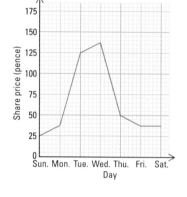

**2** The temperature of a cup of coffee is recorded every 2 minutes and a graph is drawn to show the coffee cooling.

(a) What was the temperature of the coffee at the start?

(b) What was the temperature of the coffee after 4 minutes?

(c) What was the temperature of the coffee after 10 minutes?

(d) When was the temperature 53 °C?

(e) Estimate the temperature after 3 minutes.

(f) Estimate the temperature after 11 minutes.

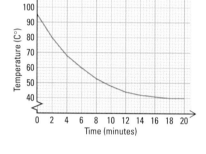

**3** This graph shows the sales of two cars, the Aurora and the Branco, for six months at the start of a year.

(a) What were the sales of the Aurora in January?

(b) What were the sales of the Branco in January?

(c) What were the smallest sales of the Aurora?

(d) When were the sales of the two cars equal?

(e) For what months were the sales of the Branco higher than of the Aurora?

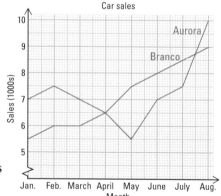

**1** A mobile phone company, Fairphone, charges its customers a fixed rate for the calls they make. Fairphone charges are shown in red on the graph.

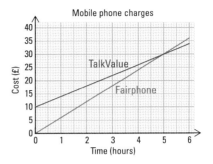

Mobile phone charges

(a) What is the cost of 5 hours of calls?

(b) What is the cost of 3 hours of calls?

(c) How much time would £15 of calls take?

(d) How much time would £24 of calls take?

**2** A second mobile phone company, TalkValue, charges its customers a fixed monthly charge and then a fixed rate for calls. TalkValue charges are shown in blue on the graph above.

(a) What is the cost of 5 hours of calls?

(b) What is the cost of 3 hours of calls?

(c) How much time would £15 of calls take?

(d) How much time would £24 of calls take?

(e) After how many hours do TalkValue and Fairphone cost the same?

**3** Which of the phone companies, Fairphone or TalkValue, would be cheaper if you made …

(a) 2 hours of calls?

(b) 6 hours of calls?

(c) very few phone calls?

(d) a lot of phone calls?

**Finished Early?**

➡ Go to page 378

# Further Practice

**F** **1** This graph shows the mean daily
temperatures for Birmingham and
Newcastle for the first 15 days of July.

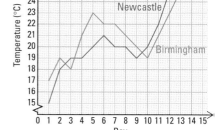

Mean daily temperature

   **(a)** What was Birmingham's highest
     temperature and on what day did
     it occur?
   **(b)** What was Newcastle's highest
     temperature and on what day
     did it occur?
   **(c)** On what day was Birmingham's temperature 20 °C?
   **(d)** On what day was Newcastle's temperature 21 °C?
   **(e)** What was the difference between the temperatures in the two cities
     on the fifth day?
   **(f)** For how many days was the temperature in Newcastle higher than the
     temperature in Birmingham?

**2** Every 2 minutes for half an hour a TV
company recorded the number of people
watching Megamovies. They produced
this graph.

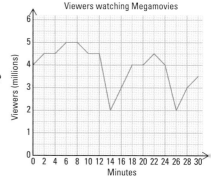

Viewers watching Megamovies

   **(a)** What was the largest number of viewers?
   **(b)** Estimate how many viewers there were
     after 11 minutes.
   **(c)** Estimate how many viewers there were
     after 25 minutes.
   **(d)** Estimate when 3.5 million viewers were
     watching.
   **(e)** When do you think the advertisements were being shown?

**G** The graph shows the connection between
the Hong Kong dollar and the Swiss franc.

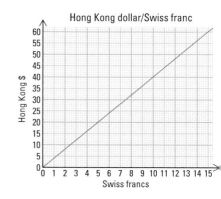

Hong Kong dollar/Swiss franc

**1** How many Swiss francs are there in
   20 Hong Kong dollars?

**2** How many Swiss francs are there in
   50 Hong Kong dollars?

**3** How many Hong Kong dollars are there in
   7 Swiss francs?

**4** How many Hong Kong dollars are there in
   11 Swiss francs?

**5** Which is worth more, 10 Swiss francs or
   30 Hong Kong dollars?

**Finished Early?**
➡ Go to page 378

# Drawing Graphs

Graph paper

## Learn About It

Jason recorded the sales in his school shop over eight weeks.

| Week | 1 | 2 | 3 | 4 | 5 | 6 | 7 | 8 |
|------|---|---|---|---|---|---|---|---|
| Sales (£) | 27 | 30 | 33 | 31 | 30 | 33 | 34 | 35 |

1 Draw a graph of these sales with the weeks on the horizontal axis and the sales on the vertical axis. Make the scale 2 cm to 1 week horizontally and 1 cm to £10 vertically. **Label** the axes and plot each point with a small cross (×). Join the points with straight lines.

2 Draw a new graph using the same data. The horizontal axis already uses the width of the page so leave it alone. A lot of the vertical axis is wasted so start from £25 by using the ⩘ symbol and a scale of 1 cm to £5.

3 Draw a new graph, starting the vertical scale from £25 and making the scale 1 cm to £1. This graph spreads out the vertical scale.

**All** of these methods are correct. If you are not told the scale to use for a graph, check the range of values you need to cover and then choose a suitable scale to go from the lowest to the highest value.

## Try It Out

The table shows the number of ice-creams sold by a shop each month for a year.

| Month | Jan. | Feb. | Mar. | Apr. | May | June | July | Aug. | Sept. | Oct. | Nov. | Dec. |
|-------|------|------|------|------|-----|------|------|------|-------|------|------|------|
| Ice-creams sold | 23 | 21 | 30 | 73 | 52 | 94 | 100 | 150 | 110 | 61 | 70 | 40 |

1 Draw a graph of the data using a scale of 1 cm to 1 month on the horizontal axis and 1 cm to 10 sales on the vertical axis.

2 Which month had the highest sales?

3 Between which months did sales increase the most?

4 Between which months did sales decrease the most?

# Learn More About It

You can draw a **conversion graph** for metres and feet. (Feet are imperial units of length.) One metre is about 3 feet.

Suppose you want to convert lengths up to 12 m. This gives the maximum value on one axis. The other axis must go up to at least 36 feet (12 × 3).

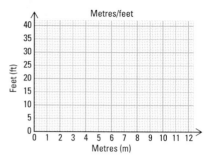

1 Draw these axes with a scale of 1 cm to 1 m horizontally and 1 cm to 5 feet vertically.

2 Take a number of metres (10, say) and work out how many feet that is (10 × 3 = 30 feet). This gives one point on the graph. Repeat this for two more points, starting with different numbers of metres.

3 Now plot your three points. You should find your points are in a straight line. Draw the line. It should pass through zero. You can now use this line to convert between metres and feet.

# Try It Out

**I** A New Zealand dollar is worth 2.5 Malaysian ringgits.

1 Draw a conversion graph for converting a maximum of 40 dollars to ringgits.

2 From your graph, find …
   (a) how many ringgits equal 15 New Zealand dollars
   (b) how many ringgits equal 23 New Zealand dollars
   (c) how many New Zealand dollars equal 52 ringgits
   (d) how many New Zealand dollars equal 33 ringgits.

# Practice

**J** 1 Jagdesh did an experiment in which the temperature of a liquid varied. He recorded the temperature of the liquid every 5 minutes for an hour.

| Time (minutes) | 0 | 5 | 10 | 15 | 20 | 25 | 30 | 35 | 40 | 45 | 50 | 55 | 60 |
|---|---|---|---|---|---|---|---|---|---|---|---|---|---|
| Temperature (°C) | 40 | 50 | 55 | 75 | 80 | 100 | 65 | 60 | 60 | 60 | 55 | 35 | 40 |

   (a) Draw a line graph to show how the temperature changed over time. Use a scale of 1 cm to 5 minutes horizontally and 1 cm to 5 °C vertically. Label the axes clearly.
   (b) What was the highest temperature?
   (c) What was the lowest temperature?
   (d) Estimate the temperature after 12 minutes.
   (e) At what times was the temperature 65 °C?

**2** The price of one share in Mega Industries during a day's trading is shown in this table.

| Time | 9am | 10am | 11am | 12 noon | 1pm | 2pm | 3pm | 4pm |
|---|---|---|---|---|---|---|---|---|
| Share price (£) | 4.00 | 3.00 | 1.80 | 0.50 | 1.10 | 1.75 | 2.25 | 2.75 |

   **(a)** Draw a graph to show how the share prices varied.
   **(b)** What was the lowest share price?
   **(c)** Estimate the share price at 10.30am.
   **(d)** When did the share price rise most quickly?

**1** The pint is an imperial unit of capacity. One litre is approximately 2 pints.
   **(a)** Draw a conversion graph to convert up to 40 litres into pints.
   **(b)** What is 30 litres in pints?
   **(c)** What is 37 pints in litres?

**2** The inch is an imperial unit of length. One inch is approximately 2.54 cm.
   **(a)** Draw a conversion graph to convert up to 10 inches into centimetres.
   **(b)** What is 4 inches in centimetres?
   **(c)** What is 12 cm in inches?

**3** To find the number of minutes needed to cook a joint of meat, you multiply the weight in kilograms by 40 and then add 30.
   **(a)** Find the time needed to cook a joint of **(i)** 2 kg **(ii)** 4 kg **(iii)** 6 kg.
   **(b)** Draw a conversion graph to show the cooking times for joints up to 6 kg.
   **(c)** What is the cooking time for a joint of 5 kg?
   **(d)** What is the cooking time for a joint of 2.5 kg?

> **Finished Early?**
> ➡ Go to page 378

## Further Practice

The sales figures for Mega Industries are given in this table.

| Month | Jan. | Feb. | Mar. | Apr. | May | June | July | Aug. | Sept. | Oct. | Nov. | Dec. |
|---|---|---|---|---|---|---|---|---|---|---|---|---|
| Sales (£1 000 000s) | 150 | 145 | 145 | 150 | 145 | 140 | 130 | 135 | 130 | 130 | 125 | 130 |

**1** Draw a graph to show Mega Industries' monthly sales.
**2** Between which months did the sales fall most steeply?
**3** When were the sales £140 000 000?

One mile is approximately equal to 1.6 km.
**1** Draw a graph to convert distances of up to 26 miles into km.
**2** What is 12 miles in km?
**3** What is 40 km in miles?
**4** What is 23 km in miles?

> **Finished Early?**
> ➡ Go to page 378

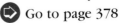

# Unit 1 *Negative Numbers and Line Graphs*

## Summary of Chapters 1 and 2

- Adding a negative number is the same as subtracting the corresponding positive number: $3 + (-2) = 3 - 2 = 1$.
- Subtracting a negative number is the same as adding the corresponding positive number: $6 - (-4) = 6 + 4 = 10$.
- Multiplying and dividing both follow the same rules:

| Same signs give + | Different signs give − |
|---|---|
| + × + gives +<br>+ ÷ + gives + | + × − gives −<br>+ ÷ − gives − |
| − × − gives +<br>− ÷ − gives + | − × + gives −<br>− ÷ + gives − |

- When you square a negative number, the answer is positive, e.g. $(-3)^2 = (-3) \times (-3) = 9$.

- **Line graphs** are often used in real life. Points are plotted and joined by straight lines. You can **estimate** the value between the plotted points.

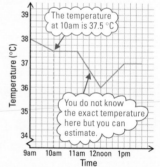

The temperature at 10am is 37.5 °C

You do not know the exact temperature here but you can estimate.

- **Conversion graphs** are used to show a link between two quantities. This graph allows you to calculate the wages for any number of hours' work up to 11. The dotted lines show that someone can earn £45 for $7\frac{1}{2}$ hours' work.

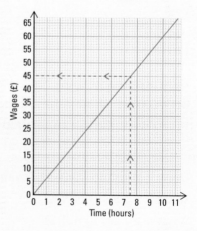

# Brush Up Your Number 2

## Computation Shortcuts and Patterns

### Learn About It

You can multiply a whole number by 10, 100, 1000, etc. by moving its digits to the left. Fill the empty places with zeros.

So $24 \times 10 = 240$, $24 \times 100 = 2400$, $24 \times 1000 = 24\,000$.

You can divide whole numbers ending in zero by 10, 100, 1000, etc. by moving digits to the right and dropping zeros.

So $240 \div 10 = 24$, $5300 \div 100 = 53$, $2\,740\,000 \div 1000 = 2740$.

### Try It Out

Work out the following.

**1** $35 \times 10$     **2** $143 \times 100$     **3** $752 \times 1000$

**4** $450 \div 10$     **5** $26\,000 \div 100$     **6** $35\,200\,000 \div 1000$

### Learn More About It

You can multiply or divide numbers by dealing with the zeros and the other digits separately.

Multiply the non-zero digits, then move the correct number of places.

$7 \times 3 = 21$, so $7 \times 30 = 210$, $70 \times 3 = 210$, $70 \times 30 = 2100$, $700 \times 30 = 21\,000$.

To divide, remove the same number of zeros from each number and then divide the rest of the number.

$21 \div 7 = 3$ and so $2100 \div 70 = 30$, $2100 \div 700 = 3$.

### Try It Out

Work out the following.

**1** $8 \times 30$     **2** $60 \times 4$     **3** $60 \times 40$

**4** $600 \times 400$     **5** $240 \div 30$     **6** $3600 \div 300$

**7** $40\,000 \div 800$     **8** $25\,000 \div 5000$     **9** $6000 \div 40$

**10** $400 \div 80$     **11** $63\,000 \div 70$     **12** $63\,000 \div 9000$

# Practice

**C** Mega Supplies makes these items and sells them. Copy and complete this table.

| Item | Cost (£) | Number | Total cost (£) |
|---|---|---|---|
| Filing cabinet | 80 | 240 | |
| Desk | 200 | 150 | |
| Table | 350 | 120 | |
| Settee | 900 | 90 | |
| Armchair | 550 | 130 | |
| Wardrobe | 240 | | 72 000 |
| Chest of drawers | 150 | | 10 500 |
| Kitchen units | | 230 | 42 550 |
| Garden seat | | 400 | 94 000 |
| Garden shed | 250 | | 40 000 |

**D** The table shows the length, width and area of rectangular fields. Copy and complete the table.

| Length (m) | Width (m) | Area (m²) |
|---|---|---|
| 120 | 50 | |
| 400 | 120 | |
| 300 | | 30 000 |
| | 250 | 100 000 |
| 160 | | 6 400 |
| 1 250 | 900 | |
| 750 | | 150 000 |
| 850 | 600 | |

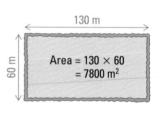

130 m

60 m

Area = 130 × 60
= 7800 m²

**E** In each question below, there are three calculations. Two have the same answer and one is different. Write down the answer to the odd one out in each set.

**1** (a) $120 \times 40$     (b) $6 \times 800$     (c) $1200 \times 3$

**2** (a) $900 \times 800$     (b) $3000 \times 120$     (c) $240 \times 3000$

**3** (a) $25\,000 \times 40$     (b) $100 \times 1000$     (c) $10\,000 \times 100$

**4** (a) $1600 \div 40$     (b) $4000 \div 10$     (c) $200 \times 2$

**5** (a) $30\,000 \div 60$     (b) $25\,000 \div 50$     (c) $50 \times 500$

**6** (a) $40 \times 80\,000$     (b) $64\,000\,000 \div 20$     (c) $2000 \times 200 \div 40$

> **Finished Early?**
>  Go to page 379

# 3 Angles

In this chapter you will learn about ...
1. angle facts
2. parallel lines

## Angle Facts

### Remember?
- Angles on a straight line add up to 180°.
  The red and the blue angles in this
  diagram add up to 180°.
- Angles at a point add up to 360°.
- You can find unknown angles using these facts.

## Try It Out

Work out the angles marked with ?.

**1**
135° ?

**2**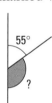
55°
?

**3**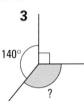
140°
?

**4**
120° 120°
?

**5**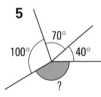
70°
100° 40°
?

## Learn About It

Protractor
**1** Measure the angles in this triangle.
Draw four more triangles, of different
shapes, and measure their
angles. Write down the sum
of the angles in each
case. What do
you notice?

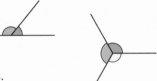

a     b     c

**2** When two straight lines cross, they form four angles.
Draw four pairs of crossing lines and measure their angles.

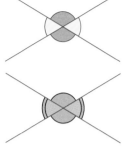

**3** The angles opposite each other where the lines cross are
called **vertically opposite angles**. The blue angles are a
pair of vertically opposite angles. So are the red angles. Write
down what you notice about these angles in your diagrams.

## Try It Out

**B** Work out the angles shown by letters.

---

**Example**

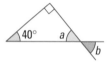

**Working**   $a = 180 - (90 + 40) = 180 - 130 = 50°$   (*The angles in a
triangle add up to 180°.*)

$b = 50°$                          (*a and b are vertically
opposite angles.*)

**Answer**    $a = 50°$,  $b = 50°$

---

**1**
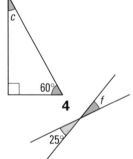

**2**
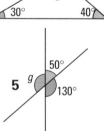

**3**
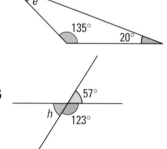

**4**

**5**

**6**

---

## Key Facts

Angles on a straight
line add up to 180°.

Angles in a triangle
add up to 180°.
$a + b + c = 180°$

Angles at a point
add up to 360°.

Vertically opposite
angles are equal.

---

## Practice

If Arnie the abstract artist knows some angles in his paintings, he can work out others. Work out the angles shown by letters.

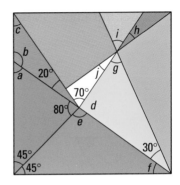

Work out the angles shown by letters.

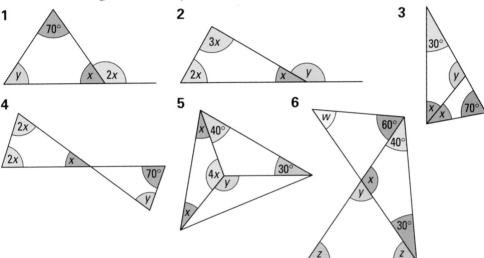

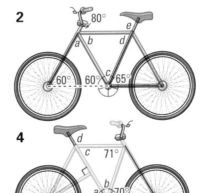

## Further Practice

Superbike make bicycles. These are some of their designs. Calculate the angles shown by letters.

**Finished Early?**
Go to page 379

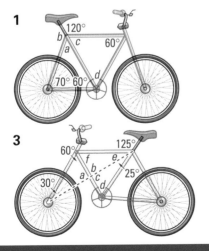

**F** Work out the angles shown by letters.

**1**
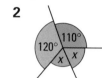

**2**
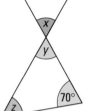

**3**
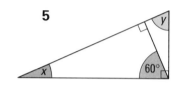

**4**
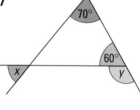

**5**
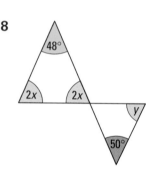

**6**

**7**

**8**

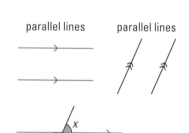

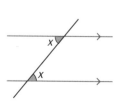

Finished Early?
➡ Go to page 379

T **2 Parallel Lines**

## Learn About It

Parallel lines never meet. They stay the same distance apart.

Arrows on the lines show they are parallel.

When a straight line crosses a pair of parallel lines, some pairs of angles at the crossing points are the same.

Angles in the same position on the two lines are equal. These are called **corresponding angles**.

**Alternate angles** are either side of the crossing lines *inside* the parallel lines. They are sometimes called Z angles. Alternate angles are also equal.

parallel lines          parallel lines

**Example** Calculate the angles shown by letters. Give reasons for your answers.

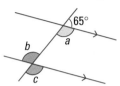

$180° - 65° = 115$

**Answer** $a = 180° - 65° = 115°$ (*Angles on a straight line*)
$b = a = 115°$ (*Alternate angles*)
$c = a = 115°$ (*Corresponding angles*)

# Try It Out

Copy each of these diagrams and mark the angle corresponding to angle $x$.

**1** 　　**2** 　　**3**

**4** 　　**5** 　　**6**

Calculate the angles shown by letters.

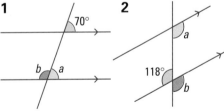

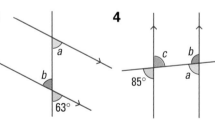

## Key Facts

Corresponding angles are equal.
Alternate angles are equal.

## Practice

**I** Calculate the angles shown by letters. Give reasons for your answers.

**1**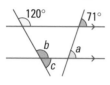

**2**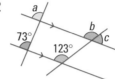

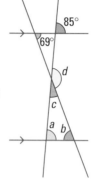

**3**

**4**

**5**

**J** Sketch these diagrams. Fill in the sizes of all the angles you can work out.

**1**

**2**

**3**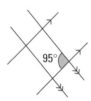

**4** **5** **6**

## Further Practice

**K** A farm has some fields with parallel sides. Copy the diagram of the farm. Using the angles given, calculate and fill in all the angles in the fields.

**Finished Early?**
Go to page 380

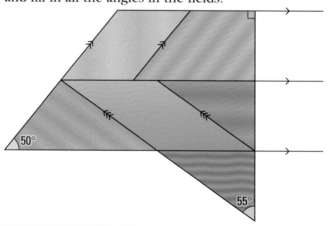

**Finished Early?**
Go to page 380

# Quadrilaterals and Polygons

In this chapter you will learn about ...
1. quadrilaterals
2. angle sums of polygons
3. interior and exterior angles
4. regular polygons

## Quadrilaterals

### Remember?

Any shape with four straight sides is called a **quadrilateral**.

There are lots of special quadrilaterals.
A **trapezium** has one pair of parallel sides.

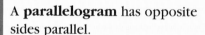

A **parallelogram** has opposite sides parallel.

This shape is called a **kite**.
It has two pairs of adjacent sides equal.

## Learn About It

When you join opposite corners of a quadrilateral you make two triangles. The red and the blue angles each add up to 180°.

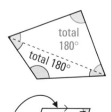
total 180°
total 180°

The angles in a quadrilateral add up to 360°.

There are several special quadrilaterals.

Parallelograms have opposite sides and angles equal. The angles marked in the parallelogram on the right are equal.

sides equal  angles equal
**parallelogram**

A rectangle is a special parallelogram. All its angles are 90°.

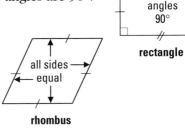

**rectangle**

A rhombus is another special parallelogram. All its sides are equal. Equal sides are shown by dashes.

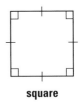

**rhombus**

A square has four equal sides and four 90° angles.

**square**

## Try It Out

**(A)** Sketch these shapes and write their names below them.

**1**   **2**   **3**   **4**

**5**   **6**

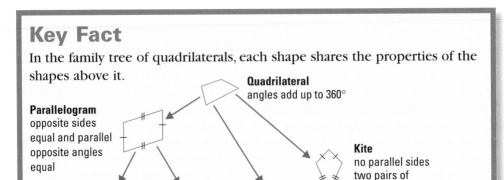

## Key Fact

In the family tree of quadrilaterals, each shape shares the properties of the shapes above it.

**Quadrilateral**
angles add up to 360°

**Parallelogram**
opposite sides
equal and parallel
opposite angles
equal

**Kite**
no parallel sides
two pairs of
adjacent sides
equal

**Rhombus**
all sides
equal

**Rectangle**
all angles 90°

**Trapezium**
one pair of
parallel sides

**Square**
all sides equal
all angles 90°

# Practice

Calculate the angles and sides shown by letters. Give reasons for your answers.

**Example**

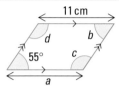

**Working**   $a = 11$ cm (*Opposite sides of parallelogram are equal.*)
$b = 55°$ (*Opposite angles of parallelogram are equal.*)
$c + d = 250°$ (*Angles of quadrilateral add up to 360°.*)
$c = d$ (*Opposite angles of parallelogram equal.*)
$c = 125°, d = 125°$

**Answer**   $a = 11$ cm, $b = 55°, c = 125°, d = 125°$

**1**   **2**  **3** 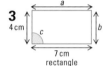 **4**  **5**

**6**    **7**   **8**    **9** 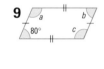   **10**

Some of the figures below are correctly labelled and some are not. For each, either write *correct* or explain why it is wrong.

**Example**

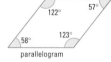
parallelogram

**Answer**   Incorrect. The opposite angles are not equal.

**1**    **2**   **3** 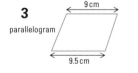   **4**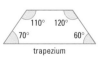

**5**   **6**    **7** 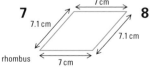   **8**

**Finished Early?**
➡ Go to page 380

# Further Practice

**D** Sketch these figures. Fill in the sizes of as many sides and angles as you can work out.

**1**   **2**   **3** 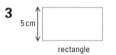  **4**

**5**   **6**   **7** 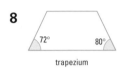  **8**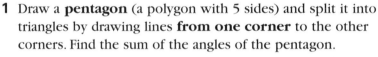

> **Finished Early?**
> ⇨ Go to page 380

## P ❷ Angle Sums of Polygons

### Learn About It

A **polygon** can have any number of sides.

A triangle has angles that add up to 180°.

A quadrilateral has four sides and you can divide it into two triangles. The sum of the angles is 360°.

**1** Draw a **pentagon** (a polygon with 5 sides) and split it into triangles by drawing lines **from one corner** to the other corners. Find the sum of the angles of the pentagon.

**2** Draw a **hexagon** (a polygon with 6 sides) and split it into triangles by drawing lines **from one corner** to the other corners. Find the sum of the angles of the hexagon.

**3** Draw a **heptagon** (a polygon with 7 sides) and split it into triangles. Find the sum of the angles of the heptagon.

**4** Write down your results in a table and continue the pattern to find the sum of the angles of polygons with 8 sides (**octagon**), 9 sides (**nonagon**) and 10 sides (**decagon**).

| Polygon | Number of sides | Number of triangles | Sum of the angles |
|---|---|---|---|
| Triangle | 3 | 1 | 180° |
| Quadrilateral | 4 | 2 | 360° |
| Pentagon | 5 | | |

**5** Write down how the sum of the angles increases.

**6** How many triangles would a 20-sided shape have? What is the rule to find the number of triangles in a polygon?

**7** Write down a rule to find the sum of the angles of a polygon with $n$ sides.

## Try It Out

Write down the sum of the angles of a polygon with …

**1** 8 sides      **2** 9 sides      **3** 10 sides

**4** 15 sides      **5** 30 sides      **6** 40 sides.

> ## Key Fact
> In a polygon with $n$ sides, there are $n - 2$ triangles.
> The sum of the interior angles of a polygon with $n$ sides is $180(n - 2)°$.

## Practice

Find the sum of the angles of each of these polygons.

**1**    **2**    **3**

**4**    **5**    **6**

14 sides

You can write the angle sum ($a$) of a polygon with $n$ sides as an equation:
$a = 180(n - 2)°$.

To find the number of sides of a polygon with a given angle sum, rearrange the equation.

> **Word Check**
> **angle sum** sum of all the interior angles in a polygon

$a = 180(n - 2)°$

$\dfrac{a}{180°} = n - 2$ (*Divide both sides by 180°.*)

$n = \dfrac{a}{180°} + 2$ (*Add 2 to both sides and swap the sides of the equation round.*)

How many sides does a polygon have if it has the following angle sums?

| | |
|---|---|
| **Example** | 540° |
| **Working** | $n = \dfrac{540°}{180°} + 2$ |
| | $n = 3 + 2$ |
| | $n = 5$ |
| **Answer** | 5 sides |

> **Finished Early?**
>  Go to page 381

**1** 720°    **2** 900°    **3** 1080°    **4** 2160°

**5** 3600°    **6** 1260°    **7** 2700°    **8** 1980°

# Further Practice

**H** Could you make a polygon with each group of angles below?

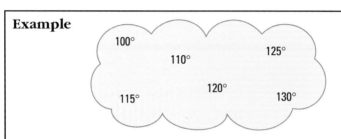

**Example**

**Working**   There are six angles so the polygon must have six sides.
A 6-sided polygon has 6 – 2 = 4 triangles.
The sum of the angles of a 6-sided polygon = 180 × 4 = 720°.
100° + 110° + 125° + 115° + 120° + 130° = 700°.

**Answer**    No

**1**
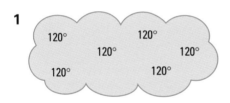

**2**
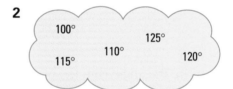

**3**
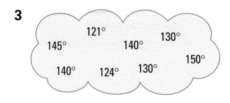

**4**
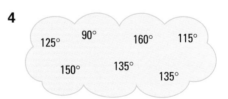

**5**
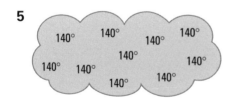

**6**
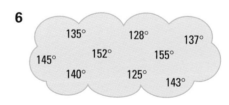

Find the angles in these polygons marked with ?.

**1**

110° ?
120°
103°
100°

**2**

150° 150°
120° 120°
120° 120°
?

**3**

?
137°

**4**
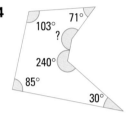
71°
103°
?
240°
85°
30°

**5**
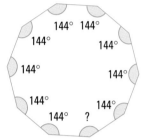
144° 144°
144° 144°
144° 144°
144° 144°
144° ?

**6**
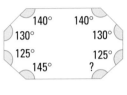
140° 140°
130° 130°
125° 125°
145° ?

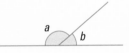
**Finished Early?**
➡ Go to page 381

# Interior and Exterior Angles

## Remember?

Angles on a straight line add up to 180°.

Here, $a + b = 180°$.

If you know one angle, you can find the other.

If $b$ is 70°, $a$ must be 110°.

a
b

## Try It Out

Find the angles marked with ?.

**1**
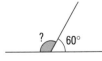
? 60°

**2**

? 125°

**3**
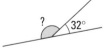
? 32°

**4**

? 51°

**5**
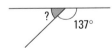
? 137°

**6**

? 101°

# Learn About It

The **interior** angles are the angles inside a shape.

Extending a side forms an **exterior** angle.

The exterior angle and the interior angle next to it add up to 180°.

If you extend each side and turn through all the exterior angles, you turn a full circle. Therefore, the exterior angles add up to 360°.

You can use these facts to find the unknown angles of polygons.

# Try It Out

**K** Work out the angles shown by letters.

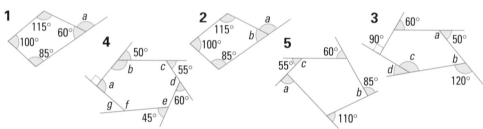

# Key Fact

An interior angle of a polygon and the exterior angle next to it add up to 180°.
The sum of the exterior angles is 360°.

# Practice

**L** Work out the angles shown by letters.

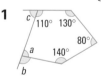
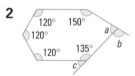
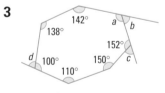
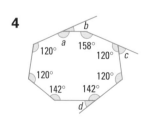
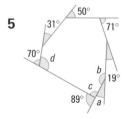
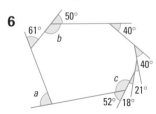

Look at each set and decide if it could be the exterior angles of a polygon.

**1**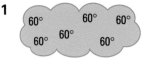
60° 60° 60°
60° 60° 60°

**2**
82° 47°
70° 101° 70°

**3**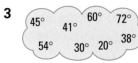
45° 60° 72°
41°
54° 30° 20° 38°

**4**
34° 125° 43°
44°
50° 51° 13°

**5**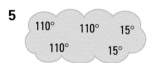
110° 110° 15°
110° 15°

**6**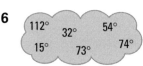
112° 32° 54°
15° 73° 74°

> **Finished Early?**
> ➡ Go to page 381

## Further Practice

Sketch these polygons and fill in as many missing angles as you can.

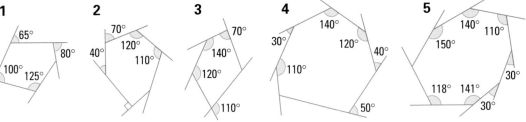

**1**
65°
80°
100° 125°

**2**
70°
120°
40° 110°

**3**
70°
140°
120°
110°

**4**
140°
30° 120°
110° 40°
50°

**5**
140° 110°
150°
30°
118° 141°
30°

> **Finished Early?**
> ➡ Go to page 381

# Regular Polygons

## Learn About It

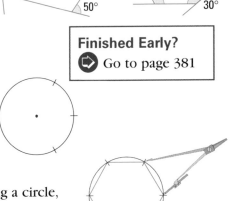

Compasses, protractor

In a **regular** polygon, all the sides are equal
and all the angles are equal.

**1** Draw a **regular hexagon** by first drawing a circle,
then marking off the length of the radius around the
circumference. Use a ruler to join the marks, in order.

**2** Use the formula for the sum of the interior angles of a polygon to find the sum
of the interior angles of a regular hexagon. Divide this by 6 to find one angle.

**3** The sum of the exterior angles is 360°. Divide this by 6 to find one
exterior angle.

**4** Use a protractor to check the results from steps 2 and 3 on your diagram.
Measure each interior and exterior angle of your regular hexagon. Each
interior angle and the exterior angle next to it should add up to 180°.

**5** Write down a way of finding the interior and exterior angles of any
regular polygon.

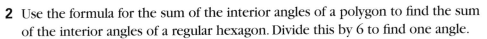

# Try It Out

Find **(a)** the size of one exterior angle and **(b)** the size of one interior angle of a regular polygon with …

**1** 5 sides      **2** 6 sides      **3** 8 sides      **4** 9 sides.

## Key Facts

To find one exterior angle of a **regular** polygon, divide 360° by the number of sides.

To find one interior angle of a **regular** polygon, divide the sum of the angles by the number of sides.

An exterior angle of a polygon and the interior angle next to it add up to 180°. If you know one you can work out the other by subtracting from 180°.

## Practice

**P** Calculate the angles shown by letters in these diagrams.

**1**
**2**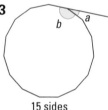
**3**
**4**
**5**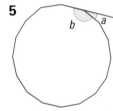

15 sides

16 sides

**Q** Find the number of sides in a regular polygon in which …

**1** every exterior angle equals 36°     **2** every exterior angle equals 12°

**3** every interior angle equals 156°     **4** every interior angle equals 135°

**5** every exterior angle equals 20°     **6** every interior angle equals 140°.

> **Finished Early?**
> ➡ Go to page 381

## Further Practice

**R** Draw up a table of the interior and exterior angles of regular polygons.

Complete the table for regular polygons with up to 25 sides.

| Number of sides | Interior angle | Exterior angle |
|---|---|---|
| 5 | 108° | 72° |
| 6 | 120° | 60° |

> **Finished Early?**
> ➡ Go to page 381

# 5 Three Dimensions

In this chapter you will learn about ...
1 drawing solids
2 nets
3 plans

## Drawing Solids

### Remember?

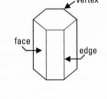

vertex

face
edge

- A **three-dimensional** (3D) shape takes up space; it is not flat. It is called a **solid**.
- A **face** of a 3D shape is a flat surface. An **edge** joins two faces. A **vertex** (plural: vertices) is a corner of a shape. Edges meet at a vertex.
- A **polyhedron** has straight edges and flat faces. There are many different sorts of polyhedron.
- A **cube** has equal square faces.
- A **cuboid** is a rectangular block.
- A pyramid has any polygon for a base. Its other faces are triangles.

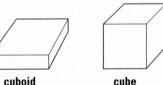

cuboid          cube

Isometric paper

## Try It Out

List the number of faces, edges and vertices of each of these solid shapes.

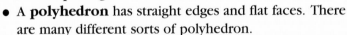

1

cuboid

2

triangular prism

3

square-based pyramid

4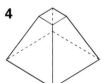

frustum (pyramid with the top cut off)

5

tetrahedron (triangle-based pyramid)

## Learn About It

You can draw a cube on squared paper but the edges will be
different lengths.

**1** Draw this cube using triangular dotted paper, known as
**isometric** paper. Make sure the paper is placed so that the
dots are in clear vertical lines. Draw the top first, then the
three downward sides and then complete the base. Use
dotted lines to show the hidden edges. Measure and label
the lengths of the edges of the cube.

**2** Draw these cubes and label their edges.

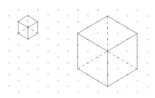

**3** Draw this cuboid in the same way. Write the lengths
of the edges on your diagram.

## Try It Out

**B** Draw these shapes and label the lengths of the edges.

**1**   **2**   **3**   **4**   **5**

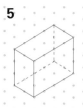

## Key Fact

Isometric paper is used to draw 3Dshapes.
Cuboids drawn on this paper have their
edges in the correct proportions.

Word Check

**isometric** equal measure

# Practice

Cubes

Make these shapes from cubes. Draw them on isometric paper.

**1**   **2**   **3**   **4**   **5**   **6**   **7**

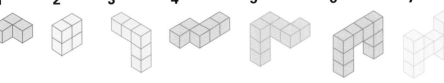

Draw these shapes on isometric paper.

**1**   **2**   **3**   **4**   **5**

  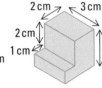 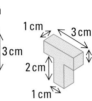 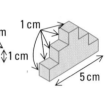

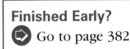

**Finished Early?**
➡ Go to page 382

# Further Practice

Draw cuboids with sides of …

**1** 3 cm, 2 cm, 4 cm    **2** 4 cm, 5 cm, 2 cm    **3** 2 cm, 4 cm, 6 cm

**4** 5 cm, 7 cm, 2 cm    **5** 6 cm, 6 cm, 6 cm.

Cubes

Each of these shapes made from cubes is shown from two different angles.
Make the shapes from cubes and draw each shape on isometric paper in
both ways.

**1 (a)**    **(b)**    **2 (a)**    **(b)**

**3 (a)**    **(b)**    **4 (a)**    **(b)**

**Finished Early?**
➡ Go to page 382

**45**

# T ❷ Nets

## Learn About It

The surface of a solid shape can be opened out to make a flat shape called a **net**.

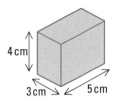

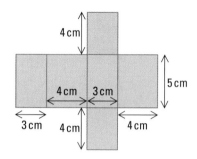

## Try It Out

Squared paper

**G** Draw the nets of these cuboids.

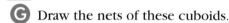

**1**                    **2**                    **3**                    **4**

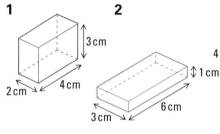
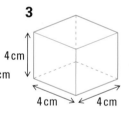
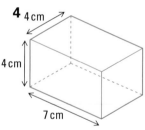

## Learn More About It

Starting with a net, you can
make a 3D shape. To make a
3D model, you need an
accurate full-scale net drawn
on card or paper. Each edge
must be the same length as
the side it will be joined to.

You need to add some **flaps** to stick the edges together.

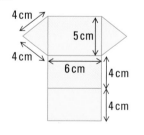
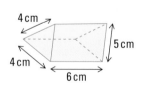
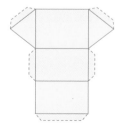

# Try It Out

Isometric paper

Draw the 3D shapes that could be made from these nets.

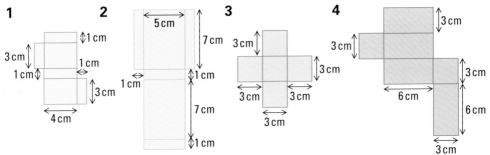

# Practice

Squared paper

Draw the nets of these 3D shapes.

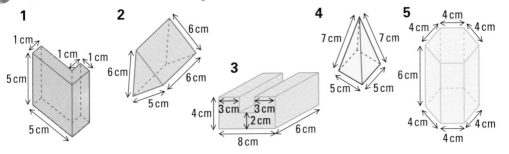

Sketch the solid shape each of these nets would make. Name the shape if you can.

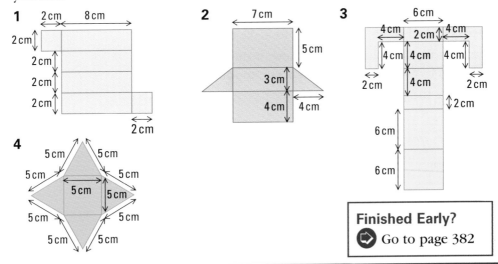

**Finished Early?**

Go to page 382

# Further Practice

Squared paper, scissors, glue

**K** Draw the net of each shape. Add flaps and cut out the net. Fold it up and stick the edges together.

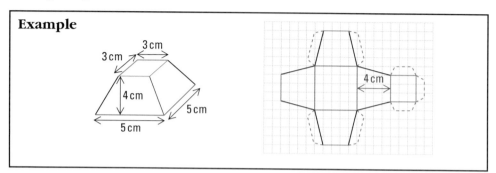

**Example**

**1**

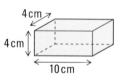

**2**

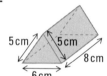

**3**

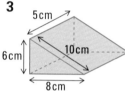

**Finished Early?**
➡ Go to page 382

Go to page 382

## T ❸ Plans

## Learn About It

Sheila is a locksmith. She is asked to make this key.

She can't find lengths from this view of the key. Unless she has a key to copy, she needs accurate **plans**.

These are the plans for the key.

plan

side elevation

end elevation

Sheila can now measure the sizes from the diagrams and make the key.

Three different views of the key are shown: **plan** view and side and end **elevations**.

Plans are either drawn full size or to scale. The plans for a house would be drawn to scale.

## Try It Out

A cube, a cuboid and a square-based pyramid are shown below in plan view and end and side elevations. The diagrams are mixed up. List the letters that go together to make the three shapes.

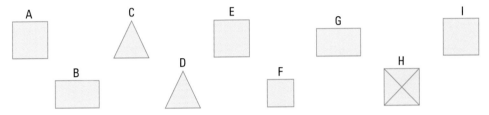

### Word Check

**plan** a view of an object from above

**side elevation** a view of an object from the side

**end elevation** a view of an object from the end

## Practice

Squared paper

Sketch each 3D shape below. Beside it draw its plan view, end elevation and side elevation accurately.

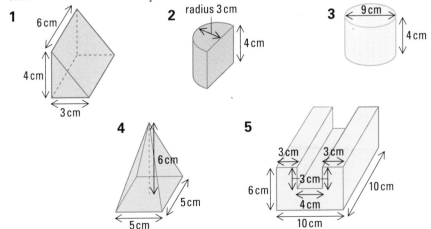

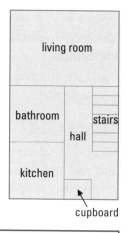

**N** The diagram shows the plan of the ground floor of a house. It is drawn to a scale of 1 cm to 2 m. Draw the plan accurately on squared paper.

Write down the real length and width of …

**1** the living room

**2** the bathroom

**3** the kitchen

**4** the cupboard

**5** the stairs.

## Further Practice

Squared paper

**Finished Early?**
➩ Go to page 382

⊙ Draw plans and elevations for these objects.
Decide on realistic lengths and draw your diagrams to scale.

**1** a toothbrush

**2** a pen

**3** a torch

**4** a bottle of correcting fluid

**P** Three different mini CD players are shown below in plan view and end and side elevations. The diagrams are in the correct proportion but are not full sized. They are mixed up. List the letters that go together to make the three CD players.

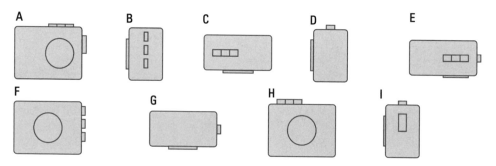

**Finished Early?**
➩ Go to page 382

# Unit 2 *Angles and Shapes*

## Summary of Chapters 3, 4 and 5

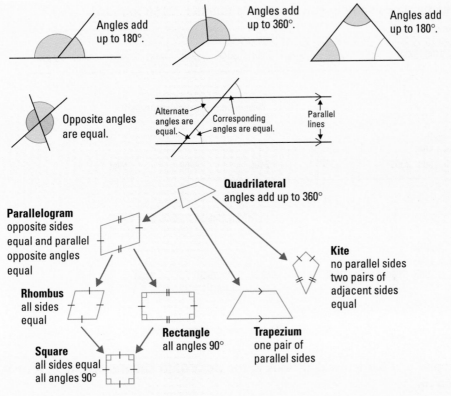

- The sum of the **interior** angles of a **polygon** with *n* sides is $180(n - 2)°$.

- The sum of the **exterior** angles of a polygon is $360°$.

- A **regular** polygon has all its sides equal and all its angles equal.

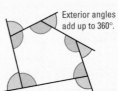

Exterior angles add up to 360°.

- A **net** is the surface of a solid, drawn flat.

- A **plan** is the view looking down on an object. The **side elevation** views the object from the side and the **end elevation** from the end.

# Brush Up Your Number 3

## Rounding Whole Numbers

### Learn About It

A number line can help you to round a number. 2456 rounded:

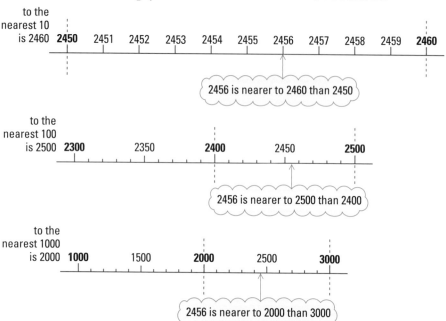

To round to a particular digit, look at the **next digit** and if it is **5, 6, 7, 8 or 9,** round up.

| | |
|---|---|
| **Example** | Round 6250 to the nearest 100. |
| **Working** | The 2 is the 100s digit. |
| | Look at the next digit. 6250. |
| | As this is 5, round up the 2 to a 3. |
| **Answer** | 6300 |

### Try It Out

 **1** Round these numbers to the nearest 10.

    **(a)** 234     **(b)** 1548     **(c)** 74     **(d)** 329

    **(e)** 7682     **(f)** 385     **(g)** 7775     **(h)** 864

**2** Round these numbers to the nearest 100.

    **(a)** 844     **(b)** 7654     **(c)** 351     **(d)** 8650

    **(e)** 2385     **(f)** 3400     **(g)** 2540     **(h)** 972

**3** Round these numbers to the nearest 1000.

(a) 3499     (b) 2527     (c) 12 672     (d) 9329

(e) 18 276     (f) 19 574     (g) 9673     (h) 8885

## Practice

The table shows the weekly sales of some magazines. For each magazine, round the sales to **(a)** the nearest 100 **(b)** the nearest 1000 **(c)** the nearest 10 000.

|    | Magazine | Sales |
|----|----------|-------|
| 1  | Good Games | 131 245 |
| 2  | Stargazing | 15 356 |
| 3  | Sport Weekly | 23 892 |
| 4  | Mega Sounds | 98 450 |
| 5  | Travel Tales | 33 420 |
| 6  | Puzzle Fun | 142 367 |
| 7  | Perfect Pets | 100 548 |
| 8  | Cookery Tips | 89 535 |
| 9  | Top Computers | 117 389 |
| 10 | Super Planes | 43 244 |

The table shows a survey of the numbers of cars using different roads in a day. Copy and complete the table.

| Road | Number of cars | Nearest 10 | Nearest 100 | Nearest 1000 |
|------|----------------|------------|-------------|--------------|
| A | 3 477 | | | |
| B | 27 869 | | | |
| C | 35 276 | | | |
| D | 2 456 | | | |
| E | 687 | | | |
| F | 32 450 | | | |
| G | 134 351 | | | |
| H | 455 | | | |

**Finished Early?**
➡ Go to page 353

# 6 Decimals

In this chapter you will learn about ...
1. decimals
2. rounding
3. calculations

## 1 Decimals

### Remember?

- The **decimal point** separates the whole number from the decimal fraction.
- The **first decimal place** shows tenths.
- The **second decimal place** shows hundredths.
- To find which is the largest number in a group of decimal numbers, look at the digits in order from left to right.

| 2·37 | 2·37 | 2·37 | 2.37 is bigger than 2.365 |
| 2·365 | 2·365 | 2·365 | |
| the same | the same | 7 is bigger than 6 | |

### Try It Out

**A** Write these groups of numbers in order, with the smallest first.

**1** 2.45, 2.38, 2.39      **2** 3.64, 3.72, 3.55

**3** 41.75, 41.71, 41.69      **4** 12.5, 12.49, 12.45

**5** 2.08, 2.07, 2.8      **6** 4.72, 4.8, 4.73

**7** 14.82, 14.87, 14.86      **8** 9.65, 9.64, 9.63

**9** 12.02, 12.16, 12.11      **10** 0.4, 0.38, 0.35

### Learn About It

**1** After the decimal point, the first place shows tenths, the second hundredths, and so on. Copy and complete this table.

| 1st place | 2nd place | 3rd place | 4th place | 5th place |
|-----------|-----------|-----------|-----------|-----------|
| $\frac{1}{10}$s | $\frac{1}{100}$s | | | |

**2** The 5 in the number 2.4254 is in the third decimal place. Its value is $\frac{5}{1000}$.
Write down the value of the digits shown in red in these numbers.

(a) 2.35             (b) 14.334             (c) 5.4765

**3** The **scale** on a ruler is used to measure lengths. The length of this leaf
is 5.6 cm.

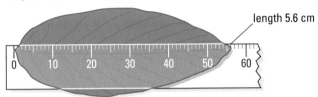

length 5.6 cm

A very accurate scale on a microscope can measure to more decimal places.
Write down the lengths of these objects.

(a) a hair        (b) a crystal        (c) a red blood cell

## Try It Out

Write down the value of the digits shown in red.

| Example | 14.534 |
|---------|--------|
| **Answer** | $\frac{3}{100}$. |

**1** 2.345          **2** 1.7          **3** 12.312

**4** 4.223          **5** 6.554 15          **6** 0.026

**7** 0.035          **8** 30.362          **9** 7.6291

**10** 0.8992          **11** 22.054 36          **12** 1.167

Write down the values marked by arrows on this scale.

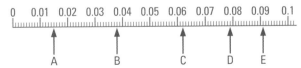

**D** Write down each of these groups of numbers in order, with the smallest first.

**1** 2.35, 2.34, 2.36, 2.345, 2.3405

**2** 0.725, 0.74, 0.739, 0.7255, 0.727

**3** 1.8001, 1.81, 1.8, 1.80001, 1.79

**4** 3.2501, 3.25, 3.249, 3.2510, 3.2495

**5** 7.227, 7.226, 7.229, 7.2266, 7.2256

**6** 8.104, 8.003, 8.103, 8.1004, 8.14

**7** 6.276, 6.2751, 6.275, 6.2752, 6.2763

**8** 5.455, 5.5545, 5.544, 5.465, 5.55451

> ## Key Fact
> The values of the decimal places are tenths, hundredths, thousandths, etc.

## Practice

**E** Write down the values marked by arrows on these scales.

**1**
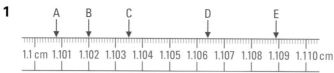

**2**
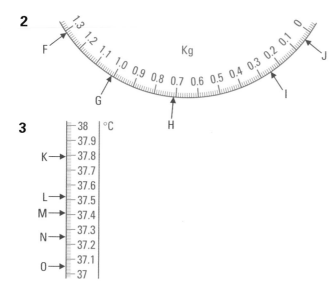

Squared paper

Copy these scales and mark in the values indicated, using arrows.

**1** **(a)** 0.2 **(b)** 0.02 **(c)** 0.45 **(d)** 0.63 **(e)** 0.79

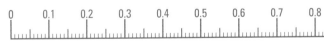

**2** **(a)** 9.103 **(b)** 9.15 **(c)** 9.135 **(d)** 9.2 **(e)** 9.25

Write each group of numbers in order, with the smallest first.

| **Example** | |
|---|---|
| | 3.51  3.56  3.53  3.52  3.49 |
| **Working** | All the numbers start with 3, so look at the next digit.<br>All the numbers have 5 in the first decimal place except 3.49,<br>so 3.49 is the smallest number.<br>Look at the second decimal place in each number. The digits<br>are 6, 1, 2 and 3.<br>Put these numbers in order: 3.51, 3.52, 3.53, 3.56. |
| **Answer** | 3.49, 3.51, 3.52, 3.53, 3.56 |

**1**

2.45  2.5450  2.454
2.5
2.444  2.4504  2.54

**2**

1.459  1.4710  1.45
1.461
1.46  1.4601  1.458

**3**

13.42  13.3621  13.365
13.36
13.362  13.341
13.3612

**4**

9.4512  9.4449  9.450
9.452
9.449  9.4518
9.45109

**5**

0.019  0.017 95  0.018
0.0179
0.02  0.015
0.1520

**6**

3.45  3.4451  3.91
3.19
3.25  3.4415  3.54

**Finished Early?**
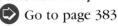 Go to page 383

## Further Practice

 **H** A scientist measured accurately the time it took four cars to cover 100 m. She timed each car five times.

100 m

**1** The times for the first car are shown on this scale.

seconds

Write down the car's times in order, with the shortest time first.

**2** The times for the second car, in seconds, are
6.91, 7.05, 7.43, 7.59, 7.75.
Mark these on a scale like that used in question 1.

**3** The times for the third car, in seconds, are
8.05, 7.71, 7.04, 6.88, 7.53.
Write these in order, with the shortest time first.

**4** The times for the fourth car, in seconds, are
7.543, 6.925, 8.04, 7.125, 7.555. Write these
in order, with the shortest time first.

**5** Which car travelled the distance in the shortest time?

**6** Which car travelled the distance in the longest time?

**Finished Early?**
 Go to page 383

Go to page 383

## **T 2 Rounding**

### Remember?

Whole numbers can be **rounded** to the nearest 10, 100, etc.

2453 rounded to the nearest 10 is 2450.

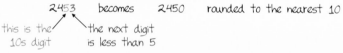

2453 rounded to the nearest 100 is 2500.

2453 rounded to the nearest 1000 is 2000.

## Try It Out

Round these numbers **(a)** to the nearest 10 **(b)** to the nearest 100.

**1** 274      **2** 134      **3** 267      **4** 585

**5** 2359      **6** 125 746      **7** 812      **8** 795

## Learn About It

You can round a number to the nearest **whole number**.

You can also round to a certain number of **decimal places, d.p.** for short.

Rounding to **one decimal place (1 d.p.)** is the same as rounding to the nearest tenth.

Rounding to **two decimal places (2 d.p.)** is rounding to the nearest hundredth.

Rounding to **three decimal places (3 d.p.)** is rounding to the nearest thousandth.

0.5641 is nearer to 1 than 0      0.5641 rounded to the nearest whole number is 1

0.5641 is nearer to 0.6 than 0.5      0.5641 rounded to 1 d.p. is 0.6

0.5641 is nearer to 0.56 than 0.57      0.5641 rounded to 2 d.p. is 0.56

0.5641 is nearer to 0.564 than 0.565      0.5641 rounded to 3 d.p. is 0.564.

If you round 6.03 to 1 d.p., you should write the answer as 6.0 to show that it is rounded.

## Try It Out

**1** Round these numbers to the nearest whole number.

     **(a)** 2.34      **(b)** 12.57      **(c)** 10.8      **(d)** 239.59

**2** Round these numbers to 1 d.p.

     **(a)** 2.34      **(b)** 15.47      **(c)** 2.02      **(d)** 4.99

**3** Round these numbers to 2 d.p.

     **(a)** 0.344      **(b)** 15.225      **(c)** 0.008      **(d)** 2.503

**4** Round these numbers to 3 d.p.

     **(a)** 5.6432      **(b)** 0.0025      **(c)** 0.3157      **(d)** 12.0005

## Learn More About It

The first **significant figure** of 2345 is 2, meaning 2 thousand.
2345 rounded to 1 significant figure is 2000.
2345 rounded to 2 significant figures is 2300.
2345 rounded to 3 significant figures is 2350.
When the number is less than 1, you find the first significant figure like this:
- start at the left
- read along the number, to the right, until you find a digit that is not zero.
Keep the zero before the decimal point, and any zeros straight after it. They are needed to keep the number the right size, but they are not significant figures.

The first significant figure of 0.066 71 is 6, meaning 6 hundredths.
0.066 71 rounded to 1 significant figure is 0.07.
0.066 71 rounded to 2 significant figures is 0.067.
0.066 71 rounded to 3 significant figures is 0.0667.

Zeros in the **middle** of a number are significant.
2035 rounded to 3 significant figures is 2040.

---

**Example**   Round 0.000 359 64 to 2 significant figures.
**Working**

0.000 359 64  rounded to 2 significant figures is 0.000 36,

2 significant figures

you need these zeros to keep the number the correct size

you do not need zeros here

**Answer**   0.00036

---

## Try It Out

**K 1** Round to 1 significant figure.
(a) 247      (b) 3500      (c) 0.046      (d) 2.5

**2** Round to 2 significant figures.
(a) 355      (b) 4644      (c) 0.0256      (d) 3.765

**3** Round to 3 significant figures.
(a) 325.75   (b) 467 999   (c) 0.022 56   (d) 4.625

---

## Key Facts

When using decimal places (d.p.), round to a given number of places after the point.

When using significant figures (s.f.), round to a given number of places from the first non-zero digit.

## Practice

A scientist is using electronic scales to measure the mass of chemicals.
Copy and complete this table of results.

| Chemical | Mass (g) | Rounded to whole number | 1 d.p. | 2 d.p. | 1 s.f. | 2 s.f. |
|---|---|---|---|---|---|---|
| Carbon | 0.025 | 0 | | | | |
| Sodium | 0.0345 | | | | | |
| Mercury | 5.0472 | | | | | |
| Strontium | 4.952 | | | | | |
| Argon | 0.000 435 | | | | | |

**1** Round these lengths of wood to 3 s.f.
  (**a**) 1.6453 m      (**b**) 2.3892 m      (**c**) 4.6435 m
  (**d**) 95.763 cm      (**e**) 35.3485 cm

**2** A racing team calculates the number of
kilometres different racing cars will travel on one
litre of petrol. Round these to (**i**) 1 d.p. (**ii**) 4 s.f.
  (**a**) 63.4235 km      (**b**) 79.514 67 km
  (**c**) 34.895 09 km      (**d**) 44.529 83 km
  (**e**) 49.954 11 km

**3** A surveyor is measuring accurately the heights of buildings. Round these
to 2 s.f.
  (**a**) 6.453 m      (**b**) 1225.64 cm      (**c**) 23.5943 m
  (**d**) 972.645 cm      (**e**) 19.875 m

**4** A bank calculates very accurately the interest it will charge on its loans and
then rounds the final answer. What will it charge if these amounts are
rounded to (**i**) 2 d.p. (**ii**) 1 s.f?
  (**a**) £342.259 42      (**b**) £1621.783 92      (**c**) £24.3467
  (**d**) £67.5463      (**e**) £749.9956

**5** A scientist measures the masses of very small amounts
of rare metals. Round these to (**i**) 5 s.f. (**ii**) 6 d.p.
  (**a**) 0.004 5783 g      (**b**) 0.000 399 74 g
  (**c**) 0.002 450 001 g      (**d**) 1.000 123 33 g
  (**e**) 0.099 543 2 g

**Finished Early?**
➡ Go to page 384

# Further Practice

 Copy and complete this table.

| | Rounded to: | | | |
|---|---|---|---|---|
| | 1 d.p. | 2 d.p. | 1 s.f. | 2 s.f. |
| 2.347 | | | | |
| 0.0585 | | | | |
| 230.235 | | | | |
| 11.957 | | | | |
| 21.075 | | | | |
| 112.507 | | | | |
| 0.4756 | | | | |
| 0.3472 | | | | |

The area of a rectangle is length × width.

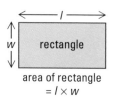

area of rectangle
= $l \times w$

Find the area of …

1 a field 63 m by 75 m, rounded to 2 s.f.

2 a garden 19.5 m by 9.2 m, rounded to 2 s.f.

3 a counter top 2.35 m by 0.67 m, rounded to 2 d.p.

4 a computer floppy disc 8.9 cm by 8.9 cm, rounded to 1 d.p.

5 a desk top 1.65 m by 0.85 m, rounded to 1 d.p.

6 a computer chip 1.25 cm by 0.995 cm, rounded to 2 d.p.

7 a metal plate 0.875 m by 0.776 m, rounded to 2 s.f.

8 a book 21 cm by 13 cm, rounded to 2 s.f.

**Finished Early?**
Go to page 384

# Calculations

## Remember?

To add and subtract decimals, line up the decimal points. Then work out as for whole numbers.

To work out 12.37 + 3.854:

```
1 2 .3 7        line up the decimal points
+ 3 .8 5 4
1 6 .2 2 4      add as for whole numbers
    1 1
```

To multiply or divide a decimal by a **whole number**, work out as for whole numbers.

12.25 × 9

```
  1 2 .2 5      2 d.p. in question and answer
×         9
1 1 0 .2 5
    2 2   4
```

17.28 ÷ 8

```
   2 .1 6        decimal points in
8)1 7 .2 8       the same position
```

To multiply or divide by 10, 100, 1000, etc., move the digits left or right.

2.54 × 10

= **25.4**  move the digits <u>one</u> place ←

32.75 ÷ 100

= 0.3275  move the digits <u>two</u> places →

## Try It Out

Work these out.

1  3.55 + 2.7
2  2.75 + 13.2
3  11.63 + 4.37
4  12.63 - 4.57
5  18.275 - 9.28
6  13.24 - 3.45
7  12.5 × 7
8  2.34 × 12
9  6.25 × 11
10  121.05 ÷ 9
11  32.4 ÷ 6
12  114.24 ÷ 7

## Learn About It

This is how to carry out the **multiplication** of decimals.

You can work out each of these multiplications from the first calculation.

12 × 13 = 156

12 × 1.3 = 15.6      (156 ÷ 10, move the digits one place right)

1.2 × 1.3 = 1.56      (156 ÷ 100, move the digits two places right)

1.2 × 0.13 = 0.156    (156 ÷ 1000, move the digits three places right)

The total number of digits after the decimal point is the same in the question and answer. To calculate $17.2 \times 3.25$, first work out $172 \times 325$:

$$
\begin{array}{r}
172 \\
\times \quad 325 \\
\hline
860 \quad \longleftarrow 172 \times 5 \\
3440 \quad \longleftarrow 172 \times 20 \\
51600 \quad \longleftarrow 172 \times 300 \\
\hline
55900 \\
\end{array}
$$

Since there are 3 d.p. in the question there must be 3 d.p. in the answer.

$17.2 \times 3.25 = 55.900$

You don't need the zeros at the end, once you have used them to put the decimal point in the correct place.

**Answer** 55.9

## Try It Out

Work these out.

**1** $3.5 \times 2.4$     **2** $2.5 \times 1.2$     **3** $2.4 \times 0.6$     **4** $3.6 \times 1.1$

**5** $2.5 \times 0.7$     **6** $0.26 \times 0.5$     **7** $0.36 \times 0.3$     **8** $0.28 \times 0.6$

## Learn More About It

You can divide a decimal by a decimal using whole number division. Remember, when the number you are dividing gets smaller, the answer gets smaller. When the number you are dividing *by* gets smaller, the answer gets bigger.

To divide 0.12 by 0.4:

$12 \div 4 = 3$      (Work with whole numbers first.)

$0.12 \div 4 = 0.03$      (Digits in the number you are dividing move right two places, so digits in the answer move right two places.)

$0.12 \div 0.4 = 0.3$      (Digits in the number you are dividing *by* move right one place, so digits in the answer move left one place.)

## Try It Out

Work these out.

| | | |
|---|---|---|
| **Example** | $7.56 \div 0.012$ | |
| **Working** | $756 \div 12 = 63$ | *(Work with whole numbers first.)* |
| | $756 \div 0.012 = 63\,000$ | *(Move digits left three places.)* |
| | $7.56 \div 0.012 = 630$ | *(Move digits right two places.)* |
| **Answer** | 630 | |

**1** $6.48 \div 1.2$     **2** $6.48 \div 0.12$     **3** $0.648 \div 1.2$     **4** $27.5 \div 1.1$

**5** $2.43 \div 0.9$     **6** $6.44 \div 0.8$     **7** $3.64 \div 0.4$     **8** $12.1 \div 0.25$

# Practice

Work these out.

| | | | |
|---|---|---|---|
| **1** $3.6 \times 2.4$ | **2** $4.8 \times 2.3$ | **3** $0.48 \times 0.23$ | **4** $6.4 \times 0.25$ |
| **5** $6.8 \times 3.5$ | **6** $5.6 \times 2.6$ | **7** $0.56 \times 0.26$ | **8** $3.5 \times 3.8$ |
| **9** $6.24 \div 1.6$ | **10** $6.75 \div 1.8$ | **11** $0.897 \div 2.3$ | **12** $12.81 \div 3.5$ |
| **13** $48.3 \div 2.8$ | **14** $48.3 \div 0.28$ | **15** $8.775 \div 2.25$ | **16** $0.8775 \div 0.225$ |

At Bean Dreams they make beanbags. There are three sizes, called Loungers (small), Floppers (medium) and Sprawlers (large).

The cover for a Sprawler weighs 0.2 kg.

**(a)** How much does a Lounger cover weigh, if it weighs 0.6 times as much as a Sprawler cover?

**(b)** How much does a Flopper cover weigh, if it weighs 0.8 times as much as a Sprawler cover?

There are three different sizes of polystyrene 'bean' for the filling.

**(c)** A small bean weighs 0.04 g. 63 000 of these are used to fill a Lounger. What does a complete Lounger weigh?

**(d)** 48 000 medium beans are used to fill a Flopper. Floppers weigh 4 kg. What is the mass of a medium bean?

**(e)** Sprawlers weigh 5.12 kg. They are filled with large beans weighing 0.12 g each. How many beans are needed to fill a Sprawler?

**(f)** One day, the supply of large beans runs out. The Sprawlers are filled with medium beans instead. How many medium beans are needed for each Sprawler?

> **Finished Early?**
> 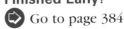 Go to page 384

# Further Practice

These calculations are correct. Use them to help you answer the questions below.

$23 \times 355 = 8165$    $27 \times 137 = 3699$    $18 \times 38 = 684$

$756 \div 42 = 18$    $493 \div 17 = 29$    $36 \times 166 = 5976$

| | | | |
|---|---|---|---|
| **1** $2.3 \times 3.55$ | **2** $0.18 \times 3.8$ | **3** $1.37 \times 2.7$ | **4** $1.66 \times 3.6$ |
| **5** $7.56 \div 4.2$ | **6** $0.493 \div 1.7$ | **7** $0.23 \times 0.355$ | **8** $0.38 \times 0.18$ |
| **9** $0.27 \times 13.7$ | **10** $0.166 \times 3.6$ | **11** $75.6 \div 0.42$ | **12** $4.93 \div 0.17$ |
| **13** $68.4 \div 3.8$ | **14** $3.699 \div 1.37$ | **15** $0.5976 \div 1.66$ | **16** $0.8165 \div 2.3$ |

> **Finished Early?**
> Go to page 384

# Unit 3 *Decimals*

## Summary of Chapter 6

- The **decimal point** separates the whole number from the decimal fraction.

- The **first decimal place** shows tenths.

  The **second decimal place** shows hundredths.

  The **third decimal place** shows thousandths.

- To find which is the larger of two decimal numbers, look at the digits in order from left to right.

  2 · 1 3 5 9   because 5 is less than 6, 2.1360 is the larger number
  2 · 1 3 6 0

- You can round to a certain number of **decimal places, d.p.** for short.

  Rounding to **one decimal place (1 d.p.)** is the same as rounding to the nearest tenth.

  *If the next digit is 5 or more, round up*

  12.43|5  rounded to 2 d.p. = 2.44

- You can round to a certain number of **significant figures (s.f.).**

  *The next digit is more than 5*

  0.004 36  rounded to 2 s.f. = 0.0044

  *2 significant figures*

- To **add** and **subtract** decimals, line up the decimal points. Then work out as for whole numbers.

- When you **multiply** decimals, you should have the same number of decimal places in the answer as in the question.

- To divide a decimal by a decimal, first use whole number division. When the number you are dividing gets smaller, the answer gets smaller. When the number you are dividing *by* gets smaller, the answer gets bigger.

# Brush Up Your Number 4

## Mixed Operations and Negative Numbers

### Learn About It

Remember the order of **operations** by BoDMAS:

**B**rackets first, then **Po**wers

**D**ivision (÷) and **M**ultiplication (×) (*Work from left to right.*)

**A**ddition (+) and **S**ubtraction (–) (*Work from left to right.*)

| | |
|---|---|
| **Example** | $12 \div 3 - 2$ |
| **Working** | $= 4 - 2$ (÷ *first.*) |
| | $= 2$ |
| **Answer** | 2 |

| | |
|---|---|
| **Example** | $6 + (5 - 2) \times 4$ |
| **Working** | $= 6 + 3 \times 4$   (*Brackets first.*) |
| | $= 6 + 12$     (× *before +.*) |
| **Answer** | 18 |

### Try It Out

Calculate these.

**1**   **(a)** $7 - 2 \times 3$      **(b)** $8 \times 2 + 4$      **(c)** $9 - 12 \div 3$

    **(d)** $3 \times 2 + 4 \times 3$      **(e)** $1 + 3 \times 5 - 2$      **(f)** $20 \div 4 + 1$

**2**   **(a)** $5 \times (3 + 6)$      **(b)** $12 - (8 - 2)$      **(c)** $(10 + 3) \times 2$

    **(d)** $36 \div (4 \times 3)$      **(e)** $(5 + 2) \times (4 + 1)$      **(f)** $(6 + 2) \div (5 - 3)$

**3**   **(a)** $5 \times (6 - 2) + 4$      **(b)** $(4 + 8) \div 3 + 1$      **(c)** $2 \times 7 - (5 - 2)$

    **(d)** $9 - (4 - 1) \times 2$      **(e)** $20 - 3(5 - 2)$      **(f)** $(7 - 4) \times 5 - 1$

### Learn More About It

You can use a number line to help you add and subtract numbers.

| | |
|---|---|
| **Example** | $3 - 7$ |
| **Working** | The number line shows the answer is negative. 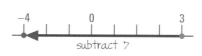 |
| | Difference $= 7 - 3 = 4$ |
| **Answer** | –4 |

Use these rules to combine + and – signs.

| Same signs give + |
|---|
| + + gives + |
| − − gives + |

| Different signs give − |
|---|
| + − gives − |
| − + gives − |

| **Example** | $3 + (-7)$ |
|---|---|
| **Working** | $= 3 - 7$ (+ – *gives* –) |
| **Answer** | –4 |

Use these rules to multiply or divide numbers.

| Same signs give + |
|---|
| + × + gives + |
| − × − gives + |

| Different signs give − |
|---|
| + × − gives − |
| − × + gives − |

| **Example** | $(-8) \div (-4)$ |
|---|---|
| **Working** | $= 8 \div 4$ (− ÷ – *gives* +) |
| **Answer** | 2 |

| Same signs give + |
|---|
| + ÷ + gives + |
| − ÷ − gives + |

| Different signs give − |
|---|
| + ÷ − gives − |
| − ÷ + gives − |

When you multiply or divide, write negative numbers in brackets, e.g. write $3 \times -2$ as $3 \times (-2)$.

## Try It Out

 Calculate the following.

**1** (a) $(-2) + 8$     (b) $(-5) - 3$     (c) $22 - 50$

**2** (a) $(-3) + 4 - 2$     (b) $(-3) - 4 - 5$     (c) $1 - 2 + 3 - 4 + 5 - 6$

**3** (a) $6 - 2$     (b) $(-3) - (-4)$     (c) $(-9) + (-2)$

**4** (a) $(-7) \times (-2)$     (b) $10 \times (-2)$     (c) $(-6)^2$

**5** (a) $10 \div (-2)$     (b) $(-20) \div (-4)$     (c) $\frac{-24}{-4}$

## C Practice

Calculate the following.

**1** $9 - (6 + 8)$     **2** $6 \times (-5) + 4$     **3** $\frac{5 + 5}{-5}$

**4** $(-7)^2$     **5** $(-2) - 4 \times (-2)$     **6** $3 \times (2 + 5) - 30$

**7** $\frac{-20}{10}$     **8** $6 - (8 - 12)$     **9** $18 \div (-3) - 1$

**10** $5 - 20 \div 2$     **11** $\frac{14}{2} - \frac{18}{2}$     **12** $\frac{4 - 20}{6 - 10}$

**13** $4 \times (-3) - 5$     **14** $2 \times (3 - 5 \times 2)$     **15** $(-6) + 3 \times (-2)$

**16** $(-20) + 3 \times 4$     **17** $(10 - 40) \div 6$     **18** $(-20) \div 2 + 3$

**Finished Early?**
➡ Go to page 385

# Formulae and Expressions

In this chapter you will learn about ...

1 substitution
2 making formulae
3 simplifying expressions
4 brackets
5 factorising

## Substitution

### Remember?

- You can use letters to stand for numbers, e.g. you could use $M$ to stand for Michael's age. If Michael's age equals Andrew's age plus 4, you can write this as $M = A + 4$.
- Miss out the multiplication sign ($\times$) when using letters, e.g. write $3a$ instead of $3 \times a$.
- Miss out the division sign ($\div$) when using letters, e.g. write $\frac{a}{5}$ instead of $a \div 5$.

## Try It Out

**1** Write a formula using the red letters and numbers from each statement.
  **(a)** Delia's age equals Joseph's age plus 6.
  **(b)** Tahir's age equals Martha's age divided by 2.
  **(c)** Roger's age equals Nathaniel's age minus 1.
  **(d)** Barbara's age equals 3 times Simon's age.

**2** Calculate the following.
  **(a)** $4^2$
  **(b)** the square of 3
  **(c)** nine squared
  **(d)** $(-5)^2$

# Learn About It

A mixture of letters ($a, b, c, x, A$, etc.), numbers ($1, 2, 3, -5, 2.6, \frac{3}{4}$, etc.) and symbols ($+, -, \times, \div, \sqrt{}$, etc.) is called an **expression**.

An expression does not have an equals sign ($=$).

Here are some short expressions:

$b - 3$ 

$a + b$

$2a$ (short for $2 \times a$)

$\frac{c}{2}$ (short for $c \div 2$)

$ab$ (short for $a \times b$)

$\frac{c}{b}$ (short for $c \div b$)

## Word Check

**expression** a mixture of numbers, letters and symbols that does not include the $=$ symbol

**substitute** put numbers in place of letters in an expression

**symbol** any sign used in mathematics, e.g. $+, -, \times, \div, \sqrt{}, =$

**value of an expression** the answer you get after substituting numbers for letters

If you know which numbers the letters stand for, you can find the **value** of an expression.

Suppose $a = 5, b = 4$ and $c = 8$. You **substitute** the numbers for letters.

$b - 3 = 4 - 3 = 1$ — The value of the expression $b - 3$ is 1.

$a + b = 5 + 4 = 9$ — The value of the expression $a + b$ is 9.

$2a = 2 \times a = 2 \times 5 = 10$ — The value of the expression $2a$ is 10.

$ab = 5 \times 4 = 20$ — The value of the expression $ab$ is 20.

$\frac{c}{b} = 8 \div 4 = 2$ — The value of the expression $\frac{c}{b}$ is 2.

The following expressions involve several operations.

Substitute $a = 5, b = 4$ and $c = 8$ again.

$3a - 2b$
$= 3 \times 5 - 2 \times 4$  *Hint: multiply first.*
$= 15 - 8$
$= 7$

$a + \frac{c}{2}$
$= 5 + 8 \div 2$  *Hint: divide first.*
$= 5 + 4$
$= 9$

You can substitute negative numbers into expressions, too. Write them in brackets. The value of an expression can be negative.

**Example** Find the value of $2a$ when $a = -5$.
**Working** $2a = 2 \times (-5)$ ($+ \times - \ gives\ -.$)
$= -10$
**Answer** $-10$

| Example | Find the value of $a + b$ when $a = -5$ and $b = -2$. |
|---|---|
| Working | $a + b = (-5) + (-2)$  (+ - *gives* -.) |
|  | $= -5 - 2$ |
|  | $= -7$ |
| Answer | -7 |

| Example | Find the value of $3x + 4y$ when $x = -2$ and $y = -1$. |
|---|---|
| Working | $3x + 4y = 3 \times (-2) + 4 \times (-1)$  (*Multiply first.*) |
|  | $= (-6) + (-4)$ |
|  | $= (-6) - 4$ |
|  | $= -10$ |
| Answer | -10 |

## Try It Out

**1** Calculate the value of each expression when $a = 3$ and $b = 6$.

(a) $a + b$    (b) $b - a$    (c) $a + 7$    (d) $2 + b$

(e) $b + 2 - a$    (f) $a - 1 + b$    (g) $3a$    (h) $2b$

(i) $5a$    (j) $2b - 4$    (k) $4a + 7$    (l) $3b + 2$

(m) $2a + 2b$    (n) $3b - 4a$    (o) $2a - b$    (p) $b + 2a + 3$

(q) $2b - 3a - 1$    (r) $ab$    (s) $a + ab$    (t) $\frac{b}{a}$

(u) $\frac{24}{b}$    (v) $a + \frac{b}{2}$    (w) $\frac{b}{a} + a$    (x) $b - \frac{6}{a}$

**2** Calculate the value of each expression in question 1 when $a = -2$ and $b = 8$.

## Learn More About It

$3^2$ means $3 \times 3$, so $a^2$ means $a \times a$.

| Example | Find the value of $a^2$ when $a = 5$. |
|---|---|
| Working | $a^2 = a \times a$ |
|  | $= 5 \times 5$ |
|  | $= 25$ |
| Answer | 25 |

| Example | Find the value of $4b^2$ when $b = 3$. |
|---|---|
| Working | $4b^2 = 4 \times b \times b$ |
|  | $= 4 \times 3 \times 3$ |
|  | $= 36$ |
| Answer | 36 |

The number 4 in $4b^2$ is not being squared; only $b$ is squared. $4b^2$ means $4 \times b \times b$.

---

**Example** Find the value of $m^2 - m$ when $m = -4$.

**Working** $m^2 - m$

$= (-4)^2 - (-4)$

$= (-4) \times (-4) - (-4)$    (*Multiply first. - × - gives +.*)

$= 16 - (-4)$    (*- - gives +.*)

$= 16 + 4$

$= 20$

**Answer** 20

---

## Try It Out

**C** **1** Calculate the value of each expression when $p = 4$ and $q = 3$.

(a) $p^2$    (b) $q^2$    (c) $p^2 + q^2$    (d) $p^2 - q^2$

(e) $q^2 + 6$    (f) $p^2 - 8$    (g) $20 - q^2$    (h) $p^2 + p$

(i) $q^2 + q$    (j) $p^2 - q$    (k) $q^2 - p - 2$    (l) $2q^2$

(m) $3p^2$    (n) $3q^2$    (o) $2p^2 + 1$    (p) $3q^2 - 20$

**2** Calculate the value of each expression in question 1 when $p = 2$ and $q = -3$.

## Practice

**D** **1** Calculate the value of each expression when $x = 6$, $y = 12$ and $z = 2$.

(a) $x + y + z$    (b) $y - x + z$    (c) $3x - 4z + 2y$    (d) $xz - y$

(e) $xz - zy$    (f) $2x - \frac{y}{z}$    (g) $x^2 - yz$    (h) $\frac{y}{x} + z^2$

(i) $yz^2$    (j) $zx^2$    (k) $zy^2$    (l) $\frac{x^2}{y}$

(m) $xyz$    (n) $xyz - x^2$

**2** Calculate the value of each expression in question 1 when $x = -3$, $y = 6$ and $z = 2$.

**E** Copy the table below. Substitute each pair of values of $m$ and $n$ into the expressions. Write the answers in the table. Write your working under the table.

|  | | $m = 3, n = 5$ | $m = 20, n = 50$ | $m = 5, n = -10$ |
|---|---|---|---|---|
| **1** | $5m - 2n$ | | | |
| **2** | $\frac{mn}{5}$ | | | |
| **3** | $2m^2 + n^2$ | | | |
| **4** | $n^2 - \frac{m}{n}$ | | | |

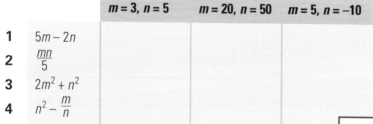

> **Finished Early?**
> ➡ Go to page 385

# Further Practice

Find the output of each machine.

| **Example** | $a = 2, b = 3$ $\boxed{5a + 4b}\!\!>$ |
|---|---|
| **Working** | Put $a = 2$ and $b = 3$ into the expression $5a + 4b$. |
| | $5a + 4b$ |
| | $= 5 \times 2 + 4 \times 3$ |
| | $= 10 + 12$ |
| **Answer** | 22 |

**1** $a = 2$ $\boxed{4a - 1}\!\!>$       **2** $a = 20$ $\boxed{\frac{a}{5}}\!\!>$

**3** $a = 6$ $\boxed{3a^2 + 3}\!\!>$       **4** $a = 4, b = 5$ $\boxed{3a + 2b}\!\!>$

**5** $a = -4, b = -5$ $\boxed{3a - 2b - 1}\!\!>$       **6** $a = -2$ $\boxed{\frac{10}{a}}\!\!>$

**7** $a = -7, b = 6$ $\boxed{a^2 + 2b^2}\!\!>$       **8** $a = 50, b = 10$ $\boxed{\frac{a}{b} + a}\!\!>$

**9** $a = -5, b = 4, c = -3$ $\boxed{abc}\!\!>$   **10** $a = 12, b = -5$ $\boxed{2a^2 - 2ab + b^2}\!\!>$

The area $A$ of a garden is given by the formula
$$A = 2b^2 + 3l - 6b.$$
Use your calculator to find $A$ when …

**1** $b = 2$ m and $l = 5$ m    **2** $b = 4$ m and $l = 12$ m   **3** $b = 20$ m and $l = 45$ m

**4** $b = 2$ m and $l = 4.8$ m  **5** $b = 1.5$ m and $l = 6$ m  **6** $b = 2.3$ m and $l = 6.2$ m.

> **Finished Early?**
> ➭ Go to page 385

# Making Formulae

## Learn About It

Stella bought 3 stamps at 20 pence each.
She calculated the total cost, $C$, like this.
$C = 3 \times 20$ pence $= 60$ pence

Stella used this formula to calculate the cost:
$C$ = number of stamps × cost of a stamp.

**1** Write down the cost $C$ of 6 stamps at 25 pence each.

Stella needs 3 stamps costing $s$ pence each to post a letter.

$C = 3 \times s$ pence $= 3s$ pence

> *Remember: $3 \times s$ is written $3s$ for short.*

**2** Write a formula for the cost, $C$, of 5 stamps at $t$ pence each.

Stella posts a parcel using $n$ stamps at 20 pence each.

$C = n \times 20$ pence $= 20n$ pence

> *Remember: $n \times 20$ is the same as $20 \times n$.*

**3** Write a formula for the cost $C$ of $m$ stamps at 20 pence each.

Stella needs $n$ stamps at $s$ pence each to send another parcel.

$C = n \times s$ pence $= ns$ pence

**4** Write a formula for the cost $C$ of $m$ stamps at $t$ pence each.

Stella has 90 pence to buy some 15-pence stamps.
The number, $N$, she can buy is:

$N = \frac{90}{15} = 90 \div 15 = 6$.

She used this formula: $N = \dfrac{\text{money to spend}}{\text{price of one stamp}}$

**5** Write formulae for the number $N$ of …
   **(a)** 20 pence stamps that can be bought for 80 pence
   **(b)** 20 pence stamps that can be bought for $x$ pence
   **(c)** $m$ pence stamps that can be bought for 80 pence
   **(d)** $m$ pence stamps that can be bought for $x$ pence.

**6** Stella buys a first-class stamp and a second-class stamp.
   Write formulae for the total cost $C$ when …
   **(a)** a first-class stamp costs 30 pence and a second-class stamp costs 20 pence
   **(b)** a first-class stamp costs $f$ pence and a second-class stamp costs 20 pence
   **(c)** a first-class stamp costs 30 pence and a second-class stamp costs $s$ pence
   **(d)** a first-class stamp costs $f$ pence and a second-class stamp costs $s$ pence.

# Try It Out

Write formulae for the total cost *C* of …
**1** 3 dice at 40 pence each  **2** 3 dice at *a* pence each
**3** *n* dice at 40 pence each  **4** *n* dice at *s* pence each
**5** a sticker costing 15 pence and a sticker costing 10 pence
**6** a sticker costing *a* pence and one costing *b* pence.

# Practice

**1** The following TV programmes have been recorded on video.
Write a formula for the total recording time, *T*, for …
**(a)** 4 chat shows lasting 20 minutes each and 15 minutes of the news
**(b)** 2 cartoons lasting *c* minutes each and a soap lasting 25 minutes
**(c)** 3 soaps lasting *s* minutes each and 2 films lasting *f* minutes each
**(d)** 3 documentaries lasting *d* minutes each and half a film lasting *f* minutes
**(e)** 4 episodes of a soap lasting *s* minutes each and *n* cartoons lasting *c* minutes each
**(f)** *m* minutes of the news and quarter of a quiz show lasting *q* minutes
**(g)** *m* adverts lasting *a* minutes each and *n* cartoons lasting *c* minutes each.

**2 (a)** Brenda spent 80 pence buying 5 pencils. Write a formula for the number, *N*, she bought.
**(b)** Charles spent 60 pence on red pencils costing *r* pence each. Write a formula for the number, *N*, that he bought.
**(c)** Kelly spent 60 pence on red pencils costing *r* pence each and 90 pence on blue pencils costing *b* pence each. Write a formula for the total number, *N*, of pencils that she bought.
**(d)** Prakesh spent *a* pence on red pencils costing *r* pence each and *b* pence on blue pencils costing *g* pence each. Write a formula for the total number, *N*, of pencils that he bought.

Find the formulae made by the following number machines.

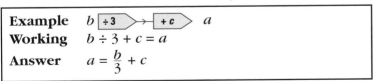

**1**   **2**   **3**
**4**   **5**   **6** 
**7** 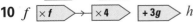  **8**   **9**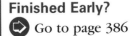
**10**

**Finished Early?**
Go to page 386

# Further Practice

 **1** Write formulae for the volume, $V$, remaining in a 50 cl bottle of juice after filling …

**(a)** a glass with 10 cl of juice    **(b)** a glass with $s$ cl of juice

**(c)** 4 glasses with 10 cl of juice each    **(d)** 4 glasses with $s$ cl of juice each

**(e)** $n$ glasses with 10 cl of juice each    **(f)** $n$ glasses with $s$ cl of juice each.

**2** Write formulae for …

**(a)** the total cost, $C$, of a book at $b$ pence and a pen at $n$ pence

**(b)** the total number, $N$, of biscuits in $m$ packets, each containing 20

**(c)** the amount, $A$, each child receives when £30 is divided among $n$ children

**(d)** the length, $l$, of each piece when a ribbon $r$ metres long is cut into $n$ equal pieces

**(e)** the total number of wine gums, $W$, contained in $m$ packets, each containing $s$ sweets

**(f)** the weight, $W$, of sugar left in a 500 g packet after $n$ spoons of 5 g have been removed

**(g)** the total length, $L$, of a train engine $t$ metres long pulling $n$ carriages, each $c$ metres long.

> **Finished Early?**
> ⇨ Go to page 386

# ⓷ Simplifying Expressions

## Learn About It

You can add the same number to itself more than once like this:
$3 + 3 + 3 + 3 = 12$.
But it is simpler to multiply:
$4 \times 3 = 12$.
So, $3 + 3 + 3 + 3$ can be **simplified** to $4 \times 3$.

You can add the *same* letter to itself more than once, too.
$a + a + a + a$ can be simplified to $4 \times a$ or even more simply $4a$.
So, $a + a + a + a = 4a$.

**1** Simplify the following.

**(a)** $b + b + b$    **(b)** $n + n + n + n + n + n$    **(c)** $F + F$

$2a = a + a$ and $3a = a + a + a$, so:
$2a + 3a = a + a + a + a + a$
$\qquad = 5a$
$2a + 3a$ can be simplified to $5a$.

**2** Simplify the following expressions.

| | |
|---|---|
| **Example** | $5b + 3b - 2b$ |
| **Working** | $5 + 3 - 2 = 6$ |
| **Answer** | $6b$ |

| | |
|---|---|
| **Example** | $2m - 5m$ |
| **Working** | $2 - 5 = -3$ |
| **Answer** | $-3m$ |

(a) $7p - 5p$     (b) $2q + 9q$     (c) $3f + f$

(d) $4x - 7x$     (e) $2s + 8s - 4s$     (f) $8k - 3k + 2k - 5k$

(g) $9t - t$

Look at this expression: $3a + 4a - 2a + 5a$.
The + and – signs break up the expression into the **terms**
$3a, + 4a, - 2a$ and $+ 5a$.
All the terms have the same letter, so they
are called **like terms**.
Expression with like terms can be
simplified, for example:
$3a + 4a - 2a + 5a = 10a$

> **Word Check**
>
> **terms** these are separated by +
> and – signs in an expression
>
> **like terms** terms that have
> exactly the same letters

The terms of $4mn + 3mn$ have exactly
the same letters too, so they are like terms and can be put together:
$4mn + 3mn = 7mn$.

**3** Simplify these expressions.

(a) $2mn + 10mn$     (b) $9ab - 4ab$     (c) $4xy + 8yx$

(d) $5ed - 2de$     (e) $8pqr - 2pqr - 3pqr$     (f) $5n^2 + 3n^2 - 4n^2$

## Try It Out

Simplify these expressions.

**1** $5p + 2p$          **2** $12m - 9m$          **3** $9r - 2r + 3r$

**4** $4t + 9t - 5t$          **5** $3tv + 5tv - 2vt$          **6** $4s + 3s - s + 5s$

**7** $4xy + 2xy - 4xy - xy$     **8** $6a - a$          **9** $8p - 12p$

**10** $6d - 8d + 5d + 4d$     **11** $7ab - 9ab + 4ab$     **12** $4y^2 - 2y^2 + 8y^2$

## Learn More About It

Look at this expression: $3a + 4a + 5b - 2b$.
$3a$ and $4a$ are like terms, so they can be combined: $3a + 4a = 7a$.
$+5b$ and $-2b$ are like terms, so they can be combined: $+ 5b - 2b = 3b$.
So $3a + 4a + 5b - 2b = 7a + 3b$.
You cannot simplify $7a + 3b$ because $7a$ and $+ 3b$ have different letters; they
are *not* like terms.

**1** Simplify these expressions.

(a) $4d + 5d + 5e - 2e$          (b) $5m - 2m + 4n - 3n$

(c) $6a + 5a + 8b - 10b$         (d) $2s - 5s + 3t + 5t$

(e) $2jk + 5jk + 6l - 2l$         (f) $5rs - 2rs + tu + 3tu$

The like terms in this expression are mixed up: $5x - 2y + 3x + 6y$.

First, move them next to each other: $5x + 3x - 2y + 6y$.

> *Remember: each sign must stay with its term.*

Then simplify:

$5x - 2y + 3x + 6y$

$= 5x + 3x - 2y + 6y$

$= 8x + 4y$

**2** Put the like terms next to each other, then simplify each expression.

(a) $2a + 3b + 5a + 2b$          (b) $4k + 9l - 2l + 5k$

(c) $6p + 4q - 2q - 3p$          (d) $g + 5h + g - 7h$

(e) $2xy + 5ab + 3xy + 2ab$       (f) $5mn + 7pq - 3mn - 2pq$

## Try It Out

Ⓜ Simplify these expressions.

**1** $4w - 2w + 3x - x$      **2** $9r - r + 8s - s$      **3** $6p - 3p - 3a + 5a$

**4** $2d - 5d + 6e - 2e$     **5** $2t - 3s + 8t + 4s$     **6** $5m - 7n + 3n - 3m$

**7** $4h - 2i - 3h + 5i$     **8** $-2u + 3v - v + 7u$     **9** $4de + 9fg - 5fg - 2de$

**10** $2rs + 5tu + 5rs - 10tu$

## Practice

Ⓝ Simplify these expressions.

**1** $y - 2y - 3y$

**2** $20a + 10a + 3 + 5$        > *Hint: 3 and 5 are like terms.*

**3** $25p - 20 - 50p + 80$                        **4** $c - 2c$

**5** $4d - 3 - 6d + 2$                             **6** $2r - 5d - 5r + 7d$

**7** $-3x + 4y - 7y - 2x$                          **8** $-3f - 2g - 5f - 7g$

**9** $5k - 6l - 7k - 8l$                           **10** $4x^2 + 3y^2 - 2x^2 + 7y^2$

**11** $5pq + 2 - 2qp - 5$                          **12** $2e + 3f - 3e + f + 6e - 2f$

**13** $3v^2 + 2w + 7v^2 - 5w - 2v^2$                **14** $5cd + 3ce - 2dc - 4ce$

**15** $3a + 4b - 5c + 2a - 3b + 7c$                **16** $2abc + 7pqr + 7abc - 3pqr$

**17** $5x - 2y - 3x - 4z + 5y - x + 5z - 2y$

**18** $2x^2 - 5tu + 6x^2 + 8ut$

> **Finished Early?**
>  Go to page 386

## Further Practice

In each question below, two of the expressions simplify to the same answer. Simplify the expressions and write down the answer to the odd one out.

**1** (a) $4m - 2m + 3m$  (b) $3m - 4m + 2m$  (c) $4m + 3m - 2m$

**2** (a) $7x + 4x - 2x - x$  (b) $4x - 2x + 7x - x$  (c) $-2x - 4x + x + 7x$

**3** (a) $2pq - 5pq - 4pq$  (b) $3pq - 5pq + 4pq$  (c) $-5pq + 4pq + 3pq$

**4** (a) $2a - 3b + 7b + 5a$  (b) $5a + 2a - 7b - 3b$  (c) $-3b + 2a + 5a + 7b$

**5** (a) $4m - 7 - 6m + 5$  (b) $4m - 5 - 6m + 7$  (c) $5 - 7 - 6m + 4m$

**6** (a) $ts + 2ab - 3ts - 5ab$  (b) $5ts - 2ab - 3ts + 2ab$
(c) $2ab - 3ts + 5ts - 2ab$

**7** (a) $3x^2 - 5y^2 + 6x^2 + 6y^2$  (b) $4x^2 - 2y^2 + 3y^2 + 5x^2$
(c) $-5y^2 + 6x^2 + 3x^2 - 6y^2$

**8** (a) $2a + b - 3c + 2b + 5c + 4a$  (b) $-2b + 2a - 4c + 7b + 4a - 5c$
(c) $6b - 2c - 7c + 4a - b + 2a$

> **Finished Early?**
> 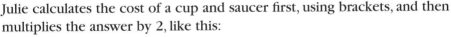 Go to page 386

# ▶ Brackets

## Learn About It

Cups cost £4 each and saucers cost £3 each.
Marlon and Julie buy 2 cups and 2 saucers.

Marlon adds the cost of two cups to the cost of two saucers, like this:

$2 \times 4 + 2 \times 3 = 8 + 6 = £14$

Julie calculates the cost of a cup and saucer first, using brackets, and then multiplies the answer by 2, like this:

$2 \times (4 + 3) = 2 \times 7 = £14$

Marlon's and Julie's calculations both give the same answer, so:

$2 \times 4 + 2 \times 3 = 2 \times (4 + 3)$

If cups cost £$c$ instead of £4, their calculations would still be the same:

$2 \times c + 2 \times 3 = 2 \times (c + 3)$

If cups cost £$c$ and saucers cost £$s$ instead of £3, their calculations would still be the same:

$2 \times c + 2 \times s = 2 \times (c + s)$

This can be simplified to:

$2c + 2s = 2(c + s)$

You can write the calculation the other way around, too:

$2(c + s) = 2c + 2s$

Removing the brackets from expressions like this is called **expanding** or **multiplying out** brackets.

| **Example** | $4(3 + c)$ |
|---|---|
| **Working** | $4 \times (3 + c)$ |
| | $= 4 \times 3 + 4 \times c$ |
| | $= 12 + 4c$ |
| **Answer** | $12 + 4c$ |

| **Example** | $2p(p + pq)$ |
|---|---|
| **Working** | $2p \times p + 2p \times pq$ |
| | $= 2p^2 + 2p^2q$ |
| **Answer** | $2p^2 + 2p^2q$ |

## Try It Out

**P** **1** Knives cost £2 each and forks cost £1 each.
   (a) Calculate the cost of 5 knives and 5 forks, using Marlon's method.
   (b) Calculate the cost of 5 knives and 5 forks, using Julie's method.

**2** Knives now cost £$k$ each. Forks are still £1 each.
   (a) Calculate the cost of 5 knives and 5 forks, using Marlon's method.
   (b) Calculate the cost of 5 knives and 5 forks, using Julie's method.

**3** Knives cost £$k$ each and forks now cost £$f$ each.
   (a) Calculate the cost of 5 knives and 5 forks, using Marlon's method.
   (b) Calculate the cost of 5 knives and 5 forks, using Julie's method.

**4** Expand these brackets.
   (a) $5(m + 2)$     (b) $7(3 + p)$
   (c) $a(b + 4)$     (d) $g(g + 8)$
   (e) $x(x + y)$     (f) $4a(a - ab)$

## Practice

**Q** Write down two ways of calculating the total, of …

| **Example** | 4 cricket balls at £$c$ each and 4 bats at £10 each |
|---|---|
| **Working** | Marlon's method: $4 \times c + 4 \times 10 = 4c + 40$ |
| | Julie's method: $4 \times (c + 10) = 4(c + 10)$ |
| **Answer** | $4(c + 10) = 4c + 40$ |

**1** 3 pairs of shorts at £4 each and 3 pairs of trousers at £10 each

**2** 4 pairs of socks at £$s$ each and 4 pairs of shoes at £15 each

**3** 12 packs of 20 screws and 12 packs of $n$ screws

**4** 100 people weighing $P$ kg each and 100 people weighing 70 kg each

**5** 12 bottles containing $W$ cl and 12 bottles containing $T$ cl of wine

**6** 4 giant footprints $g$ cm long and 4 small footprints $s$ cm long

**7** 3 large packets containing $L$ crisps, 3 medium packets containing $M$ crisps and 3 small packets containing $S$ crisps

**8** $n$ cars with 2 passengers and $n$ cars with 3 passengers

**9** $m$ books with $p$ pages and $m$ books with 100 pages

**10** $m$ boxes of $G$ green pencils and $m$ boxes of $R$ red pencils.

Expand the following brackets.

**1** $5(a + 2)$          **2** $7(5 + b)$          **3** $2(s + t)$          **4** $6(d - 7)$

**5** $m(3 + 2)$          **6** $4(a + b + c)$          **7** $n(x - y)$          **8** $t(v + w)$

**9** $A(B - 2)$          **10** $2(a + b)$          **11** $m(m + n)$          **12** $5c(d - c)$

**13** $3(2f + 4)$          **14** $j(jk - 5)$          **15** $ab(b + c)$          **16** $2r(rs + t)$

> **Finished Early?**
> ⇨ Go to page 387

## Further Practice

Copy the calculations, filling in the boxes.

**1** $3(\square + 2) = 3 \times 5 + 3 \times 2$          **2** $7(\square + \square) = 21 + 14$

**3** $\square(5 - 3) = 30 - 18$          **4** $10(m + 2) = 10\square + 10 \times \square$

**5** $\square(v - e) = 4v - 4\square$          **6** $5(p - \square) = \square p - 15$

**7** $20(\square + d) = 100 + \square d$          **8** $2(\square + f) = \square k + 2\square$

**9** $a(\square + \square) = ab + ac$          **10** $p(q - \square + \square) = p\square - pt + 2p$

Match each box with another box that means the same. Write the pairs of letters.

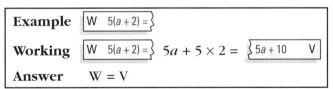

> **Finished Early?**
>  Go to page 387

# T ⑤ Factorising

## Learn About It

**Factorising** is the reverse of expanding the brackets of an expression. It involves writing an expression using brackets.

Factorisation involves finding **common factors** in terms. The common factors are written outside the bracket and the remaining terms are written inside.

The answer can be checked by expanding the bracket to see if the expression is the same as the one you started with.

| | |
|---|---|
| **Example** | Factorise $3m + 3n$. |
| **Working** | 3 is a factor of both $3m$ and $3n$. So 3 goes outside the brackets and $m + n$ inside the brackets. |
| **Answer** | $3(m + n)$      *Check*: $3(m + n) = 3m + 3n$      ✓ |

### Word Check

**factor of a term** a whole number or letter which divides exactly into another term

**common factor** a number or letter that is a factor of two or more terms

| | |
|---|---|
| **Example** | Factorise $2x - 8y$. |
| **Working** | 2 is a factor of $2x$ and $8y$. |
| | $2x = 2 \times x$ |
| | $-8y = 2 \times (-4y)$ |
| | So 2 goes outside the brackets and $x - 4y$ inside. |
| **Answer** | $2(x - 4y)$ |

## Try It Out

**1** Find the missing factor shown by ?.

(**a**) $2a + 2b = ?(a + b)$        (**b**) $3c + 3d = ?(c + d)$

(**c**) $12e - 6f = ?(2e + f)$      (**d**) $34g - 17h = ?(2g - h)$

(**e**) $2i + 4j = ?(i + 2j)$        (**f**) $3k - 6l = ?(k - 2l)$

(**g**) $2m - 6n = ?(m - 3n)$      (**h**) $9x + 12y = ?(3x + 4y)$

**2** Factorise these expressions. Check your answers by expanding the brackets.

(**a**) $2n + 2p$      (**b**) $3q + 3r$      (**c**) $2s + 4t$      (**d**) $3u - 6v$

(**e**) $3w - 9x$      (**f**) $15y + 10z$      (**g**) $12x + 8y$      (**h**) $30q - 18r$

# Learn More About It

Common factors can include letters as well as numbers.

| | |
|---|---|
| **Example** | Factorise $ax + ay$. |
| **Working** | The common factor is $a$. |
| **Answer** | $a(x + y)$ |

Sometimes you may need to take out more than one common factor.

| | |
|---|---|
| **Example** | Factorise $4pt - 6pu$. |
| **Working** | 2 is a common factor. $4pt - 6pu = 2(2pt - 3pu)$ |
| | There is another common factor, $p$. |
| | $2(2pt - 3pu) = 2p(2t - 3u)$ |
| **Answer** | $2p(2t - 3u)$ |

Be careful when expressions include powers.

| | |
|---|---|
| **Example** | Factorise $a^2 + ab$. |
| **Working** | $a$ is a common factor. |
| | $a^2 = a \times a$ |
| | $ab = a \times b$ |
| | So $a$ goes outside the bracket, $a + b$ inside. |
| **Answer** | $a(a + b)$ |

Sometimes the common factor is actually one of the terms.

| | |
|---|---|
| **Example** | Factorise $4x^2 + 2x$. |
| **Working** | 2 is a common factor. |
| | So $4x^2 + 2x = 2(2x^2 + x)$ |
| | $x$ is also a common factor. |
| | $2x^2 = x \times 2x$ |
| | $x = x \times 1$ |
| | So $2(2x^2 + x) = 2x(2x + 1)$ |
| **Answer** | $2x(2x + 1)$ |

# Try It Out

**1** Find the missing factors.

There may be more than one missing factor!

(a) $ax + bx = ?(a + b)$
(b) $ax + ay = ?(x + y)$
(c) $bx + 2b = ?(x + 2)$
(d) $3ax + 3ab = ?(x + b)$
(e) $2ax + 2bx = ?(a + b)$
(f) $16y + 8xy = ?(2 + x)$
(g) $24xyz + 6xz = ?(4y + 1)$

**2** Fill in the brackets.

(a) $4a + 2b = 2(\quad + \quad)$     (b) $4cd + 8de = 4d(\quad + \quad)$

(c) $fgh - 3fhi = fh(\quad - \quad)$     (d) $6jk + 2kl = 2k(\quad + \quad)$

(e) $m^2 + m = m(\quad + \quad)$     (f) $a^2b^2 - ab = ab(\quad - \quad)$

You have to insert the correct sign now!

(g) $op^2q - pq = pq(\qquad)$     (h) $r^2s + rs^2 = rs(\qquad)$

**3** Factorise these.

(a) $ab + bc$     (b) $2b - 2c$     (c) $2a^2 + a$     (d) $3a^2 + 6a$

(e) $2ab - 4b$     (f) $7ab + 14a$     (g) $3abc + 2ac$

# Practice

**1** Find the missing factors. There may be more than one missing factor.

(a) $2a + 6b = ?(a + 3b)$     (b) $3c - 6d = ?(c - 2d)$

(c) $5e - 15f = ?(e - 3f)$     (d) $14g + 10h = ?(7g + 5h)$

(e) $2i + 3i = ?(2 + 3) = 5?$     (f) $4j - 3j = ?(4 - 3) = ?$

(g) $2jk + 4jl = ?(jk + 2jl) = ?(k + 2l)$     (h) $3mn - 6mr = ?(n - 2r)$

(i) $15pq + 20ps = ?(3q + 4s)$

(j) $2t^2u + 4t = ?(t^2u + 2t) = ?(tu + 2)$

(k) $3v^2w + 6vx = ?(v^2w + 2vx) = ?(vw + 2x)$

(l) $10y^2z + 5yx = ?(2yz + x)$

(m) $18xy^2z - 9xy = ?(2yz - 1)$

**2** Factorise these.

(a) $2y + xy$     (b) $2x^2 + 4x$     (c) $12xz - 6yx$

(d) $5x^2 + 10xy$     (e) $12x - 4x^2$     (f) $12xy + 4y$

(g) $18xz^2 + 3yz$     (h) $2x^2y^2 + 3x^2y + 5xy$     (i) $3x^2y + 3xy^2 + 4xy$

> **Finished Early?**
> ➡ Go to page 387

# Further Practice

**1** Find the missing factors.

(a) $7a - 7b = ?(a - b)$     (b) $3c - 3d = ?(c - d)$

(c) $2e + 4f = ?(e + 2f)$     (d) $12g + 24h = ?(g + 2h)$

(e) $15i - 10j = ?(3i - 2j)$     (f) $3k + 2kl = ?(3 + 2l)$

(g) $m - mn = ?(1 - n)$     (h) $2pq + 2pr = ?(q + r)$

(i) $stu + tuv = ?(s + v)$     (j) $2wx + 4xyz = ?(w + 2yz)$

**2** Factorise these expressions.

(a) $10a + 10b$     (b) $3c - 3d$     (c) $3e + 3f + 3g$

(d) $hi + hj$     (e) $kl + km + kn$     (f) $2xp + 2xq$

(g) $2rs + 4rt$     (h) $5st + 15su$     (i) $v^2 + 2v$

(j) $wx^2 + wx$     (k) $3y^2 + 6yz$

> **Finished Early?**
> ➡ Go to page 387

# Equations and Inequalities

In this chapter you will learn about …
1. solving equations
2. simplifying equations
3. trial and improvement
4. inequalities

## Solving Equations

### Remember?

- An **inverse** is the opposite of an operation.
  Addition (+) and subtraction (–) are inverses of each other.
  Multiplication (×) and division (÷) are inverses of each other.
- Number machines can be reversed to show their inverses:
  20 ÷4 ▷ 5 becomes 20 ◁ ×4 5
- You can write and solve an equation using a number machine:

| | |
|---|---|
| **Example** | Solve $a + 3 = 5$. |
| **Working** | $a$ +3 ▷ 5     (*Write the equation using a number machine.*) |
| | $a$ ◁ –3 5     (*Reverse the number machine and work backwards.*) |
| **Answer** | $a = 2$ |

## Try It Out

**1** Reverse these number machines to find the missing numbers.

(a) ? +20 ▷ 50

(b) ? –45 ▷ 38

(c) ? ×5 ▷ 65

(d) ? ÷3 ▷ 14

**2** Write these equations using number machines, then solve them.

(a) $k + 10 = 25$

(b) $x - 5 = 12$

(c) $4m = 24$

(d) $\frac{c}{2} = 4$

# Learn About It

An equation is like a set of weighing scales.

Equations have two sides, the left-hand side and the right-hand side.
You can shorten these to LHS and RHS.

The two sides of the equation are equal, so the scale pans
balance.

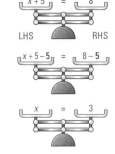

Take 5 away from both sides to keep the balance.

Now simplify to find the answer.

You can solve equations without using scales. Always do the same thing to
both sides of an equation. This way, the two sides will always balance.

| | | |
|---|---|---|
| **Example** | $x + 12 = 20$ | |
| **Working** | $x + 12 - 12 = 20 - 12$ | *(Subtract 12 from both sides.)* |
| **Answer** | $x = 8$ | *(Simplify both sides.)* |

| | | |
|---|---|---|
| **Example** | $p - 7 = 10$ | |
| **Working** | $p - 7 + 7 = 10 + 7$ | *(Add 7 to both sides.)* |
| **Answer** | $p = 17$ | *(Simplify both sides.)* |

| | | |
|---|---|---|
| **Example** | $3a = 15$ | |
| **Working** | $\frac{3a}{3} = \frac{15}{3}$ | *(Divide both sides by 3.)* |
| **Answer** | $a = 5$ | *(Simplify both sides.)* |

| | | |
|---|---|---|
| **Example** | $\frac{n}{2} = 6$ | |
| **Working** | $\frac{n}{2} \times 2 = 6 \times 2$ | *(Multiply both sides by 2.)* |
| **Answer** | $n = 12$ | *(Simplify both sides.)* |

## Key Fact

When solving equations:
- always write each step on a new line
- keep the LHS and RHS balanced
- simplify expressions whenever you can.

### Word Check

**equation** two expressions
joined by an equals sign to
show that one expression
equals the other

# Try It Out

| | |
|---|---|
| **Example** | Solve $\frac{x}{3} = 5$    *(Remember: $\frac{x}{3}$ means x ÷ 3.)* |
| **Working** | $\frac{x}{3} = 5$         *(Write down the equation.)* |
| | $\frac{x}{3} \times 3 = 5 \times 3$   *(Multiply both sides by 3.)* |
| **Answer** | $x = 15$ |

Solve the following equations. Write each step on a new line.

**1** $x - 2 = 7$      **2** $2x = 12$      **3** $\frac{y}{5} = 8$      **4** $y + 7 = 30$

**5** $\frac{z}{3} = 4$      **6** $15z = 60$      **7** $t - 200 = 450$      **8** $\frac{t}{25} = 17$

# Learn More About It

This equation has two operations, × and −.

$$3x - 5 = 10$$

Here is the solution using scales.

Write the equation.

Add 5 to both sides.

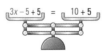

Simplify both sides.

Divide both sides by 3.

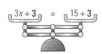

Simplify both sides.

## Key Fact

When solving equations,
reverse the order of operations.

**Example**  Solve $\dfrac{x}{5} - 2 = 4$.

**Working**  $\dfrac{x}{5} - 2 + 2 = 4 + 2$  *(Add 2 to both sides.)*

$\dfrac{x}{5} = 6$  *(Simplify.)*

$\dfrac{x}{5} \times 5 = 6 \times 5$  *(Multiply both sides by 5.)*

**Answer**  $x = 30$

## Try It Out

**C** Solve these equations. Remember to write each step on a new line.

**1** $2a + 4 = 10$   **2** $5g + 2 = 27$   **3** $4m + 11 = 27$   **4** $2b - 3 = 11$

**5** $10p - 8 = 52$   **6** $6b - 3 = 15$   **7** $\dfrac{b}{4} + 2 = 22$   **8** $\dfrac{x}{10} + 3 = 7$

**9** $\dfrac{a}{2} - 3 = 5$   **10** $\dfrac{x}{5} - 4 = 0$

## Practice

**D**

**1** Solve these equations. Remember to write each step on a new line. Some of the answers include fractions.

(a) $4t = 3$     (b) $5x = 22$     (c) $6a + 2 = 20$

(d) $\dfrac{c}{10} = 5$     (e) $\dfrac{k}{6} - 5 = 3$     (f) $4p - 16 = 2$

(g) $8x = 17$     (h) $\dfrac{r}{3} - 16 = 4$     (i) $5p - 1 = 27$

(j) $2s + 3 = 14$     (k) $\dfrac{w}{20} - 200 = 100$     (l) $50d - 75 = 48$

**2** Solve these equations. Some of the answers are negative.

(a) $t + 8 = 3$     (b) $a + 17 = 2$     (c) $5x = -30$

(d) $9q = -27$     (e) $\dfrac{d}{8} = -5$     (f) $\dfrac{m}{4} = -3$

(g) $4p + 13 = 1$     (h) $2x + 35 = 15$     (i) $\dfrac{r}{7} + 9 = 4$

(j) $\dfrac{p}{2} + 30 = 20$     (k) $2s + 6 = -10$     (l) $\dfrac{v}{4} + 2 = -7$

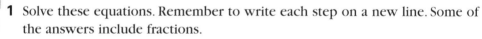

For each question, make up an equation and solve it. You can use any letter you like to stand for the number.

**Example** Class 8G's teacher said:

> I thought of a number, doubled it and then added 3. The answer was 9. What was my number?

**Working** Choose a letter to stand for the teacher's number, say, $n$.
Write an equation that matches what she said: $2n + 3 = 9$.
Now solve the equation.

$2n + 3 = 9$
$2n = 6$ _(Subtract 3 from both sides.)_
$n = 3$ _(Divide both sides by 2.)_

**Answer** The teacher's number was 3.

**1** I thought of a number, multiplied it by 4, then took 2 away. The result was 12. What was my number?

**2** If you divide my number by 3 and then add 4 you get 10. What is my number?

**3** I thought of a number, multiplied by 10, then added 5. The result was 28. What was my number?

**4** Multiply my number by 4, then subtract 9. You get 14. What is my number?

**5** I thought of a number, divided by 8 then added 25. The result was 200. What was my number?

**6** If I double my age and take away 5, I get 20. How old am I?

**7** If you divide the number of marks I got in my maths test by 7, then add 32, you get 34. How many marks did I get?

**Finished Early?**
Go to page 390

## Further Practice

The following equations have been written using number machines. Write them using algebra, then solve them.

**Example** $n$ $\boxed{-5}$ 17
**Working** $n - 5 = 17$
**Answer** $n = 22$ _(Add 5 to both sides.)_

**1** (a) $x$ $\boxed{+10}$ 25  (b) $p$ $\boxed{+2}$ 6.5  (c) $s$ $\boxed{-3}$ 1
  (d) $A$ $\boxed{-11}$ 11  (e) $m$ $\boxed{\times 5}$ 20  (f) $T$ $\boxed{\div 8}$ 1.5

**2** (a) $e$ $\boxed{\times 2}$ $\boxed{+5}$ 17  (b) $q$ $\boxed{\times 4}$ $\boxed{+1}$ 37
  (c) $L$ $\boxed{\div 6}$ $\boxed{-9}$ 2  (d) $j$ $\boxed{\times 100}$ $\boxed{-27}$ 0

**Finished Early?**
Go to page 390

# T② Simplifying Equations

## Learn About It

$x = 3$ and $3 = x$ mean the same thing.

If you have to solve this equation: $\quad 10 = x + 3$
you can turn it around: $\quad\quad\quad\quad x + 3 = 10$

The **terms** of equations are separated by +, – and = signs.
In the equation $5x + 3x = 7 + 9$ the terms are $5x$, $3x$, $7$ and $9$.

$5x$ and $3x$ are **like terms**, so $5x + 3x$ can be simplified to $8x$.
$7$ and $9$ are like terms, so $7 + 9$ can be simplified to $16$.

Now you can solve the equation:

$$5x + 3x = 7 + 9$$
$$8x = 16 \quad \text{(Simplify the terms.)}$$
$$x = 2 \quad \text{(Divide both sides by 8.)}$$

You can make up an equation to describe a problem. If you solve the equation, you solve the problem.

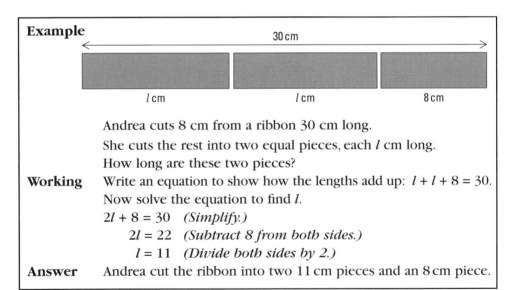

**Example**

30 cm

*l* cm      *l* cm      8 cm

Andrea cuts 8 cm from a ribbon 30 cm long.
She cuts the rest into two equal pieces, each *l* cm long.
How long are these two pieces?

**Working**   Write an equation to show how the lengths add up: $l + l + 8 = 30$.
Now solve the equation to find *l*.

$$2l + 8 = 30 \quad \text{(Simplify.)}$$
$$2l = 22 \quad \text{(Subtract 8 from both sides.)}$$
$$l = 11 \quad \text{(Divide both sides by 2.)}$$

**Answer**   Andrea cut the ribbon into two 11 cm pieces and an 8 cm piece.

## Try It Out

G **1** Turn these equations around and solve them.

     **(a)** $5 = x + 3$      **(b)** $10 = \frac{y}{4}$      **(c)** $1 = t - 5$      **(d)** $45 = 5x$

**2** Solve these equations. Simplify them first.

     **(a)** $7m - 5m = 6 + 8$      **(b)** $4x - x = 16 - 10$      **(c)** $4p + 3p = 10 + 11$
     **(d)** $4x + 2x = 12$      **(e)** $5x = 10 + 25$      **(f)** $5x - 2x = 6$

Write an equation for each of the following problems. Solve the equations.

| Example | Linda needs 20 light bulbs altogether. Full boxes contain $b$ light bulbs. She uses 3 boxes and another 2 light bulbs. How many light bulbs are there in a box? |
|---|---|
| Working | Linda uses 3 boxes of $b$ light bulbs. That's $3 \times b$ or $3b$ light bulbs. Linda uses another 2 light bulbs. That's $3b + 2$ altogether. So $3b + 2 = 20$. Now solve the equation. $$3b + 2 = 20$$ $$3b = 18$$ $$b = 6$$ |
| Answer | There are 6 light bulbs in a box. |

**1** A maths lesson lasts $m$ minutes and a history lesson lasts 40 minutes. Together, both lessons last 90 minutes. How long does a maths lesson last?

**2** Packets contain $p$ crisps each. Four packets contain 100 crisps. How many crisps does a packet contain?

**3** A length of 2 m is cut from a roll of wallpaper $w$ metres long. There are 8 m left on the roll. How long is a roll of wallpaper?

**4** Three chocolates at $c$ pence each and a 7p toffee cost 43 pence altogether. How much does one chocolate cost?

**5** Four adults weigh $W$ kg each. A child weighs 40 kg. They weigh 360 kg altogether. How much does an adult weigh?

**6** Jan recorded five songs, lasting $s$ minutes each, on a 30 minute tape. There was 10 minutes left on the tape. How long does each song last?

## Learn More About It

$$6m - 4 = 2m + 6$$

In this equation, $6m$ and $2m$ are like terms. You could combine them if they were on the same side of the equation.

$$6m - 4 = 2m + 6$$

| | |
|---|---|
| $6m - 2m - 4 = 6$ | *(Subtract 2m from both sides.)* |
| $4m - 4 = 6$ | *(Simplify the LHS.)* |
| $4m = 10$ | *(Add 4 to both sides.)* |
| $m = \dfrac{10}{4}$ | *(Divide both sides by 4.)* |
| $m = 2.5$ | *(Simplify the RHS.)* |

## Try It Out

**1** Solve these equations. Some answers are negative.

(a) $3r = r + 6$     (b) $5t = 2t + 12$     (c) $8w = 7w + 20$

(d) $10x = 3x + 14$     (e) $25n = 20n + 50$     (f) $7P = 3P + 8$

(g) $4m = 2m - 12$     (h) $6y = 5y - 2$     (i) $9q = 4q - 20$

**2** Solve these equations.

(a) $4t + 3 = 2t + 9$     (b) $8q + 1 = 3q + 16$     (c) $5r - 6 = 3r + 4$

(d) $4v + 3 = v + 9$     (e) $5M + 2 = 3M + 8$     (f) $7x - 8 = 3x + 12$

(g) $4d + 1 = d + 16$     (h) $9n - 10 = 2n + 4$     (i) $5z - 2 = 2z - 5$

## Practice

**J** Solve these equations.

**1** $10 = k - 7$     **2** $12 = \frac{t}{4} + 9$     **3** $5c - 2c = 15$

**4** $6r + r = 35$     **5** $4p = 2p + 10$     **6** $9y = y + 40$

**7** $9m - 1 = 6m + 5$     **8** $5d + 3 = 3d + 7$     **9** $2p + 3p + 4p = 36$

**10** $6v - 2v + 2 = 2v + 8$

**K** Write an equation for each of these problems. Solve the equations to answer the questions.

**1** A 30-litre tank of water fills 4 buckets containing $J$ litres each, with 10 litres left over. How much water does a bucket hold?

**2** A packet contains $s$ sweets. Holly and her friends ate 3 whole packets and 4 sweets from another packet. They ate 25 sweets altogether. How many sweets does a packet contain?

**3** The lengths of the sides of this rectangle add up to 96 cm. Find $x$.

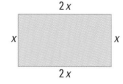

**4** I am thinking of a number, $n$. If I multiply the number by 5, I get the same answer as adding 24 to the number. What is my number?

**5** The picture shows the capacity, in millilitres, of a cup, a mug and a jug. The jug fills three cups and a mug.

(a) Make an equation for the amount of liquid the jug holds.

(b) How much does a cup hold?

(c) How much does a mug hold?

(d) How much does the jug hold?

$C$

$3C - 150$     $5C$

**Finished Early?**
➡ Go to page 390

## Further Practice

Two equations in each question have the same answer. Solve them *all* to find out which is the odd one out.

**1 (a)** $4 = x - 2$      **(b)** $16 = 2x$      **(c)** $2 = \frac{x}{3}$

**2 (a)** $2m + m = 12$      **(b)** $3m = -12$      **(c)** $-2 = \frac{m}{2}$

**3 (a)** $4A = 2A + 6$      **(b)** $9A = 3A + 18$      **(c)** $5A = 4A + 2$

**4 (a)** $4e + 8 = 12$      **(b)** $3e + 3 = 9$      **(c)** $2e + 6 = 10$

**5 (a)** $6k + 2 = 3k + 14$      **(b)** $4k - 3 = 5k + 1$      **(c)** $5k - 3 = 3k + 5$

> **Finished Early?**
> ➡ Go to page 390

# Trial and Improvement

## Learn About It

Trial and improvement is a mathematical method for 'guessing' the solution of an equation. To make a **trial**:
- guess the solution of the equation
- substitute your guess into the equation
- use the result to improve your guess.

Solve $x^2 = 34$, correct to 2 d.p.

$6^2 = 36$, so $x = 6$ would be a good first trial.

| Trial, $x$ | $x^2$ | Comments |
|---|---|---|
| 6 | $6^2 = 36$ | Too high. $x$ is smaller than 6. |
| 5 | $5^2 = 25$ | Too low. $x$ is bigger than 5. |
| | | Try 5.5 next, because it's exactly halfway between 5 and 6. |
| 5.5 | $5.5^2 = 30.25$ | Too low. $x$ is bigger than 5.5. |
| | | Try 5.7 because it's about halfway between 5.5 and 6. |
| 5.7 | $5.7^2 = 32.49$ | Too low. Try 5.8. |
| 5.8 | $5.8^2 = 33.64$ | Close but still too low. $x$ is bigger than 5.8. |
| 5.9 | $5.9^2 = 34.81$ | Close but still too high. $x$ is smaller than 5.9. |
| | | Try 5.85 next, because it's exactly halfway between 5.8 and 5.9. |
| 5.85 | $5.85^2 = 34.2225$ | Too high. $x$ is smaller than 5.85. |
| 5.83 | $5.83^2 = 33.9889$ | Too low. $x$ is bigger than 5.83. |
| 5.84 | $5.84^2 = 34.1056$ | Too high. $x$ is smaller than 5.84. |
| | | To find out which one is closer, try 5.835. |
| 5.835 | $5.835^2 = 34.047\,225$ | Too high. So $x$ is between 5.83 and 5.835. |

So the solution of $x^2 = 34$ is $x = 5.83$ to 2 d.p.

# Try It Out

 **1** Solve the equation $x^2 = 53$ to 2 d.p. Follow these steps.

    **(a)** Draw this table at the top of a page.

| Trial, $x$ | $x^2$ | Comments |
|---|---|---|
| 7 | $7^2 =$ | |

    **(b)** Try $x = 7$ and write a comment.

    **(c)** Try more whole numbers until you find the two whole numbers on either side of $x$ and closest to it.

    **(d)** Try numbers with one decimal place until you find the two on either side of $x$ and closest to it.

    **(e)** Try numbers with two decimal places until you find the two on either side of $x$ and closest to it.

    **(f)** Find out which answer from (e) is closer, by testing halfway between them.

**2** Copy the table below and use it to help you solve the equation $x^2 + 5 = 40$ correct to 1 d.p.

| Trial, $x$ | $x^2 + 5$ | Comments |
|---|---|---|
| 4 | $4^2 + 5 = 16 + 5 = 21$ | Too low. $x$ is bigger than 4 |
| 5 | $5^2 + 5 =$ | |

**3** Solve these equations correct to 1 d.p.

    **(a)** $x^2 + 2 = 16$      Try $x = 1$ as your first guess.

    **(b)** $x^2 - 12 = 82$    Try $x = 12$ as your first guess.

    **(c)** $x^2 + 9 = 29$     Make your own first guess.

# Practice

Solve these equations to the accuracy given. Make a table like the one above to help you.

**1** $x^2 = 120$            Try $x = 10$ as your first guess.
                             Give your answer correct to 2 d.p.

**2** $x^2 + x = 35$         Try $x = 5$ as your first guess.
                             Give your answer correct to 1 d.p.

**3** $x^2 - x = 16$         Try $x = 6$ as your first guess.
                             Give your answer correct to 1 d.p.

**4** $x^2 + x = 140$        Try $x = 13$ as your first guess.
                             Give your answer correct to 2 d.p.

**5** $x^2 - 10x = 100$      Make your own first guess.
                             Give your answer correct to 1 d.p.

**6** $x^2 + x = 0.8$        Make your own first guess.
                             Give your answer correct to 2 d.p.

**Finished Early?**
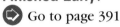 Go to page 391

# Further Practice

Write an equation for the area of each rectangle. Solve your equation, correct to 1 d.p.

| **Example** | Area = 65m², $x + 2$, $x$ |
|---|---|
| **Working** | Area of a rectangle = base × height |
| | $= x \times (x + 2)$ |
| | $= x^2 + 2x$ |
| | $x^2 + 2x = 65$ *(Use trial and improvement to solve correct to 1 d.p.)* |
| **Answer** | $x = 7.1$m (to 1 d.p.) |

**1**
Area = 28 cm², $x + 5$, $x$

**2**
Area = 55 mm², $x - 2$, $x$

**3**
Area = 120 m², $x + 3$, $x$

**Finished Early?**
 Go to page 391

# T ④ Inequalities

## Learn About It

A statement such as 6 > 5 is an **inequality**. You can use inequalities to represent a set of numbers.

$x > 2$ means numbers greater than 2.

If you are talking about whole numbers or **integers**, it means the numbers 3, 4, 5, 6, … and so on.

If you are talking about **all** numbers, you can get as close to 2 as you like, as long as you don't include it. This is shown by the open circle on the arrow.

$x \leqslant 8$ (less than or equal to 8) means numbers that are 8 or less. As 8 is included in the possible values, the circle at the end of the arrow is solid.

You can also give a **range** between two numbers.

$-6 \leqslant x < 4$ means numbers that are −6 or more, but less than 4.

### Word Check

**inequality** a statement showing that one number is bigger or smaller than another; a statement giving a range of values for a number

> greater than

< less than

⩾ greater than or equal to

⩽ less than or equal to

**integers** positive or negative whole numbers

**range** a limited set of numbers with a maximum and minimum

# Try It Out

Copy each statement. Write *True* or *False* next to each one.

**1** $3 < 10$      **2** $5 > 5$      **3** $5 \geqslant 5$

**4** $-6 > -4$      **5** $3 \leqslant 4$      **6** $-3 \leqslant 4$

**7** $1.52 > 1.51$      **8** $1.51 < -1.52$      **9** $1 \geqslant 0.999$

**10** $1 \leqslant 1$

Draw number lines from –8 to 8 and use them to illustrate these inequalities.

**1** $x \leqslant 7$ (integers)      **2** $x \leqslant 7$ (all numbers)

**3** $x > 4$ (integers)      **4** $x > 4$ (all numbers)

**5** $x < -6$ (all numbers)      **6** $x \geqslant -3$ (all numbers)

**6** $-2 < x < 4$ (integers)      **8** $-2 < x < 4$ (all numbers)

**7** $2 < x < 4$ (integers)      **10** $-7 \leqslant x \leqslant 3.5$ (all numbers)

# Learn More About It

An inequality can also be a type of puzzle, like an equation.

$x + 2 > 8$ means that if you take a number and add 2 to it, the answer must be greater than 8.

Solve it like an equation.

$x + 2 > 8$      (*Write the inequality.*)

$x + 2 - 2 > 8 - 2$      (*Subtract 2 from both sides.*)

$x > 6.$      (*Simplify.*)

So the number is greater than 6.

Other puzzles can be solved in similar ways.

$x - 5 \leqslant 6$      $3x \geqslant 3$      $\dfrac{x}{5} > 4$

$x - 5 + 5 \leqslant 6 + 5$      $3x \div 3 \geqslant 3 \div 3$      $\dfrac{x}{5} \times 5 > 4 \times 5$

$x \leqslant 11$      $x \geqslant 1$      $x > 20$

You have to be careful with range inequalities like this.

$-8 < 2x < 3$

$-8 \div 2 < 2x \div 2 < 3 \div 2$      (*Divide **all three parts** by 2.*)

$-4 < x < 1.5$      (*Simplify.*)

## Try It Out

**(R)** Solve these inequalities.

**1** $x + 5 < 10$        **2** $x - 2 \leqslant 4$        **3** $x + 1 > -5$

**4** $2x < 18$        **5** $10x \geqslant 36$        **6** $\dfrac{x}{4} > 8$

**7** $5 < x + 4 < 11$      **8** $-2 \leqslant x - 1 \leqslant 5$      **9** $-6 < 4x < 0$

**10** $12 \leqslant \dfrac{x}{5} < 16$

## Practice

**(S)** Write an inequality statement to match each number line.

**1**

**2**

**3**

**4**

**5**

**6**

**(T)** Solve each pair of inequalities. Write SAME if they have the same solution, DIFFERENT if they don't.

**1 (a)** $x + 5 < 10$      **2 (a)** $2x \geqslant 15$      **3 (a)** $x + 6 \leqslant 2$
   **(b)** $x - 3 < 2$          **(b)** $x - 7 \geqslant 0.5$       **(b)** $\dfrac{x}{4} \leqslant -16$

**4 (a)** $5x > 15$       **5 (a)** $0 < x + 10 < 6$
   **(b)** $2x \geqslant 6$        **(b)** $-5 < \dfrac{x}{2} < -2$

> **Finished Early?**
> ⇨ Go to page 391

## Further Practice

**(U)** Solve each inequality, then draw a number line to illustrate it.

**1** $2x \leqslant 7$ (integers)        **2** $x + 1 \leqslant 7$ (all numbers)

**3** $x - 8 > 4$ (integers)        **4** $5x \geqslant 0$ (all numbers)

**5** $\dfrac{x}{10} < -3$ (all numbers)      **6** $2 < x - 5 < 4$ (integers)

**7** $-1 < x + 1 \leqslant 1$ (all numbers)    **8** $-4 < 2x < -2$ (integers)

> **Finished Early?**
> ⇨ Go to page 3

# Unit 4 *Algebra 1*

## Summary of Chapters 7 and 8

- Find the value of an expression by substituting numbers for its letters, e.g. if $a = 2$ and $b = 5$, then the value of $a + b$ is $2 + 5 = 7$.
- Like terms contain exactly the same letters, so $2m$ and $5m$ are like terms, and $3mn$ and $-4mn$ are like terms.
  Simplify an expression by combining like terms, e.g.
  $3a + 5a + 6b - 2b = 8a + 4b$.
- To expand brackets, multiply all of its terms, e.g.
  $3(a - b) = 3 \times a - 3 \times b = 3a - 3b$.
- Factorising is the reverse of expanding brackets.
- To solve an equation, always do the same thing to both sides to keep balanced.
- Rearrange and simplify equations before you start to solve them.

| | | |
|---|---|---|
| **Example** | Solve $5x - 6 = 19$ | |
| **Working** | $5x - 6 + 6 = 19 + 6$ | (*Add 6 to both sides.*) |
| | $5x = 25$ | (*Simplify both sides.*) |
| **Answer** | $x = 5$ | (*Divide both sides by 5 and simplify.*) |

- Some equations can't be solved exactly, but you can get as close as you like to the solution by **trial and improvement**. Use the result of each trial to make a more accurate guess.

$$x \leqslant 5 \qquad x \geqslant 5 \qquad x < 5$$

This range inequality shows that $5 \leqslant x < 10$.
- Solve inequalities using the rules for equations.

# Brush Up Your Number 5

 **More Computation Shortcuts and Patterns**

## Learn About It

Use these shortcuts to make it easier to add and subtract in your head.

| Example | Shortcut | Working |
|---|---|---|
| | **Subtract 9** | |
| 36 – 9 = 27 | Subtract 10<br>Add 1 | 36 – 10 = 26<br>26 + 1 = 27 |
| | **Add 99** | |
| 73 + 99 = 172 | Add 100<br>Subtract 1 | 73 + 100 = 173<br>173 – 1 = 172 |
| | **Subtract 99** | |
| 248 – 99 = 149 | Subtract 100<br>Add 1 | 248 – 100 = 148<br>148 + 1 = 149 |

## Try It Out

**A** Calculate the following using a shortcut. Explain how you worked out each answer.

| | | | |
|---|---|---|---|
| **1** 26 + 9 | **2** 45 + 9 | **3** 94 + 9 | **4** 138 + 9 |
| **5** 37 – 9 | **6** 72 – 9 | **7** 166 – 9 | **8** 331 – 9 |
| **9** 27 + 99 | **10** 135 + 99 | **11** 252 + 99 | **12** 585 + 99 |
| **13** 136 – 99 | **14** 290 – 99 | **15** 462 – 99 | **16** 948 – 99 |

## Learn More About It

Use these shortcuts to make it easier to multiply and divide in your head.

| Example | Shortcut | Working |
|---|---|---|
| | **Multiply by 9** | |
| 23 × 9 = 207 | Multiply by 10<br>Subtract number | 23 × 10 = 230<br>230 – 23 = 207 |
| | **Multiply by 99** | |
| 7 × 99 = 693 | Multiply by 100<br>Subtract number | 7 × 100 = 700<br>700 – 7 = 693 |

| Example | Shortcut | Working |
|---|---|---|
| | **Multiply by *0** | |
| $12 \times 30 = 360$ | Multiply by * <br> Multiply by 10 | $12 \times 3 = 36$ <br> $36 \times 10 = 360$ |
| | **Multiply by *00** | |
| $8 \times 400 = 3200$ | Multiply by * <br> Multiply by 100 | $8 \times 4 = 32$ <br> $32 \times 100 = 3200$ |
| | **Divide by *0** | |
| $35 \div 50 = 0.7$ | Divide by * <br> Divide by 10 | $35 \div 5 = 7$ <br> $7 \div 10 = 0.7$ |
| | **Divide by *00** | |
| $36 \div 400 = 0.09$ | Divide by * <br> Divide by 100 | $36 \div 4 = 9$ <br> $9 \div 100 = 0.09$ |

## Try It Out

Calculate the following using a shortcut. Explain how you worked out each answer.

1 $13 \times 9$    2 $25 \times 9$    3 $78 \times 9$    4 $560 \times 9$
5 $7 \times 99$    6 $14 \times 99$    7 $35 \times 99$    8 $89 \times 99$
9 $17 \times 20$    10 $23 \times 30$    11 $51 \times 60$    12 $35 \times 40$
13 $12 \times 200$    14 $32 \times 600$    15 $88 \times 500$    16 $57 \times 400$
17 $12 \div 30$    18 $45 \div 50$    19 $21 \div 70$    20 $144 \div 60$
21 $6 \div 200$    22 $28 \div 400$    23 $95 \div 500$    24 $261 \div 300$

## Practice

Find your own shortcuts to work out these calculations. Explain how you worked out each answer.

1 $26 + 999$    2 $372 + 999$    3 $5200 - 999$    4 $8524 - 999$
5 $17 \times 999$    6 $56 \times 999$    7 $12 \times 3000$    8 $63 \times 5000$
9 $24 \div 3000$    10 $252 \times 7000$    11 $28 + 19$    12 $57 - 19$
13 $45 + 39$    14 $76 - 29$    15 $52 + 69$    16 $23 + 98$
17 $65 + 93$    18 $145 - 97$    19 $358 - 92$    20 $320 + 490$
21 $750 - 390$    22 $2500 + 5900$    23 $8 \times 990$    24 $25 \times 990$
25 $15 \times 98$    26 $7 \times 994$    27 $20 \times 30$    28 $60 \times 50$
29 $500 \times 40$    30 $2000 \times 800$    31 $800 \div 40$    32 $9000 \div 30$
33 $60\,000 \div 20$    34 $20\,000 \div 500$

**Finished Early?**
Go to page 390

# 9 Calculating with Confidence

In this chapter you will learn about …
**1** using your calculator
**2** checking your answer

## 1 Using Your Calculator

### Remember?

Calculate using the correct order of operations.
Remember this as BoDMAS:
**B**rackets first
**P**owers
**D**ivide and **M**ultiply (work
from left to right)
**A**dd and **S**ubtract (work from
left to right).

| | |
|---|---|
| **Example** | $6 + (5 - 2) \times 4$ |
| **Working** | $= 6 + 3 \times 4$ (*Brackets first.*) |
| | $= 6 + 12$ (*× before +.*) |
| | $= 18$ |
| **Answer** | 18 |

### Try It Out

**A** Calculate the following.

**1** $4 + 2 \times 3$    **2** $8 - 6 \div 2$    **3** $9 \times 2 - 5$    **4** $2 + 6 \div 3 - 1$

**5** $3 \times (8 - 2)$    **6** $16 \div (4 \div 2)$    **7** $12 - (9 - 7)$    **8** $3 + (4 + 1) \times 6 - 2$

### Learn About It

**1** Blake, Daisy and Sonly make some cakes. Blake makes 5, Sonly 4 and Daisy 9.
They decide to share them out equally among themselves. They have to add
up the number of cakes and divide by 3, like this:

$$\frac{\text{total number of cakes}}{3} = \frac{5 + 4 + 9}{3}$$

What is the answer?

**2** Sonly uses her calculator this way. Try it out.
First she calculates the total.

[ 5 ] [ + ] [ 4 ] [ + ] [ 9 ] [ = ]   `18.`

Then she divides by 3.

[ ÷ ] [ 3 ] [ = ]   `6.`

Each person gets 6 cakes.

Daisy knows that calculators work out brackets first before going on to the next part of a calculation. So she uses brackets, like this:

Daisy gets the same answer as Sonly.

**3** Press **AC** to start a new calculation, then try Daisy's method. Press **C** if you do not have **AC** on your calculator.

On some calculators, pressing **C** only cancels the last part of a calculation. It may not start a new calculation. Check with your teacher if you are not sure.

**4** Blake makes a mistake. He puts the numbers into his calculator as he reads them, like this:

**5** **+** **4** **+** **9** **÷** **3**

He is only dividing 9 by 3, not the total number of cakes. Work out his answer in your head.

Press **AC** to clear the last calculation and try Blake's method.

**5** **+** **4** **+** **9** **÷** **3** **=** ⌈ *12.* ⌉

They cannot have 12 cakes each!

---

## Key Fact

Press **AC** or **C** to clear the last calculation before starting a new one.

---

**5** Calculate these. First use Sonly's method, then Daisy's.

(a) $\dfrac{12 + 7 + 16}{7}$   (b) $\dfrac{100 - 20 - 25}{11}$   (c) $\dfrac{1 + 2 + 3 + 4 + 5 + 6}{6}$

**6** Blake and Daisy calculate $\dfrac{12}{2 + 3 + 1}$ like this.

Blake: **12** **÷** **2** **+** **3** **+** **1** **=** ⌈ *10.* ⌉
He calculates $12 \div 2 + 3 + 1$.

Daisy: **12** **÷** **(** **2** **+** **3** **+** **1** **)** **=** ⌈ *2.* ⌉
She calculates $12 \div (2 + 3 + 1)$.

Try both ways. Who is correct? Explain why.

## Try It Out

Calculate the following. Use brackets only if you need to. Check your answers with your neighbour.

**1** $\dfrac{35 + 20}{5}$   **2** $\dfrac{60}{8 + 4}$   **3** $\dfrac{17 + 25 - 10}{8}$

**4** $\dfrac{98}{7 + 4 + 29 - 15}$   **5** $\dfrac{16 + 14}{32 - 27}$

# Learn More About It

Your calculator can store numbers in its memory. Use this Key Facts box to check which keys on *your* calculator allow you to use the memory.

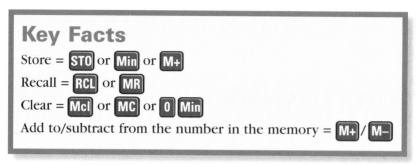

**Key Facts**

Store = STO or Min or M+
Recall = RCL or MR
Clear = Mcl or MC or 0 Min
Add to/subtract from the number in the memory = M+ / M−

Follow these steps to check the memory on your calculator.

**1** If 'M' is showing in your calculator display, it means there is already a number stored there. Clear the memory. The 'M' should disappear.

**2** Store 5 in the memory. The 'M' should reappear.

**3** Work through these steps on your calculator:
(a) Clear the memory.
(b) Store 10 in the memory.
(c) Add 7 to the memory.
(d) Subtract 9 from the memory.
(e) Add 3 to the memory five times.
(f) Add $4 \times 6$ to the memory.
(g) Recall the memory and write down your answer.
(h) Clear the memory. Check that it is cleared.

**4** You can use the memory to store parts of a calculation. Try it.

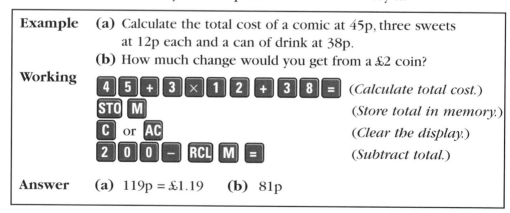

| **Example** | (a) Calculate the total cost of a comic at 45p, three sweets at 12p each and a can of drink at 38p. |
| | (b) How much change would you get from a £2 coin? |

**Working**

4 5 + 3 × 1 2 + 3 8 =  (*Calculate total cost.*)
STO M  (*Store total in memory.*)
C or AC  (*Clear the display.*)
2 0 0 − RCL M =  (*Subtract total.*)

**Answer**   (a) 119p = £1.19   (b) 81p

# Try It Out

**1** Follow these instructions and write down the final answer:

   **(a)** Clear the display.

   **(b)** Store 125 in the memory.

   **(c)** Subtract 49 from the memory.

   **(d)** Add 94 to the memory.

   **(e)** Calculate $5 \times 7$ and add it to the memory.

   **(f)** Recall the memory.

**2** Calculate the total cost of 3 pencils at 35p each, a notepad at 74p and 2 erasers at 48p. Store the answer in the memory. Calculate the change from a £10 note.

# Practice

**1** Use brackets to calculate the following. Try this worked example on your calculator first.

**Example** $\dfrac{15 + 25}{8} - \dfrac{150}{8 \times 15}$

**Working** Put in brackets: $\dfrac{(15 + 25)}{8} - \dfrac{150}{8 \times 15}$

**Answer** 3.75

   **(a)** $\dfrac{52 + 56}{18}$

   **(b)** $\dfrac{285}{43 - 18}$

   **(c)** $\dfrac{42}{1 + 5 \times 1.2}$

   **(d)** $\dfrac{4 \times 4.94}{1.9 + 3.3}$

   **(e)** $15 + \dfrac{20}{1.8 + 0.7}$

   **(f)** $\dfrac{1000 - 244}{29 + 35} - 7$

   **(g)** $\dfrac{125.46}{5} - \dfrac{2.2 + 6.5}{1.6}$

   **(h)** $\dfrac{1}{0.02} + \dfrac{1}{0.04 + 50}$

**2** Calculate the answers to question 1 without using brackets. Use the memory of your calculator, if necessary.

**E** Use the information in the box to work out the calculations below.

Word Check
..........................................
**convert** change

| Foreign Currency Exchange Rates | | |
|---|---|---|
| **£1 buys ...** | | |
| US dollars | $ | 1.55 |
| French francs | FFr | 9.71 |
| German marks | DM | 2.98 |
| Portuguese escudos | Esc | 296.79 |
| Italian lire | L | 2866 |

| | |
|---|---|
| **Example** | Convert to US dollars ($): **(a)** £20  **(b)** £74  **(c)** £325 |
| **Working** | The number of dollars to the £1 is: 1.55. Store this in the memory. |

`1` `.` `5` `5` `STO` `M`

Multiply the figure in the memory by the number of pounds in each part of the question:

`2` `0` `×` `RCL` `M` `=`  31.

`7` `4` `×` `RCL` `M` `=`  114.7

`3` `2` `5` `×` `RCL` `M` `=`  503.75

| | |
|---|---|
| **Answer** | **(a)** $31  **(b)** $114.7  **(c)** $503.75 |

**1** Convert to French francs (FFr) ...

   **(a)** £60  **(b)** £140  **(c)** £2300.

**2** Convert to German marks (DM) ...

   **(a)** £950  **(b)** £75 320  **(c)** £4 523 000.

**3** Convert to Portuguese escudos (Esc) ...

   **(a)** £70  **(b)** £2800  **(c)** £6 million.

**4** Convert to Italian lire (L) ...

   **(a)** 40p  **(b)** £9.60  **(c)** £735.

**Finished Early?**
➡ Go to page 390

# Further Practice

**1** $\dfrac{1800}{36 - 27}$

**2** $\dfrac{6 + 3 \times 14}{16}$

**3** $\dfrac{17 + 3 \times 11}{20}$

**4** $\dfrac{450 - 170}{40 - 26}$

**5** $\dfrac{3.2 + 2.8}{1.4 + 6.6}$

**6** $100 + \dfrac{120}{80 - 55}$

**Finished Early?**
⇨ Go to page 390

# Checking Your Answer

## Remember?

Count the significant figures of a number from left to right, from the first non–zero digit to the last.

| Examples | 4 000 000 has 1 s.f. |
| --- | --- |
| | 930 has 2 s.f. |
| | 300 500 has 4 s.f. |
| | 0.00253 has 3 s.f. |

You can round numbers to a given number of significant figures.

**Example** Round 3 262 652 to 2 s.f.

**Working**

2nd s.f.  3rd s.f.

3 262 652

≈ 3 300 000

round up when 3rd s.f. is 5, 6, 7, 8 or 9

**Answer** 3 300 000

≈ means 'approximately equals'.

# Try It Out

**1** Write down each number below. Draw a line under the significant figures. How many significant figures does each number have?
   **(a)** 59 300
   **(b)** 71 592 000
   **(c)** 0.053
   **(d)** 9 300 400

**2** Round these numbers.
   **(a)** 9268 (to 1 s.f.)
   **(b)** 637.4 (to 2 s.f.)
   **(c)** 4 592 800 (to 1 s.f.)
   **(d)** 0.057 72 (to 1 s.f.)

# Learn About It

Always estimate the answer to a calculation, using rounded numbers. Round to 1 s.f. This helps you check you haven't made a mistake.

| **Example** | $29 \times 194 = 5626$ |
|---|---|
| **Working** | $29 = 30$ to 1 s.f. |
| | $194 = 200$ to 1 s.f. |
| | $30 \times 200 = 6000$ |
| **Answer** | 5626 is very close to 6000. |
| | It's probably correct. |

| **Example** | $58928 \div 63 = 5321$ |
|---|---|
| **Working** | $58928 = 60000$ to 1 s.f. |
| | $63 = 60$ to 1 s.f. |
| | $60000 \div 60 = 1000$ |
| **Answer** | 5321 is more than five times greater than 1000. |
| | It's probably incorrect. |

You should always round rough answers, too.
$143 \div 26$ gives a rough calculation.
$100 \div 30 = 3.333\,333\ \ldots$ !

3 is accurate enough to check the main calculation.

### Word Check
**estimate** calculate a rough answer

# Try It Out

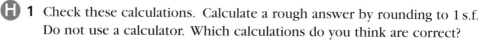

**1** Check these calculations. Calculate a rough answer by rounding to 1 s.f. Do not use a calculator. Which calculations do you think are correct?

(a) $12 \times 42 = 504$      (b) $58 \times 74 = 4292$
(c) $209 \div 38 = 15.5$      (d) $750 \times 97 = 727\,500$

**2** Calculate a rough answer to these calculations.

(a) $102 \div 28$      (b) $218 \div 19$
(c) $153 \times 22$      (d) $359 \div 43$

# Practice

Turn off your calculator. **Estimate** each calculation using 1 s.f. With a partner, use a calculator to check each other's estimates.

**1** (a) $26 \times 32$    (b) $62 \div 16$    (c) $148 \div 46$
    (d) $170 + 34 \times 18$    (e) $2420 \times 37$    (f) $209 \div 24 + 100$

**2** Estimate the answers to these calculations.

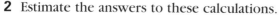

| **Example** | $43 \times 0.27$ |
|---|---|
| **Working** | $= 40 \times 0.3$ to 1 s.f. |
| **Answer** | 12 |

| **Example** | $6.4 \div 0.213$ |
|---|---|
| **Working** | $= 6 \div 0.2$ to 1 s.f. |
| **Answer** | 30 |

(a) $9.6 \times 724$    (b) $25.8 \div 12.6$    (c) $29 \times 0.18$
(d) $3.8 \div 4.6$    (e) $0.613 \times 0.152$    (f) $1.05 \div 0.243$

Estimate the answers to these questions. Write down a rough calculation.

**1** A box contains 27 screws. How many screws in 36 boxes altogether?

**2** How many 17 cm lengths can be cut from a rope 6 m long?

**3** What is the total cost of 42 candles at 23p each and 38 boxes of matches at 13p each?

**4** An aeroplane carries 357 crates. Each crate weighs 64 kg. How much do the crates weigh altogether?

**5** A jar of coffee costs £2.35.
   **(a)** How much do 38 jars cost?
   **(b)** How many jars can be bought for £55?

**6** **(a)** Calculate the cost of 120 concrete slabs at £3.54 each.
   **(b)** How many slabs can be bought for £700?

**7** A pen weighs 5.3 g and a pencil 4.2 g.
   **(a)** How many pens weigh 519.4 g?
   **(b)** How many pencils weigh 625.8 g?
   **(c)** A pack contains a pen and a pencil.
       How many packs weigh 921.5 g?

> **Finished Early?**
>  Go to page 391

# Further Practice

Check these calculations by working out a rough answer. Show your working. Do not use a calculator. Which calculations do you think are correct?

**1** $5628 \div 8.4 = 670$

**2** $46 \times 73 + 2130 = 75\,238$

**3** $24 \times 132 \div 18 = 376$

**4** $1.46 \times 5.83 = 8.5118$

**5** $6283 - 23 \times 23 = 5754$

**6** $57 \times 34 - 15 \times 92 = 558$

**7** $\dfrac{8602}{422 + 770} = 0.45$

**8** $380 \times 742 \times 194 = 427\,090$

**9** $5850 \times 0.18 = 1053$

**10** $942\,381 \times 4632 = 4\,365\,108\,792$

> **Finished Early?**
>  Go to page 391

# 10 Powers and Roots

In this chapter you will learn about ...

**1** powers
**2** square roots and cube roots
**3** powers of 10

## P **1** Powers

### Remember?

- To square a number, multiply it by itself.
  For example:
  3 squared $= 3^2 = 3 \times 3 = 9$.
- The cube of a number is the number multiplied by itself and by itself again
  For example:
  2 cubed $= 2^3 = 2 \times 2 \times 2 = 8$.
- You can round numbers using decimal places (d.p.) or significant figures (s.f.).

**Examples**
$239.275 \approx 239.3$ (1 d.p.)
$239.275 \approx 239.28$ (2 d.p.)
$239.275 \approx 200$ (1 s.f.)
$239.275 \approx 240$ (2 s.f.)

### Try It Out

 **1** Calculate the following.
(a) $5^2$ **(b)** the square of 7 **(c)** 4 squared **(d)** $12^2$

**2** Which of the numbers below are the squares of whole numbers?

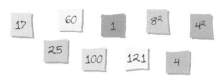

17    60    1    $8^2$    $4^2$
25    100    121    4

**3** Calculate the following.
(a) $2^3$ **(b)** $4^3$ **(c)** the cube of 5 **(d)** 10 cubed

**4** Round these numbers.
(a) 6.3742 (to 2 d.p.) **(b)** 0.4831 (to 1 d.p.)
(c) 5739 (to 1 s.f.) **(d)** 443 671 (to 2 s.f.)

## Learn About It

When you multiply a number by itself, you get a **power** of that number.

Here are some powers of 3:

$3 \times 3$             $= 9$

$3 \times 3 \times 3$         $= 27$

$3 \times 3 \times 3 \times 3$     $= 81$

$3 \times 3 \times 3 \times 3 \times 3 = 243$

The more times you multiply that number, the higher the power.

$3 \times 3 \times 3 \times 3 \times 3$ is the *fifth power of 3* because five 3s have been multiplied together. You can also say *3 raised to the fifth power* or simply *3 to the fifth*.

$3^5$ does not mean $3 \times 5$.

> ### Word Check
> **power** a number multiplied by itself one or more times
>
> **base** the number being multiplied in a power
>
> **index** how many of the number are multiplied together

$3^5$

index: tells you how many of the number to multiply together

base: the number being multiplied

**1** Work out the next power of 3.

**2** Write these powers the short way, using a base and index.

(a) $5 \times 5 \times 5$        (b) $10 \times 10 \times 10 \times 10 \times 10 \times 10$

(c) $6 \times 6 \times 6 \times 6$        (d) $3 \times 3$

**3** Write these powers the long way and calculate them.

| | |
|---|---|
| **Example** | $6^5$ |
| **Working** | $6 \times 6 \times 6 \times 6 \times 6$ |
| **Answer** | $7776$ |

(a) $2^7$        (b) $4^4$        (c) third power of 5        (d) $2^5$

You can calculate powers of negative numbers, too. Remember to write them in brackets.

$(-2)^4 = (-2) \times (-2) \times (-2) \times (-2)$

$\quad\quad\ = 4 \times (-2) \times (-2)$

$\quad\quad\ = (-8) \times (-2)$

$\quad\quad\ = 16$

> *Remember:* $- \times -$ *gives* $+$
> $+ \times -$ *gives* $-$

$-2^4$ does not mean the same as $(-2)^4$.

$-2^4$ means $-(2 \times 2 \times 2 \times 2) = -16$

**4** Calculate the following.

(a) $(-4)^3$        (b) $(-5)^2$        (c) $-3^4$        (d) $(-2)^5$

You can calculate powers using the power key $x^y$ or $y^x$ on your calculator.

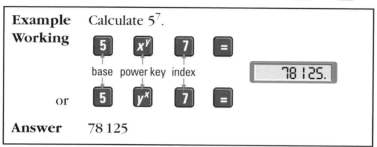

**Example**   Calculate $5^7$.

**Working**

base   power key   index

or

**Answer**   78 125

---

**Example**   Calculate $(-2)^6$.

**Working**

**Answer**   64

---

**5** Calculate the following.

(a) $5^3$    (b) $10^6$    (c) $6.2^4$    (d) $(-4)^5$    (e) $-7^4$

**6** Work out these calculations. Only use a calculator for parts (c) and (d).
Show your working.

**Example**   $10^6 \div 5^4$

**Working**   $= 1\,000\,000 \div 625$   (*Calculate powers before division.*)
$= 1600$

**Answer**   1600

**Key Fact**

When a calculation involves powers, use **BoDMAS**:

1 **B**rackets
2 **P**owers
3 **D**ivision and **M**ultiplication (left to right)
4 **A**ddition and **S**ubtraction (left to right)

---

**Example**   $4^2 - 2^3$

**Working**   $4 \times 4 - 2 \times 2 \times 2$
$= 16 - 8$   (*Multiply before subtracting.*)
$= 8$

**Answer**   8

---

(a) $3 \times 2^4$    (b) $3^3 - 4^2$    (c) $\dfrac{5^4}{2^3}$    (d) $4^4 - 3^3$

# Try It Out

**1** Write these powers the short way, using a base and index, e.g. $3^4$.

(a) $7 \times 7 \times 7 \times 7$         (b) $10 \times 10 \times 10 \times 10 \times 10 \times 10 \times 10$

(c) $6 \times 6 \times 6$         (d) $9 \times 9 \times 9 \times 9 \times 9$

**2** Calculate the following powers without using a calculator. Show your working.

(a) fifth power of 2         (b) $10^9$         (c) $(-3)^4$

(d) $3 \times 10^5$         (e) $-2^8$         (f) $(-10)^7$

**3** Calculate the following powers using your calculator.

(a) $2^{12}$      (b) $1.6^3$      (c) $\dfrac{3^5}{2^4}$      (d) $(-8)^6$

(e) $-6^6$      (f) $(-4)^5$      (g) $7^4 - 4^5$      (h) $3^3 \times 5^2$

# Practice

Write the following calculations the long way. Then work them out. Do not use a calculator. Show your working.

**1** $2^4$     **2** $4^3$     **3** $10^5$     **4** $(-3)^2$     **5** $-2^4$

**6** $3^2 - 2^3$     **7** $4 \times 2^4$     **8** $5^2 + 2^5$     **9** $3^2 \times 2^3$     **10** $\dfrac{4^3}{2^4}$

**1** Calculate the values of the following expressions. Do not use a calculator.

| | |
|---|---|
| **Example** | Calculate $a^3 + b^4$ when $a = 2$ and $b = 3$. |
| **Working** | $a^3 + b^4$ |
| | $= 2^3 + 3^4$ |
| | $= 2 \times 2 \times 2 + 3 \times 3 \times 3 \times 3$ |
| | $= 8 + 81$ |
| | $= 89$ |
| **Answer** | 89 |

(a) $a^5$ when $a = 2$         (b) $x^3$ when $x = 5$

(c) $m^5$ when $m = -2$         (d) $r^7$ when $r = 10$

(e) $4 \times b^3$ when $b = 2$         (f) $3 \times t^4$ when $t = 3$

(g) $\dfrac{p^3}{4}$ when $p = 2$

(h) $c^4 - d^3$ when $c = 3$ and $d = 4$

(i) $x^3 + y^2$ when $x = -2$ and $y = 3$

(j) $a^3 \times b^3$ when $a = 4$ and $b = 10$

**2** Calculate the values of these expressions.

| Example | $m^3$ when $m = 5.1$ |
| --- | --- |
| Working | $\boxed{5}\ \boxed{.}\ \boxed{1}\ \boxed{x^y}\ \boxed{3}\ \boxed{=}$ |
| | $\boxed{132.651}$ |
| Answer | 132.651 |

| Example | $v^3 - w^2$ when $v = 3.2$ and $w = 2.8$ |
| --- | --- |
| Working | $\boxed{3}\ \boxed{.}\ \boxed{2}\ \boxed{x^y}\ \boxed{3}\ \boxed{-}$ |
| | $\boxed{2}\ \boxed{.}\ \boxed{8}\ \boxed{x^2}\ \boxed{=}$ |
| | $\boxed{24.928}$ |
| Answer | 24.928 |

**(a)** $g^3$ when $g = 4.7$        **(b)** $j^5$ when $j = 7$

**(c)** $p^4$ when $p = 0.3$        **(d)** $z^3$ when $z = 29$

**(e)** $r^7$ when $r = -3$        **(f)** $4 \times b^3$ when $b = 6$

**(g)** $2.5 \times n^4$ when $n = 1.2$    **(h)** $d^5 - e^3$ when $d = 17$ and $e = 105$

**(i)** $f^3 - g^2$ when $f = 6.1$ and $g = 5.8$    **(j)** $a^3 + b^4$ when $a = 5.3$ and $b = 1.8$

**(k)** $\dfrac{a^7}{125}$ when $a = 5$        **(l)** $1000 + b^9$ when $b = -2$

**(m)** $\dfrac{m^3}{n^2}$ when $m = 16$ and $n = 5$    **(n)** $a^4 \times b^3$ when $a = 2.5$ and $b = 4$

> **Finished Early?**
> ⇨ Go to page 391

## Further Practice

**E** Write the following calculations in full and work them out. Do not use a calculator. Show your working.

**1** $2^3$      **2** $5^2$      **3** $10^8$      **4** $(-3)^2$      **5** $-4^2$

**6** $3^3 + 2^4$      **7** $4^3 - 2^5$      **8** $2 \times 3^2$      **9** $2^3 \times 2^2$      **10** $\dfrac{3^4}{3^2}$

**F** Calculate the output numbers from the following number machines. The second number machine shows how to round your answer.

| Example | $2.1 \rightarrow \boxed{x^6} \rightarrow \langle R(2\,d.p.)\rangle$ |
| --- | --- |
| Working | Calculate $2.1^6$ using a calculator. |
| | $\boxed{2}\ \boxed{.}\ \boxed{1}\ \boxed{x^y}\ \boxed{6}\ \boxed{=}\ \boxed{85.766121}$ |
| | Round the answer to 2 decimal places. |
| Answer | 85.77 to 2 d.p. |

**1** (a) 4.2  (b) 5.3  (c) 9.8 $x^6$ ➤ R(2 d.p.)   **2** (a) 2 (b) 6 (c) 9 $x^9$ ➤ R(2 s.f.)

**3** (a) –2  (b) –25  (c) –100 $x^4$ ➤ R(2 s.f.)   **4** (a) 2 (b) 3 (c) 4 $x^{13}$ ➤ R(3 s.f.)

**5** (a) –15 (b) –32 (c) –43 $x^5$ ➤ R(2 s.f.)

**6** (a) 0.85 (b) 1.24 (c) 1.12 $x^{25}$ ➤ R(3 d.p.)

**Finished Early?**
➡ Go to page 391

## Square Roots and Cube Roots

**Remember?**
You can find the square root of a number using the √ key on a calculator. To calculate $\sqrt{9}$, press: √ 9 = | 3. |

## Try It Out
Use your calculator to find these square roots.

**1** $\sqrt{25}$    **2** $\sqrt{81}$    **3** $\sqrt{100}$    **4** $\sqrt{144}$

## Learn About It
Squaring 3 gives an answer of 9.
The square of $3 = 3^2 = 3 \times 3 = 9$.
The square root of 9 is 3. $\sqrt{9} = 3$.

Finding the square root is the inverse (opposite) of finding the square.

You know that $4^2 = 16$, so $\sqrt{16} = 4$.

You have to use a calculator to find $\sqrt{12}$.

You can see that the answer is a number between 3 and 4.

√ 1 2 = | 3.464101615 |

$\sqrt{12} = 3.46$ correct to 2 d.p.

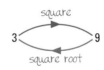

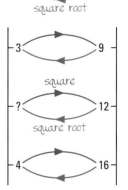

# Try It Out

 **1** Copy the diagrams. Fill in the missing numbers.

**(a)** $7^2 = ?$
$\sqrt{?} = 7$

**(b)** $10^2 = ?$
$\sqrt{?} = 10$

**(c)** $?^2 = 25$
$\sqrt{25} = ?$

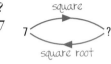

**(d)** $?^2 = 81$
$\sqrt{81} = ?$

 **2** Use your calculator to find these square roots. Write your answers correct to 2 decimal places.

**(a)** $\sqrt{17}$      **(b)** $\sqrt{250}$      **(c)** $\sqrt{1000}$      **(d)** $\sqrt{2}$

# Learn More About It

Cubing 2 gives an answer of 8.

The cube of $2 = 2^3 = 2 \times 2 \times 2 = 8$.

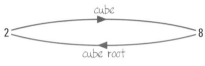

Finding the cube root is the inverse (opposite) of cubing.
You write it like this: $\sqrt[3]{\ }$ .

The **cube root** of $8 = \sqrt[3]{8} = 2$.

You know that $3^3 = 3 \times 3 \times 3 = 27$, so $\sqrt[3]{27} = 3$.

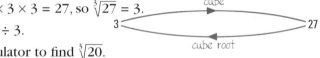

$\sqrt[3]{27}$ does not mean $27 \div 3$.

You have to use a calculator to find $\sqrt[3]{20}$.

Press  2.714417617

$\sqrt[3]{20} = 2.71$ correct to 2 d.p.

# Try It Out

 **1** Fill in the missing numbers.

**(a)** $5^3 = ?$
$\sqrt[3]{?} = 5$

**(b)** $6^3 = ?$
$\sqrt[3]{?} = 6$

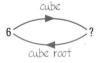

**(c)** $?^3 = 1000$
$\sqrt[3]{1000} = ?$

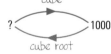

**(d)** $?^3 = 64$
$\sqrt[3]{64} = ?$

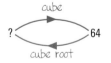

 **2** Calculate these cube roots correct to 2 d.p. Use your calculator.

**(a)** $\sqrt[3]{50}$          **(b)** $\sqrt[3]{834}$

**(c)** $\sqrt[3]{9}$          **(d)** $\sqrt[3]{100}$

# Practice

Copy these diagrams and fill in the missing numbers.

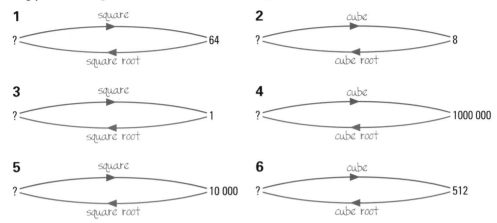

**1**  square
?  64
square root

**2**  cube
?  8
cube root

**3**  square
?  1
square root

**4**  cube
?  1000 000
cube root

**5**  square
?  10 000
square root

**6**  cube
?  512
cube root

**1**  Copy this page of roots from Mario's exercise book. Check his calculations by squaring or cubing the answers. Tick the correct answers, cross the ones that are wrong. Do not use the $\sqrt[3]{\phantom{x}}$ key of your calculator. Show your working. The first one has been done for you

| | |
|---|---|
| **Example** | $\sqrt[3]{729} = 9$ |
| **Working** | $9^3 = 9 \times 9 \times 9 = 81 \times 9 = 729$ |
| **Answer** | $\sqrt[3]{729} = 9.$ ✓ |

(a)  $\sqrt[3]{729} = 9$

(b)  $\sqrt[3]{64} = 8$

(c)  $\sqrt{169} = 13$

(d)  $\sqrt{289} = 19$

(e)  $\sqrt[3]{625} = 5$

(f)  $\sqrt[3]{343} = 11$

(g)  $\sqrt{1\,000\,000} = 1000$

(h)  $\sqrt[3]{8000} = 40$

(i)  $\sqrt[3]{9261} = 21$

(j)  $\sqrt{0.9} = 0.3$

(k)  $\sqrt[3]{125\,000\,000} = 350$

**2**  Correct Mario's mistakes. Use the $\sqrt{\phantom{x}}$ or $\sqrt[3]{\phantom{x}}$ key of your calculator.

**L** Calculate the output numbers from these number machines. The second
number machine shows how to round your answer.

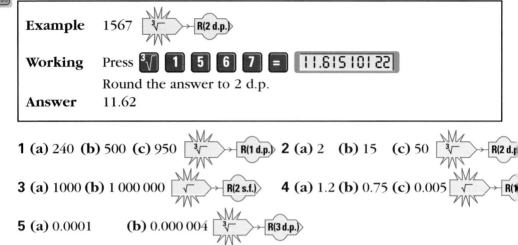

**1 (a)** 240 **(b)** 500 **(c)** 950 [³√ → R(1 d.p.)]  **2 (a)** 2  **(b)** 15  **(c)** 50 [³√ → R(2 d.p.)]

**3 (a)** 1000 **(b)** 1 000 000 [√ → R(2 s.f.)]  **4 (a)** 1.2 **(b)** 0.75 **(c)** 0.005 [√ → R(1

**5 (a)** 0.0001  **(b)** 0.000 004 [³√ → R(3 d.p.)]

**6 (a)** 123 456 789 **(b)** 999 999 [√ → R(2 s.f.)]

**7 (a)** 555 555  **(b)** 50 000 [√ → R(1 s.f.)]

> **Finished Early?**
> Go to page 392

**8 (a)** 0.8  **(b)** 0.88 **(c)** 0.088 [³√ → R(2 d.p.)]

## Further Practice

**M** Calculate the length of a side of each square or cube below.

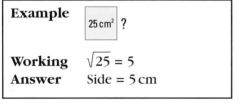
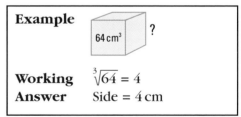

**1** 36 cm² ?  **2** 81 cm² ?  **3** 20 cm² ?  **4** 0.7 cm² ?

**5** 216 cm³ ?  **6** 1000 m³ ?  **7** 8000 mm³ ?  **8** 12 m³ ?

> **Finished Early?**
> Go to page 392

# Powers of 10

## Remember?

$10^2$, $10^3$, $10^4$, etc. are called powers of 10.

| Name | Number | Power of 10 |
|---|---:|---|
| ten | 10 | $10^1$ |
| one hundred | 100 | $10^2$ |
| one thousand | 1000 | $10^3$ |
| ten thousand | 10 000 | $10^4$ |
| one hundred thousand | 100 000 | $10^5$ |
| one million | 1 000 000 | $10^6$ |
| ten million | 10 000 000 | $10^7$ |
| one hundred million | 100 000 000 | $10^8$ |
| one billion | 1 000 000 000 | $10^9$ |
| one trillion | 1 000 000 000 000 | $10^{12}$ |
| one quadrillion | 1 000 000 000 000 000 | $10^{15}$ |

You can calculate using powers of 10, e.g. $5 \times 10^4 = 5 \times 10\,000 = 50\,000$.

$10^2 = 10 \times 10 = 100$, so you can write 100 as $10^2$.

$10^3 = 10 \times 10 \times 10 = 1000$, so you can write 1000 as $10^3$.

$10^4 = 10 \times 10 \times 10 \times 10 = 10\,000$, so you can write 10 000 as $10^4$.

## Try It Out

**1** Write these numbers as powers of 10.
  **(a)** 100 000          **(b)** 10 000 000
  **(c)** 100 000 000 000

**2** Calculate the following.
  **(a)** $10^6$          **(b)** $10^9$
  **(c)** $10^{12}$

**3** Calculate the following.
  **(a)** $6 \times 10^2$      **(b)** $9 \times 10^6$
  **(c)** $4 \times 10^8$      **(d)** $7 \times 10^1$

# Learn About It

It is often quicker to write large numbers using powers of 10.

$500 = 5 \times 100$

$\phantom{500} = 5 \times 10^2$

$3000 = 3 \times 1000$

$\phantom{3000} = 3 \times 10^3$

$8\,000\,000 = 8 \times 1\,000\,000$

$\phantom{8\,000\,000} = 8 \times 10^6$

$4\,000\,000\,000 = 4 \times 1\,000\,000\,000$

$\phantom{4\,000\,000\,000} = 4 \times 10^9$

> *Remember: the bigger the number, the higher the power of 10.*

Writing numbers using powers of 10 is called **standard form**. The red numbers that multiply the powers of 10 are always from 1 to 10 (1 may be used but 10 may not).

## Word Check

**standard form**  writing a number as a number from 1 to 10 multiplied by a power of 10

**1**  Write the following numbers using standard form. Copy the method above.
   (a) 4000       (b) 800 000       (c) 300 000 000    (d) 50

The power of 10 shows you roughly how big the number is.
$2 \times 10^7$ is bigger than $9 \times 10^6$ because $10^7$ is bigger than $10^6$.
Check:  $2 \times 10^7 = 20\,000\,000$
$\phantom{Check:\,} 9 \times 10^6 = \phantom{0}9\,000\,000$

**2**  Write these numbers in order, from smallest to largest.
   $7 \times 10^6$     $9 \times 10^4$     $3 \times 10^{12}$     $5 \times 10^6$

# Try It Out

**1**  Write these numbers using standard form.
   (a) 60 000            (b) 20 000 000            (c) 10 000
   (d) 500               (e) 7 000 000 000         (f) 20

**2**  Calculate the following.
   (a) $4 \times 10^3$     (b) $9 \times 10^6$     (c) $1 \times 10^5$     (d) $3 \times 10^1$

**3**  Write these in order, from smallest to largest.
   $7 \times 10^9$     $9 \times 10^7$     $5 \times 10^6$     $8 \times 10^7$     $1 \times 10^6$     $9 \times 10^5$

# Learn More About It

This large number has 3 significant figures:

561 000

Follow these steps to write it in standard form:

- Put a decimal point after the first significant figure to make a number between 1 and 10: 5.61
- Multiply this number by the power of 10 that gives the original number:
  $561\,000 = 5.61 \times 100\,000 = 5.61 \times 10^5$.

To change a number written in standard form to an ordinary number:

- Write the power of 10 out in full, e.g. $3.26 \times 10^8 = 3.26 \times 100\,000\,000$
- Work out the 'answer' to this calculation:
  $3.26 \times 100\,000\,000 = 326\,000\,000$.

# Try It Out

**1** Write these numbers in standard form.

| | | |
|---|---|---|
| **(a)** 46 000 | **(b)** 980 | **(c)** 230 000 |
| **(d)** 1100 | **(e)** 720 000 000 000 | **(f)** 32 500 |
| **(g)** 666 000 | **(h)** 9 050 000 | **(i)** 515 000 000 000 |
| **(j)** 8 940 000 000 000 000 | | |

**2** Write these numbers in full.

| | | |
|---|---|---|
| **(a)** $4.3 \times 10^4$ | **(b)** $9.5 \times 10^6$ | **(c)** $1.2 \times 10^{10}$ |
| **(d)** $3.15 \times 10^7$ | **(e)** $8.47 \times 10^{12}$ | **(f)** $6.03 \times 10^8$ |

# Practice

Write the red numbers in standard form. Write the blue numbers in full.

**1** There are over 15 000 different kinds of flatworm.

**2** The Earth is 4 500 000 000 years old.

**3** 1 cm$^3$ of oxygen contains over $2 \times 10^{19}$ molecules.

**4** Light travels 299 000 000 m per second.

**5** The area of the Sahara Desert is about 17 000 000 square kilometres.

**6** In 1969, the tanker *Keo* spilled $8.8 \times 10^7$ gallons of oil into the sea.

**7** The highest mountain in the world is Mount Everest. It is almost 8850 m high.

**8** The population of the world will be over ten billion by the year 2050.

**9** The distance from the Earth to the Moon is about 382 000 km.

**10** The Sun has a mass of about $2 \times 10^{30}$ kg.

**R** These planets and stars are shown in order of their distance from the Sun. The distances, in metres, are written underneath, in standard form.

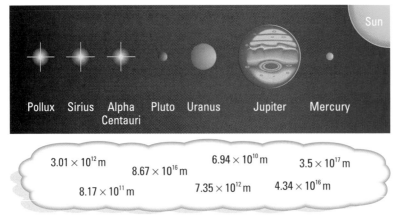

Pollux    Sirius    Alpha    Pluto    Uranus    Jupiter    Mercury    Sun
Centauri

$3.01 \times 10^{12}$ m

$8.67 \times 10^{16}$ m

$6.94 \times 10^{10}$ m

$3.5 \times 10^{17}$ m

$8.17 \times 10^{11}$ m

$7.35 \times 10^{12}$ m

$4.34 \times 10^{16}$ m

**1** Write the distances in order, from smallest to largest.

**2** Write the name of each planet or star with its distance from the Sun written in full.

> **Finished Early?**
> ➡ Go to page 392

## Further Practice

**S** **1** **(a)** A trillion is $10^{12}$. Write the number in full.
**(b)** A quadrillion is 1 000 000 000 000 000. Write it as a power of 10.
**(c)** Find out what a googol is.

**2** Write these numbers using standard form.
**(a)** 4 trillion          **(b)** 9 quadrillion          **(c)** 6 googol

**T** Write each set of numbers in order, from smallest to largest. Change them all to standard form first.

**1** $10^4$, 2000, twenty thousand, $3 \times 10^3$, one thousand

**2** one million, $3.5 \times 10^7$, nine hundred and twenty thousand, $7.1 \times 10^6$, $52\,000 \times 10^8$

**3** five billion, $8.4 \times 10^9$, 260 000 000, $7.6 \times 10^7$, forty-two million, $4.1 \times 10^8$

**4** thirty thousand five hundred, $2.59 \times 10^4$, $9.35 \times 10^4$, 4 850 000, $8.59 \times 10^3$, 485 000

> **Finished Early?**
> ➡ Go to page 392

# Unit 5 *Computation*

## Summary of Chapters 9 and 10

- Use the memory of your calculator like this:

  [5] [STO] [M]  stores 5 in the memory

  [5] [M+]  adds 5 to the memory

  [5] [M−]  subtracts 5 from the memory

  [RCL] [M]  recalls the memory

  [0] [STO] [M]  clears the memory.

  > Note: Some calculators use different keys.

  Always clear the memory of your calculator between calculations.
- To check your answer to a calculation, round the numbers to 1 s.f. and calculate a rough answer.
- Write a power using a base and an index.

  $$2^{\overset{\text{index}}{3}} = 2 \times 2 \times 2$$
  
  base

- $(-2)^2$ means $(-2) \times (-2) = 4$ but $-2^2$ means $-(2 \times 2) = -4$
- The third power of a number is called its cube, e.g. the cube of $2 = 2^3 = 8$.
- Use the power key [$x^y$] or [$y^x$] of your calculator to find powers, e.g. to calculate $1.4^3$ press [1] [.] [4] [$x^y$] [3] [=].
- Calculate with powers using this order of operations (**BoDMAS**): **B**rackets, **P**owers, **D**ivision and **M**ultiplication, **A**ddition and **S**ubtraction, for example, $2^3 \times 3^2 = 8 \times 9 = 72$.
- Finding the square root ($\sqrt{\phantom{x}}$) of a number is the inverse of finding the square.

  Finding the cube root ($\sqrt[3]{\phantom{x}}$) of a number is the inverse of finding the cube.

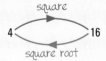

The square root of 16 is 4.

$\sqrt{16} = 4$

4 squared is 16.  $4^2 = 16$.

The cube root of 8 is 2.

$\sqrt[3]{8} = 2$

2 cubed is 8.  $2^3 = 8$.

- Large numbers can be written using standard form, e.g.
  $32\,400\,000 = 3.24 \times 10^7$.
  The red number must be at least 1 and smaller than 10.

# Brush Up Your Number 6

##  Multiplication Tables

### Learn About It

It is important to know your multiplication tables by heart. Practise them every day until you know them.

### Try It Out

 **A** Take turns to ask your partner a multiplication fact. Check each other's answers.

### Practice

**B** Answer these questions.

**1** There are six cars in a car park. Each has four wheels. How many wheels are there altogether?

**2** Stamps cost 7p each. How much do nine cost?

**3** There are 10 mm in 1 cm. How many mm are there in 8 cm?

**4** Charles eats three sandwiches for lunch every day. How many does he eat in five days?

**5** Bradley has six hours of lessons a day. How many hours does he have in six days?

**6** There are eight coloured pencils in a pack. How many are there in four packs?

**7** There are five teams in a five-a-side football league. How many players are there altogether?

**8** A bar of chocolate has eight squares. How many squares do five bars have?

**9** Each box contains six eggs. How many eggs are there in nine boxes?

**10** Eight pupils wear gym shoes. How many gym shoes are worn altogether?

**11** Tim and Pak each buy a bus ticket each day. How many do they buy between them in six days?

**12** Mark hits eight sixes in a cricket match. How many runs does he score altogether?

**13** What is the total length of nine rolls of fencing if each roll is 9 m long?

**14** Desks have four legs each. How many legs do seven desks have?

**15** How many days are there in eight weeks?

**16** Five people drink four cups of tea each. How many cups do they drink altogether?

**17** A tent holds eight children. How many children could six tents hold?

**18** It takes four apples to make a pie. How many apples does it take to make nine pies?

**19** Bags of potatoes weigh 5 kg each. How much do seven bags weigh?

**20** May Ling gets £3 a week for pocket money. How much does she get in eight weeks?

**21** A can holds five litres of oil. How much oil do six cans hold?

**22** Nine playing cards are dealt to each of five children. How many cards are dealt altogether?

**23** A box contains ten floppy disks. How many do ten boxes contain?

**24** A lift can hold six people. How many people can it carry in three journeys?

**25** Umbrellas cost £9 each. How much do three cost?

**26** A snail crawls 7 cm a minute. How far does it crawl in seven minutes?

**27** Batteries are sold in packs of four. How many batteries are there in ten packs?

**28** A kite takes nine hours to make. How long would four kites take?

**29** Three people each bring seven friends to a party. How many friends do they bring altogether?

**30** Sandy works eight hours a day. How long does she work in ten days?

**31** Seven apples weigh 1 kg. How many apples weigh 6 kg?

**32** Four people can play on a tennis court. How many can play on eight courts?

Dice

**1** Take turns to throw a dice twice. Multiply the numbers together. Write down the multiplication fact.

**2** When you have ten multiplication facts, check them with a partner.

**Finished Early?**
➡ Go to page 393

# 11  Coordinates

In this chapter you will learn about ...
1. straight lines
2. more straight-line graphs
3. regions
4. curved graphs

## ᵀ 1 Straight Lines

### Learn About It

The points marked in blue have the
coordinates $(-6, 4), (-2, 4), (0, 4),$
$(2, 4), (6, 4).$

Any point on the blue line has a
$y$-coordinate of 4.
The equation of this line is $y = 4$.

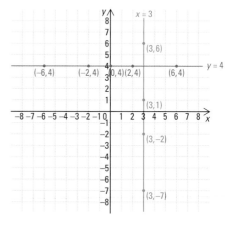

| $x$ | −6 | −2 | 0 |
|---|---|---|---|
| $y$ | 4 | 4 | 4 |

On the line, the
$y$-coordinate is
always 4.

The points marked in red have the coordinates
$(3, -7), (3, -2), (3, 1), (3, 6).$

Any point on the red line has an $x$-coordinate of 3.
The equation of this line is $x = 3$.

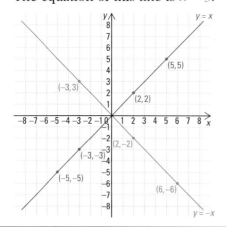

The points marked in blue have the
coordinates $(-5, -5), (-3, -3), (2, 2), (5, 5).$
Any point on the blue line has its $x$- and
$y$-coordinates equal.

The equation of this line is $y = x$.

The points marked in red have the
coordinates $(-3, 3), (2, -2), (6, -6).$ On the
red line, the $y$-coordinate equals $-x$.

The equation of this line is $y = -x$.

# Try It Out

Write down the equation of each line below. Choosing points on the line and writing them in a table may help you see the pattern.

**Word Check**

**equation of a line** the rule for points on that line

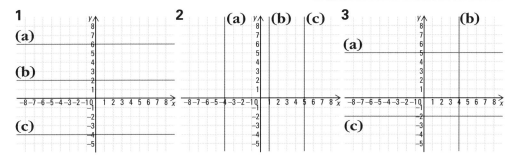

**1**
(a) _____
(b) _____
(c) _____

**2** (a) (b) (c)

**3**
(a)
(b)
(c)

# Practice

Squared paper

Draw a set of axes labelled from –8 to 8 and plot the following points. Draw a straight line through each group of points and label each line with its equation.

**1** $(2, 4), (2, 0), (2, -3)$

**2** $(3, 1), (5, 1), (-6, 1)$

**3** $(4, -3), (3, -3), (-4, -3)$

**4** $(-2, -2), (-2, 0), (-2, 7)$

**5** $(-5, 2), (-5, -3), (-5, -5)$

**6** $(-5, 5), (-2, 2), (0, 0), (3, -3), (5, -5)$

Write down the equation of each line and the coordinates of the points where lines cross.

**1**

**2**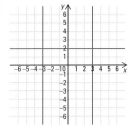

**3**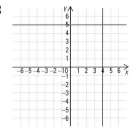

**4**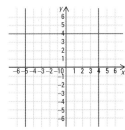

**5**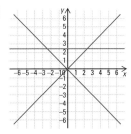

**6**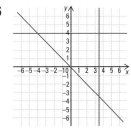

Squared paper

**D** For each question below, draw a suitable set of axes and draw a line for the $x$ equation and a line for the $y$ equation. Label the lines.

**1** $x = 3$, $y = -2$

**2** $x = -5$, $y = 4$

**3** $y = -7$, $x = -4$

**4** $x = 7$, $y = x$

**5** $x = 0$, $y = 0$

**6** $x = 4.5$, $y = 3\frac{1}{2}$

> **Finished Early?**
> Go to page 393

## Further Practice

**E** Write down the equation of each line.

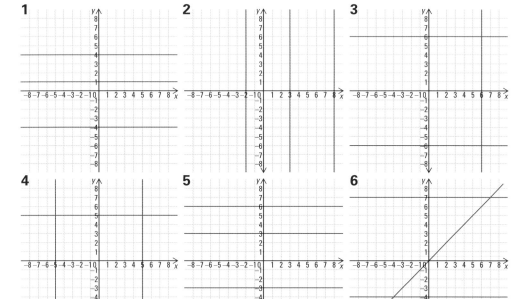

**1**

**2**

**3**

**4**

**5**

**6**

  Squared paper

**F** Draw axes and plot these lines. You may be able to fit several lines on the same axes.

**1** $x = 8$

**2** $y = 4$

**3** $y = -3$

**4** $x = -6$

**5** $y = -1$

**6** $x = -1$

**7** $y = 0$

**8** $x = 0$

**9** $y = -2.5$

**10** $x = -5\frac{1}{2}$

**11** $y = -x$

**12** $y = \frac{1}{2}$

> **Finished Early?**
>  Go to page 393

# More Straight-Line Graphs

## Learn About It

Squared paper

To draw the line $y = 2x$, you need to work out coordinates of points on the line. Choose three values for $x$ and use them to find the values for $y$, then plot the points and draw the line.

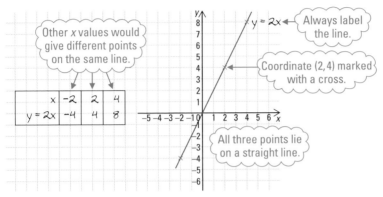

Three values of $x$ were **substituted** in the equation. You need to plot **three** points so that mistakes show up.

Any **equation** in which $x$ and $y$ are in proportion to each other (e.g. $y = 2x$, $y = x + 1$, $y = 4x$), will give a straight-line graph.

To draw the line $y = x + 2$, you also work out and plot coordinates of three points.

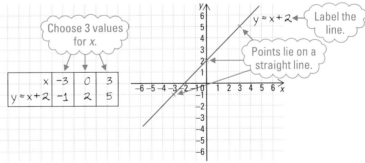

## Key Fact

To draw a **straight-line** graph, find the coordinates of three points, plot them and then draw a line through them.

## Word Check

substitute  replace a letter with a number

## Try It Out

**G** Draw the graphs of these lines.

**1** $y = 3x$      **2** $y = x + 3$      **3** $y = 4x$      **4** $y = x + 4$

## Learn More About It

Equations can involve multiplying and adding. They can also contain negative numbers. To draw the graph of $y = -2x + 3$, again substitute three values for $x$.

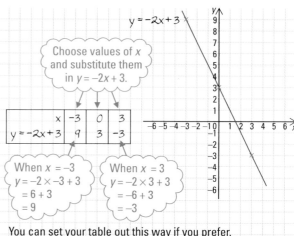

| $x$ | -3 | 0 | 3 |
|-----|-----|-----|-----|
| $y = -2x + 3$ | 9 | 3 | -3 |

When $x = -3$
$y = -2 \times -3 + 3$
$= 6 + 3$
$= 9$

When $x = 3$
$y = -2 \times 3 + 3$
$= -6 + 3$
$= -3$

You can set your table out this way if you prefer.

| $x$ | -3 | 0 | 3 |
|-----|-----|-----|-----|
| $-2x$ | 6 | 0 | -6 |
| $+3$ | 3 | 3 | 3 |
| $y$ | 9 | 3 | -3 |

Add these two rows to find the value of $y$.

## Try It Out

**H** Draw graphs for the following equations on the same axes.

**1** $y = 2x + 1$     **2** $y = 2x - 1$     **3** $y = -2x + 1$     **4** $y = -2x - 1$

## Practice

**I** Draw graphs for the following equations. Use separate axes for each one.

**1** $y = 3x + 2$     **2** $y = 3x - 4$     **3** $y = 2x + 3$     **4** $y = x - 4$
**5** $y = 2x - 5$     **6** $y = -2x + 4$     **7** $y = -3x - 2$     **8** $y = -2x - 5$

**J** Draw graphs for the following equations. Use separate axes for each one.

**1** $y = 1.5x + 2$    **2** $y = 2.5x - 1$    **3** $y = -1.5x + 1$    **4** $y = x - 2.5$
**5** $y = 2.5x - 1.5$    **6** $y = -2.5x + 1.5$   **7** $y = -1.5x + 2.5$   **8** $y = -2.5x - 3$

**Finished Early?**
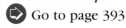 Go to page 393

## Further Practice

Draw graphs for the following equations. Use one set of axes for each pair.

**1** (a) $y = 2x$  (b) $y = -2x$  **2** (a) $y = 3x$  (b) $y = -3x$
**3** (a) $y = x$  (b) $y = -x$  **4** (a) $y = x + 4$  (b) $y = -x + 4$
**5** (a) $y = 2x + 5$  (b) $y = -2x - 5$  **6** (a) $y = 2x + 4$  (b) $y = -2x - 4$
**7** (a) $y = 3x + 4$  (b) $y = -3x - 4$  **8** (a) $y = 4x + 1$  (b) $y = -4x - 1$

> **Finished Early?**
> ➡ Go to page 393

# Regions

Graph paper

## Learn About It

The line on this graph shows $x = 3$.
To the left of the line is the region
$x < 3$ ($x$ is less than 3). To the right is
the region $x > 3$ ($x$ is greater than 3).

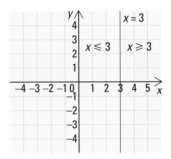

The line on this graph shows $y = 2$.
Below the line is the region $y < 2$
($y$ is less than 2).
Above the line is the region $y > 2$
($y$ is greater than 2).

**131**

The shaded region on this graph is bordered by two lines.

We can describe this region using the inequalities $x > 1$ and $x < 3$, which can be combined as $1 < x < 3$, meaning '$x$ is greater than 1 and less than 3'.

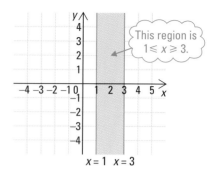

This region is $1 \leqslant x \geqslant 3$.

$x = 1$  $x = 3$

## Try It Out

**L** **1** Describe the shaded region on each graph using inequalities.

(a)

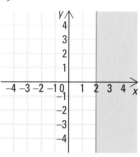

(b)

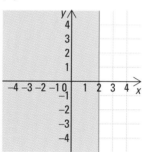

(c)

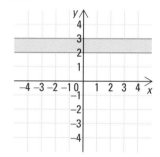

(d)

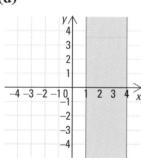

(e)

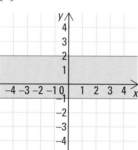

(f)

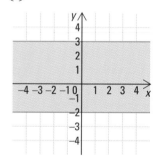

**2** On separate graphs, draw the following. Use axes labelled from –4 to +4.

   (a) the line $y = 3$; shade the region $y < 3$

   (b) the line $x = 2$; shade the region $x < 2$

   (c) the line $y = -1$; shade the region $y > -1$

   (d) the line $x = -3$; shade the region $x > -3$

**3** On separate graphs with axes labelled from –4 to +4, draw the following.

   **(a)** the lines $y = 1$ and $y = 2$; shade the region $1 < y < 2$

   **(b)** the lines $x = 3$ and $x = 2$; shade the region $2 < x < 3$

   **(c)** the line $y = -1$ and $y = 2$; shade the region $2 > y > -1$ (this is the same as $-1 < y < 2$)

   **(d)** the line $x = -3$ and $x = 1$; shade the region $1 > x > -3$ (this is the same as $-3 < x < 1$)

## Learn More About It

We can use four lines to define a rectangular region.

The rectangle of coordinates $(1, 1)$, $(1, 2)$, $(3, 1)$ and $(3, 2)$ is trapped between the lines $x = 1$ and $x = 3$ and the lines $y = 1$ and $y = 2$.

The rectangular region can be described as $1 < x < 3$ and $1 < y < 2$.

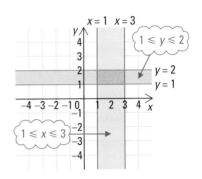

## Try It Out

Write inequalities to describe the rectangular area on each graph.

**1**

**2**

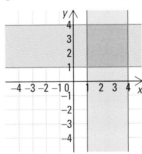

**3**

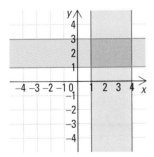

**4**

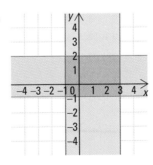

## Practice

**N** **1** Write inequalities to describe the shaded region on each graph.

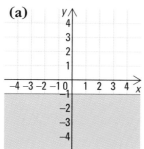
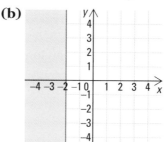
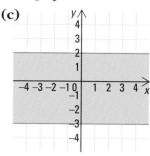

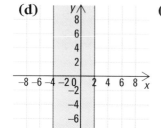
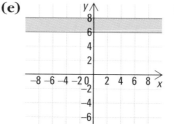
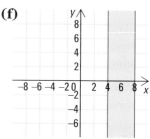

**2** Write inequalities to describe the shaded rectangular area on each graph.

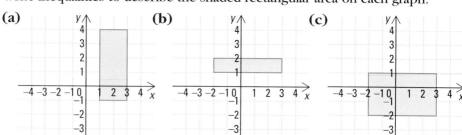

**O** On graph paper, plot the following sets of coordinates and join them to make rectangles. Write inequalities to describe the region which each rectangle represent

**1** $(0, 0), (2, 0), (2, 2), (0, 2)$        **2** $(1, 0), (1, 5), (3, 5), (3, 0)$

**3** $(-1, -1), (-1, 1), (2, -1), (2, 1)$

> **Finished Early?**
> ➡ Go to page 394

## Further Practice

**P** **1** Draw the following regions on graph paper (label axes from –6 to +6).
     **(a)** $3 < y < 5$     **(b)** $1 < y < 6$     **(c)** $-1 < x < 1$     **(d)** $-4 < x < 0$
     **(e)** $-5 < y < 0$     **(f)** $-3 < y < 3$     **(g)** $0.5 < x < 5.5$

**2** Write down the coordinates of the corners of the rectangle represented by each of the following pairs of inequalities.

(a) $1 < y < 6$ and $1 < x < 3$      (b) $-4 < y < 5$ and $1 < x < 3$

(c) $-5 < y < 1$ and $-6 < x < -4$      (d) $-1 < y < 1$ and $0.5 < x < 5.5$

**Finished Early?**

➡ Go to page 394

# Curved Graphs

Graph paper

## Learn About It

**1** Not all graphs are straight lines.
Copy and complete this table for $y = x^2$.

| $x$ | −5 | −4 | −3 | −2 | −1 | 0 | 1 | 2 | 3 | 4 | 5 |
|---|---|---|---|---|---|---|---|---|---|---|---|
| $y$ | 25 |  |  |  |  |  | 1 |  |  | 16 |  |

Draw a graph and plot the coordinates. Use these axes: $-5 \leqslant x \leqslant 5$, *scale*: 1 cm to 1 unit. $0 \leqslant y \leqslant 25$ *scale*: 1 cm to 2 units.
Join the points with a **smooth curve**.

Do not join the dots with straight lines!

**2** Copy and complete this table for $y = x^3$.

| $x$ | −3 | −2 | −1 | 0 | 1 | 2 | 3 |
|---|---|---|---|---|---|---|---|
| $y$ | −27 |  |  |  |  | 8 |  |

Draw a graph and plot the coordinates. Use these axes: $-5 \leqslant x \leqslant 5$, *scale*: 1 cm to 1 unit. $-30 \leqslant y \leqslant 30$, scale: 1 cm to 5 units.
Join the points with a **smooth curve**.

**3** You are going to plot the curve $y = \frac{1}{x}$.
Copy this table.

| $x$ | −2 | −1 | −0.75 | −0.5 | −0.25 | 0.25 | 0.5 | 0.75 | 1 | 2 |
|---|---|---|---|---|---|---|---|---|---|---|
| $y$ | −0.5 |  |  |  | −4 | 4 |  |  |  | 0.5 |

For each value of $x$, find the corresponding value of $y$ by dividing 1 by the value of $x$. For example, when $x = 2$ then $y = \frac{1}{2} = 0.5$ and when $x = 0.25$, $y = \frac{1}{0.25} = 4$. Check with a calculator.
Plot the points. Use these axes: $-2 \leqslant x \leqslant 2$, *scale*: 2 cm to 1 unit.
$-4 \leqslant y \leqslant 4$, *scale*: 2 cm to 1 unit.
Join the points with a **smooth curve**.
Note that the graph has two separate parts. There is no solution for $x = 0$ as $\frac{1}{0}$ cannot be worked out.

# Try It Out

**Q** **1** Identify which of these curves are based on (i) $y = x^2$ (ii) $y = x^3$
(iii) $y = \frac{1}{x}$ (iv) none of these.

**(a)** 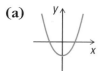 **(b)** 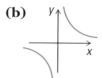 **(c)** 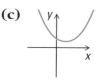 **(d)**

**(e)** 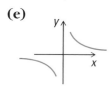 **(f)**  **(g)** 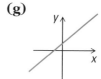 **(h)**

**2** Draw suitable axes and plot the following curves.

(a) $y = x^2 + 1$  (b) $y = \frac{1}{x} + 2$  (c) $y = x^3 + 1$

# Practice

**R** **1** Plot the following curves on the same graph. Use these axes: $-5 \leqslant x \leqslant 5$, *scale*:1 cm to 1 unit. $0 \leqslant y \leqslant 80$, *scale*: 1 cm to 5 units. What do you notice?
(a) $y = x^2$  (b) $y = 2x^2$  (c) $y = 3x^2$

**2** Plot the following curves on the same graph. Use these axes: $-5 \leqslant x \leqslant 5$, *scale*:1 cm to 1 unit. $0 \leqslant y \leqslant 30$, *scale*: 2 cm to 5 units. What do you notice?
(a) $y = x^2$  (b) $y = x^2 + 1$
(c) $y = x^2 + 2$  (d) $y = x^2 + 3$

**Finished Early?**
 Go to page 394

# Further Practice

**S** **1** Match each equation below to one of the following graphs. Write the letter of the correct graph for each equation.

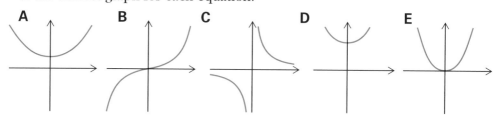

A    B    C    D    E

(a) $y = x^3$  (b) $y = x^2 + 1$  (c) $y = 2x^2$
(d) $y = x^2 + 5$  (e) $y = \frac{1}{x}$

**2** *Sketch* these curves.
(a) $y = x^2$  (b) $y = x^3$  (c) $y = \frac{1}{x}$

**Finished Early?**
Go to page 394

# 12 Simultaneous Equations

In this chapter you will learn about ...
1. changing the subject
2. simultaneous equations and graphs

## Changing the Subject

### Remember?

When solving equations you sometimes need to rearrange them.

$$8n + 5 = 5n + 50$$

| | |
|---|---|
| $8n + 5 - 5 = 5n + 50 - 5$ | (Subtract 5 from both sides.) |
| $8n = 5n + 45$ | (Simplify both sides.) |
| $8n - 5n = 5n + 45 - 5n$ | (Subtract 5n from both sides.) |
| $3n = 45$ | (Simplify both sides.) |
| $3n \div 3 = 45 \div 3$ | (Divide both sides by 3.) |
| $n = 15$ | (Simplify RHS.) |

Always **simplify** equations as much as possible before you solve them.

## Try It Out

Simplify, rearrange and solve each equation.

1. $2y + 3 = y + 5$
2. $4d - 3 = 2d + 7$
3. $3X + 5 = X + 12$
4. $8m + 15 = m - 6$
5. $2q = 3q - 8$
6. $3(L - 3) = 9$
7. $3(5 - t) = 15$
8. $2(3v + 1) = 4v$
9. $6(5a - 2) = 2(a + 8)$
10. $7(k - 5) = 2(2 - 3k)$

# Learn About It

A formula usually has a **subject**. This is what the formula helps you work out.

Luke fixes TVs. He charges £15 call-out fee and £5 an hour. This formula tells you how much it *c*osts if you know the *h*ours:

$$c = 5h + 15$$

$c$ is the subject of this formula.

Suppose you know what a repair cost and needed to work out how many hours it took. You need a formula with $h$ as the subject. This is called **changing the subject**.

You do this by rearranging the terms.

| | |
|---|---|
| $c = 5h + 15$ | *(Write the formula down.)* |
| $c - 15 = 5h + 15 - 15$ | *(Subtract 15 from both sides.)* |
| $c - 15 = 5h$ | *(Simplify RHS.)* |
| $\dfrac{c - 15}{5} = \dfrac{5h}{5}$ | *(Divide both sides by 5.)* |
| $\dfrac{c - 15}{5} = h$ | *(Simplify RHS.)* |
| $h = \dfrac{c - 15}{5}$ | *(Swap sides for neatness.)* |

Sometimes the formula has no subject.

| **Example** | Make $x$ the subject of $2x + 3y = 12$. | |
|---|---|---|
| **Working** | $2x + 3y = 12$ | *(Write the formula down.)* |
| | $2x + 3y - 3y = 12 - 3y$ | *(Subtract 3y from both sides.)* |
| | $2x = 12 - 3y$ | *(Simplify LHS.)* |
| | $\dfrac{2x}{2} = \dfrac{12 - 3y}{2}$ | *(Divide both sides by 2.)* |
| **Answer** | $x = \dfrac{12 - 3y}{2}$ | *(Simplify LHS.)* |

## Word Check

**formula** mathematical instructions for working something out

**subject** the term being worked out

**rearrange** move terms around in a formula or equation

## Try It Out

In each formula below, one letter is red. Make that letter the subject.

**1** $B = A - 30$      **2** $d = 2r$

**3** $S = \dfrac{n}{10} + 5$      **4** $t = 2b + 40$

**5** $e = a + b$      **6** $f = pv$

**7** $3x = 4y + 5$      **8** $5x + 4y = 20$

**9** $r = \sqrt{s}$      **10** $C = 3r^2$

## Practice

In each question, two of the formulae mean the same thing. One is different. Rearrange them to find out which is the odd one out.

| | |
|---|---|
| **Example** | **(a)** $p - q = r$    **(b)** $q - r = p$    **(c)** $p - r = q$ |
| **Working** | Make $p$ the subject of each one. |
| | **(a)** $\quad p - q = r$ |
| | $\quad p - q + q = r + q$      *(Add q to both sides.)* |
| | $\quad\quad p = r + q$      *(Simplify LHS.)* |
| | **(b)** $\quad q - r = p$ |
| | $\quad\quad p = q - r$      *(Swap sides.)* |
| | **(c)** $\quad p - r = q$ |
| | $\quad p - r + r = q + r$      *(Add r to both sides.)* |
| | $\quad\quad p = q + r$      *(Simplify LHS.)* |
| **Answer** | **(a)** and **(c)** match, **(b)** is different. |

**1** **(a)** $y = x - 5$    **(b)** $x = y + 5$    **(c)** $y = x + 5$

**2** **(a)** $d = 2C - 10$    **(b)** $C = 2d + 10$    **(c)** $d = \dfrac{C - 10}{2}$

**3** **(a)** $s = \dfrac{n}{2} + 3$    **(b)** $n = 2s - 3$    **(c)** $n = 2(s - 3)$

**4** **(a)** $a = b - c$    **(b)** $b = c - a$    **(c)** $c = a + b$

**5** **(a)** $2v - 3w = 1$    **(b)** $v = \dfrac{3w + 1}{2}$    **(c)** $w = \dfrac{2v + 1}{3}$

**1** Make $y$ the subject of each of these equations.
 **(a)** $2x + y = 13$    **(b)** $x - y = 1$    **(c)** $6x + 2y = 9$
 **(d)** $2x - 5y = 13$    **(e)** $4x + 3y = 0$

**2** For each part of question 1, find the value of $y$ if $x = 2$.

Cars pass two emergency phones on the motorway.

The speed at the first phone is $u$ m/s.

The speed at the second phone is $v$ m/s.

Cars travel from the first phone to the second in $t$ seconds.

The acceleration of the cars is $a$ m/s$^2$.

The formula connecting these is $v = u + at$.

**1** (a) Make $u$ the subject of the formula.

   (b) Make $t$ the subject of the formula.

   (c) Make $a$ the subject of the formula.

**2** Use your formulae to fill in this table.

| | Speed at 1ˢᵗ phone ($u$ m/s) | Speed at 2ⁿᵈ phone ($v$ m/s) | Time taken ($t$ seconds) | Acceleration ($a$ m/s$^2$) |
|---|---|---|---|---|
| Car A | 15 | | 50 | 0.2 |
| Car B | 10 | 15 | | 0.0625 |
| Car C | | 30 | 40 | 0.25 |
| Car D | 15 | 5 | 100 | |

> **Finished Early?**
> ➡ Go to page 394

## Further Practice

**F** **1** In each formula, one letter is red. Make that letter the subject.

   (a) $G = g + 100$

   (b) $a = 5b$

   (c) $f = \dfrac{e}{3} - 3$

   (d) $q = 10p - 8$

   (e) $V = lbh$

**2** Make $y$ the subject of each of these formulae.

   (a) $3x + y = 10$

   (b) $x - y = -6$

   (c) $4x + 3y = 20$

   (d) $-7x - 2y = 1$

   (e) $7x - 5y = 0$

**3** For each part of question 2, find the value of $y$ if $x = 5$.

> **Finished Early?**
> ➡ Go to page 394

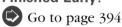

# Simultaneous Equations and Graphs

Squared paper

## Learn About It

This grid shows the graphs of
$y = x + 2$ and $y = 3x$.

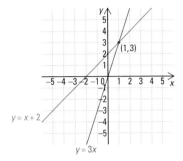

All the points on the red line satisfy the
equation $y = x + 2$.

All the points on the blue line satisfy the
equation $y = 3x$.

There is one point that satisfies both
equations. It's where the lines cross, at $(1, 3)$.

Equations that are true at the same time are called **simultaneous equations**.
The solution for a pair of simultaneous equations will always have **two** parts:
one for each variable. The solution of these two equations is $x = 1$ and $y = 3$.
You get these answers from the coordinates of the point where the lines cross.

Always check the solutions by substituting them into the original equations.

| | | | |
|---|---|---|---|
| $y = x + 2$ | *(Original equation.)* | $y = 3x$ | *(Original equation.)* |
| $3 = 1 + 2$ | *(Substitute.)* | $3 = 3 \times 1$ | *(Substitute.)* |
| $3 = 3$ | *(Simplify RHS.)* | $3 = 3$ | *(Simplify RHS.)* |
| This is correct. | | This is correct. | |

The solutions work in both equations.

## Word Check

simultaneous equations  equations that are true at the same time

## Key Fact

To solve a pair of simultaneous equations:
- Plot the graphs of both equations on a single grid.
- Find the point where the lines cross.
- Write down the $x$ and $y$ values of the coordinates of this point,
  to give the solution.
- Check the solution by substitution.

## Try It Out

**G** Plot graphs to solve these pairs of simultaneous equations. Both axes should go from –10 to 10.

**1** $y = 2x + 2$          **2** $y = 3x - 4$
    $y = x + 4$                   $y = 1 - 2x$

## Learn More About It

Sometimes you have to change the subject of an equation before you can plot its graph.

| | |
|---|---|
| **Example** | Solve the simultaneous equations $x + 2y = 1$, $2x + y = 8$. |
| **Working** | Make $y$ the subject of the first equation. |

$$x + 2y = 1$$
$$x + 2y - x = 1 - x \qquad \textit{(Subtract x from both sides.)}$$
$$2y = 1 - x \qquad \textit{(Simplify LHS.)}$$
$$\frac{2y}{2} = \frac{1 - x}{2} \qquad \textit{(Divide both sides by 2.)}$$
$$y = \frac{1 - x}{2} \qquad \textit{(Simplify LHS.)}$$

Make $y$ the subject of the second equation.

$$2x + y = 8$$
$$2x + y - 2x = 8 - 2x \qquad \textit{(Subtract 2x from both sides.)}$$
$$y = 8 - 2x \qquad \textit{(Simplify LHS.)}$$

Plot the graphs.

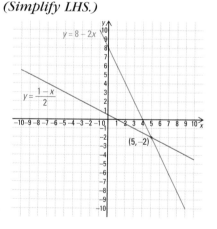

The graphs cross at (5, –2).

| | |
|---|---|
| **Answer** | $x = 5, y = -2$. |
| **Check** | The solution to the equations is $x = 5, y = -2$. |

$$\begin{array}{ll} x + 2y = 1 & 2x + y = 8 \\ 5 + 2 \times (-2) = 1 & 2 \times 5 + (-2) = 8 \\ 5 - 4 = 1 & 10 - 2 = 8 \end{array}$$

This is correct.      This is correct.

The solution works in both equations.

You can use simultaneous equations to solve problems.

| | |
|---|---|
| **Example** | Suppose you are trying to find the mass of a 20p coin and a 1p coin. |
| | You find that 62 pence weighs 22 grams and 24 pence weighs 19 grams. |
| **Working** | Use $x$ to stand for the mass of a 1p coin. |
| | Use $y$ to stand for the mass of a 20p coin. |
| | *(Note: it doesn't matter which one is x and which is y.)* |
| | 62 pence is 2 pennies and three 20p coins, $2x + 3y$. |
| | 24 pence is 4 pennies and one 20p coin, $4x + y$. |
| | The equations are $2x + 3y = 22$, $4x + y = 19$. |
| | Solving these gives $x = 3.5$ and $y = 5$. |
| **Answer** | A penny weighs 3.5 grams and a 20p coin weighs 5 grams. |

**Check**

| | |
|---|---|
| $2x + 3y = 22$ | $4x + y = 19$ |
| $2 \times 3.5 + 3 \times 5 = 22$ | $4 \times 3.5 + 5 = 19$ |
| $7 + 15 = 22$ | $14 + 5 = 19$ |
| This is correct. | This is correct. |

The solutions work in both equations.

## Word Check

**rearrange** change the subject of a formula or equation

## Try It Out

Rearrange these pairs of simultaneous equations so that $y$ is the subject, then draw graphs to solve them.  Both axes should go from –10 to 10.

**1** $x + 5y = 6$
$2x + 3y = -2$

**2** $x - 2y = 2$
$2x + y = 7$

## Practice

 For each question, make a pair of simultaneous equations and solve them using graphs. Both axes should go from –10 to 10.

**1** A construction set has long pieces and short pieces. Laid end to end, a long piece and two short pieces measure 11 cm. Two long pieces and a short piece measure 13 cm.

How long are the two kinds of piece?

**2** At a concert, three adult and two child tickets cost £34. One adult with four children pays £28.

How much are the tickets?

**3** If filled completely, two small buckets and two large buckets fill a 9 litre container.

Six small buckets and one large bucket fill a 12 litre container.

What does each bucket hold?

> **Finished Early?**
> Go to page 395

## Further Practice

 Solve these pairs of simultaneous equations by drawing graphs.

**1** (a) $y = 2x + 3$
    $y = x - 2$
   (b) $y = 4 - x$
    $y = \frac{1}{4}x + 1$

**2** (a) $x + y = 2$
    $2x - 3y = -5$
   (b) $3x - 2y = 7$
    $x + 4y = 0$

**3** Rashid takes $6\frac{1}{2}$ minutes to eat two sandwiches and a piece of fruit. He takes $5\frac{1}{2}$ minutes to eat one sandwich and two pieces of fruit. How long does he take to eat a sandwich? How long does he take to eat a piece of fruit?

> **Finished Early?**
> Go to page 395

# Unit 6 *Algebra 2*

## Summary of Chapters 11 and 12

- Every straight line on a coordinate grid can be described by an **equation**.

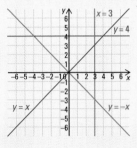 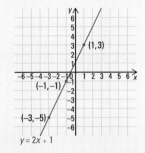

- Graphs can be used to show **regions**. The regions are described using inequalities.

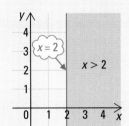 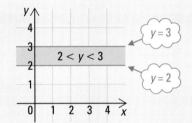

- Some common **curved graphs** are:

 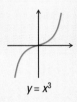 

$y = x^2$      $y = x^3$      $y = \frac{1}{x}$

- Simultaneous equations are both true at the same time. You can find the solution by plotting the graphs of both equations on one grid.

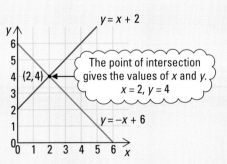

The point of intersection gives the values of $x$ and $y$. $x = 2$, $y = 4$

# Brush Up Your Number 7

 **Multiplying Whole Numbers**

## Learn About It

To be able to multiply numbers, you need to know your **multiplication tables**.

To multiply by 10, 100 or 1000, move the digits to the **left** 1, 2 or 3 places. Fill empty columns with zeros. For example, $23 \times 10 = 230$, $410 \times 100 = 41\,000$.

To multiply 1 s.f. numbers, use tables **and** move digits.

| | |
|---|---|
| **Example** | $600 \times 30$ |
| **Working** | $6 \times 3 = 18$ |
| | There are three zeros in the question, so move the digits three places to the left. |
| **Answer** | $18\,000$ |

To multiply by a 2-digit number, use the box method or set out the calculation in columns.

**Example**   $435 \times 27$
**Working**                                          **Working**
Box method:                                          Column method:

| × | **400** | **30** | **5** |
|---|---|---|---|
| **20** | 8000 | 600 | 100 |
| **7** | 2800 | 210 | 35 |

**Totals**   10 800     810     135

$10\,800 + 810 + 135 = 11\,745$

```
      4 3 5
  ×     2 7
    3 0 4 5
    8 7 0 0
  1 1 7 4 5
```

**Answer**      11 745

## Try It Out

 Calculate the following.

**1 (a)** $31 \times 7$      **(b)** $975 \times 6$      **(c)** $42\,628 \times 8$

**2 (a)** $41 \times 10$      **(b)** $703 \times 100$      **(c)** $250 \times 1000$

**3 (a)** $60 \times 7$      **(b)** $400 \times 6$      **(c)** $300 \times 40$

**4 (a)** $55 \times 25$      **(b)** $126 \times 63$      **(c)** $2605 \times 42$

# Practice

**1** Mallinson's make cakes. The cakes are packed into boxes. Copy and complete this production sheet for one week. Write your working underneath.

| Type of cake | Number per box | Number of boxes | Number of cakes |
|---|---|---|---|
| Cherry bakewell | 5 | 690 | |
| Choc sponge roll | 6 | 1235 | |
| Mini battenburg | 8 | 562 | |
| Jam tarts | 6 | 348 | |
| Strawberry tarts | 4 | 744 | |

Their target is to make 20 000 cakes a week. Have they done it this week?

**2** The number in the middle of this multiplication square is 120 because $2 \times 3 \times 4 \times 5 = 120$.

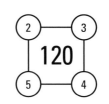

Copy the shapes below. Multiply **all** the numbers at the corners of each shape to find the number that goes in the middle.

**(a)**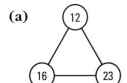

**(b)**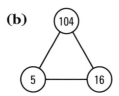

**(c)**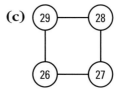

**(d)**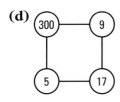

**(e)**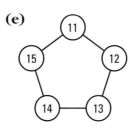

**(f)**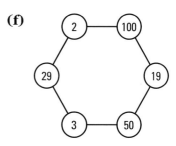

**3** Work out these powers.

  **(a)** $24^2$      **(b)** $53^2$      **(c)** $85^2$      **(d)** $13^3$

  **(e)** $30^3$      **(f)** $77^3$

> *Remember:* **squaring** *a number means multiplying it by itself.* **Cubing** *means multiplying it by itself twice.*

**Finished Early?**
 Go to page 395

# 13 Fractions

In this chapter you will learn about ...

1 decimals and fractions
2 mixed numbers
3 fraction calculations
4 fractions of an amount

## 1 Decimals and Fractions

### Learn About It

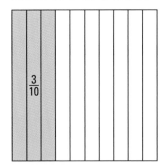

Each strip is one tenth ($\frac{1}{10}$) of the square.

3 tenths ($\frac{3}{10}$) are shaded red.

You can write $\frac{3}{10}$ as the decimal: 0.3.

0.3 tenths

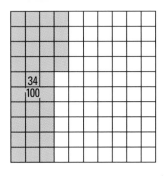

Each small square is one hundredth ($\frac{1}{100}$) of the large square.

4 hundredths ($\frac{4}{100}$) are shaded blue.

3 tenths ($\frac{3}{10}$) and 4 hundredths ($\frac{4}{100}$) are shaded altogether.

You can write this as the decimal: 0.34.

34 hundredths ($\frac{34}{100}$) are shaded altogether.

So 0.34 also means $\frac{34}{100}$.

0.34 tenths hundredths

0.03 means 3 hundredths ($\frac{3}{100}$).

0.207 means 207 thousandths ($\frac{207}{1000}$).

0.125 means 125 thousandths ($\frac{125}{1000}$) which cancels to $\frac{1}{8}$.

**NUMBER SKILLS Know the columns of the decimal system, multiply/divide HTU**

# Try It Out

**1** Write these decimals as fractions.

| | |
|---|---|
| **Example** | 0.245 |
| **Working** | Look at the last column: thousandths. |
| | So 0.245 = 245 thousandths |
| **Answer** | $\frac{245}{1000}$ |

tenths hundredths thousandths

0.2 4 5

(a) 0.7    (b) 0.93    (c) 0.491    (d) 0.03    (e) 0.017

(f) 0.009    (g) 0.307    (h) 0.2939    (i) 0.0009    (j) 0.0027

**2** Write these fractions as decimals.

| | |
|---|---|
| **Example** | $\frac{29}{1000}$ |
| **Working** | The last digit will be thousandths. |
| **Answer** | 0.029 |

tenths hundredths thousandths

0.0 2 9

(a) $\frac{9}{10}$    (b) $\frac{23}{100}$    (c) $\frac{9}{100}$    (d) $\frac{237}{1000}$

(e) $\frac{3}{1000}$    (f) $\frac{58}{1000}$    (g) $\frac{6957}{10\,000}$    (h) $\frac{23}{10\,000}$

# Learn More About It

You can change any fraction into a decimal. There are several methods.

**1** Change the denominator to 10, 100 or 1000.

| | | |
|---|---|---|
| **Example** | Change $\frac{2}{5}$ to a decimal. | Change $\frac{4}{25}$ to a decimal. |
| **Working** | $\frac{2}{5} = \frac{4}{10}$ = 4 tenths = 0.4 (× 2) | $\frac{4}{25} = \frac{16}{100}$ = 16 hundredths = 0.16 (× 4) |
| **Answer** | 0.4 | 0.16 |

**2** Divide the numerator by the denominator.

$\frac{19}{4}$ means $19 \div 4 = 4.75$

$$\begin{array}{r} 4.75 \\ 4\overline{)19.^30^20} \end{array}$$

**3**  Use your calculator.

---

**Example**   Change $\frac{19}{40}$ to a decimal.

**Working**   $\frac{19}{40}$ means $19 \div 40$

$$\boxed{1}\boxed{9}\boxed{\div}\boxed{4}\boxed{0}\boxed{=}\quad\boxed{0.475}$$

**Answer**   0.475

---

You can write mixed numbers as decimals too, and decimals as mixed numbers.

---

**Example**   Change $2\frac{3}{20}$ to a decimal.

**Working**   $2\frac{3}{20} = 2 + \frac{3}{20} = 2 + \frac{15}{100} = 2 + 0.15 = 2.15$

Or, using a calculator:

$$\boxed{2}\boxed{+}\boxed{3}\boxed{\div}\boxed{2}\boxed{0}\boxed{=}\quad\boxed{2.15}$$

**Answer**   2.15

---

**Example**   Change 3.4 to a mixed number.

**Working**   $3.4 = 3 + 0.4 = 3 + \frac{4}{10} = 3 + \frac{2}{5} = 3\frac{2}{5}$

**Answer**   $3\frac{2}{5}$

---

## Try It Out

**B** **1**  Convert each fraction to an equivalent fraction with denominator 10, 100 or 1000. Write the fraction as a decimal. Do not use your calculator.

(a) $\frac{3}{5}$        (b) $\frac{7}{20}$        (c) $\frac{9}{25}$        (d) $\frac{32}{50}$

(e) $\frac{2}{25}$        (f) $\frac{24}{200}$        (g) $\frac{2}{500}$        (h) $2\frac{3}{25}$

**2**  Use short or long division to convert these fractions to decimals.

(a) $\frac{2}{5}$        (b) $\frac{7}{8}$        (c) $\frac{13}{20}$        (d) $\frac{9}{40}$

 **3**  Use your calculator to convert these fractions to decimals.

(a) $\frac{3}{8}$        (b) $\frac{37}{40}$        (c) $2\frac{5}{8}$        (d) $15\frac{7}{16}$

**4**  Write these decimals as mixed numbers.

(a) 1.3        (b) 4.6        (c) 3.25        (d) 2.45

(e) 3.04        (f) 6.025

# Practice

**1** Convert these decimals to fractions and then cancel them to their lowest terms.

**Example** 0.625 **Working**

$$0.625 = \frac{625}{1000} = \frac{5}{8}$$

**Answer** $\frac{5}{8}$

**(a)** 0.8    **(b)** 0.45    **(c)** 0.36    **(d)** 0.025

**(e)** 0.625    **(f)** 0.3375    **(g)** 0.256    **(h)** 0.1024

**2** Convert these fractions to equivalent fractions with denominators 100, 1000 or 10 000. Write them as decimals. Do not use a calculator.

*Hint: multiply by 5 as many times as you need to.*

**(a)** $\frac{11}{20}$    **(b)** $\frac{43}{200}$    **(c)** $\frac{9}{40}$    **(d)** $\frac{1}{8}$

**(e)** $\frac{45}{400}$    **(f)** $\frac{3}{16}$    **(g)** $\frac{3}{2000}$    **(h)** $\frac{21}{80}$

Write each group of numbers in order, from smallest to largest. Convert the fractions to decimals first.

**Example** $\frac{3}{5}$   $\frac{5}{8}$   0.45

**Working** Convert fractions to decimals: $\frac{3}{5} = 0.6$ and $\frac{5}{8} = 0.625$.

Put the decimals in order: 0.45   0.6   0.625

**Answer** 0.45   $\frac{3}{5}$   $\frac{5}{8}$

**1** $\frac{3}{8}$   $\frac{2}{5}$   0.35    **2** $\frac{9}{4}$   2.33   $\frac{43}{20}$    **3** $\frac{29}{8}$   3.7   $\frac{69}{20}$

**4** $\frac{116}{20}$   $\frac{23}{4}$   5.64    **5** 0.09   $\frac{2}{25}$   $\frac{17}{200}$    **6** 2.853   $\frac{231}{80}$   $\frac{714}{250}$

**Finished Early?**
➡ Go to page 396

# Further Practice

Copy and complete these tables. Write all the fractions in their lowest terms.

| Fraction | Decimal | Fraction | Decimal | Fraction | Decimal |
|---|---|---|---|---|---|
| $\frac{1}{2}$ | | $\frac{3}{8}$ | | $\frac{3}{16}$ | |
| | 0.25 | | 0.625 | | 0.3125 |
| $\frac{3}{4}$ | | $\frac{7}{8}$ | | $\frac{3}{100}$ | |
| | 0.2 | | 0.1 | | 0.23 |
| $\frac{2}{5}$ | | $\frac{3}{10}$ | | $\frac{1}{200}$ | |
| | 0.6 | | 0.7 | | 0.004 |
| $\frac{4}{5}$ | | $\frac{9}{10}$ | | $\frac{34}{1000}$ | |
| | 0.125 | | 0.0625 | | 0.234 |

**F** Find a fraction that lies between the fractions in each pair. Convert the fractions to decimals first. There will be more than one correct answer.

**1** $\frac{3}{4}$ and $\frac{9}{10}$     **2** $\frac{1}{5}$ and $\frac{1}{4}$     **3** $\frac{3}{25}$ and $\frac{19}{40}$     **4** $\frac{13}{20}$ and $\frac{31}{50}$

| | |
|---|---|
| **Example** | $\frac{2}{5}$ and $\frac{7}{8}$ |
| **Working** | Convert to decimals: $\frac{2}{5} = 0.4$ and $\frac{7}{8} = 0.875$. |
| | Choose a decimal between 0.4 and 0.875, for example 0.6. |
| | Convert 0.6 to a fraction: $0.6 = \frac{6}{10} = \frac{3}{5}$. |
| **Answer** | $\frac{3}{5}$ |

**5** $\frac{3}{8}$ and $\frac{9}{25}$     **6** $\frac{1}{50}$ and $\frac{4}{125}$     **7** $\frac{7}{80}$ and $\frac{23}{250}$     **8** $\frac{12}{5}$ and $\frac{47}{20}$

**9** $\frac{31}{8}$ and $\frac{97}{25}$     **10** $\frac{21}{16}$ and $\frac{53}{40}$

> **Finished Early?**
> ➡ Go to page 396

## **T②** Mixed Numbers

### Learn About It

Darren has cut this whole pizza into four equal parts.

You can write a whole (1) as the fraction $\frac{4}{4}$ (4 quarters).

Darren bakes two more pizzas. He has three whole pizzas.

You can write 3 as the fraction $\frac{12}{4}$ (12 quarters).

Darren ate one quarter of a pizza. He has 11 quarters left. You can write this as a fraction: $\frac{11}{4}$. The fraction $\frac{11}{4}$ is called an **improper fraction** or a **top-heavy fraction** because the numerator (11) is bigger than the denominator (4).

Darren has 2 whole pizzas and $\frac{3}{4}$ of a pizza left. You can write $2 + \frac{3}{4}$ as the **mixed number** $2\frac{3}{4}$.

   **NUMBER SKILLS** Know the columns of the decimal system, multiply/divide HTU

You can **convert** the mixed number $2\frac{3}{4}$ to the improper fraction $\frac{11}{4}$ like this:

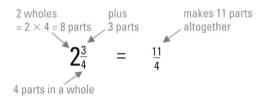

$$2\frac{3}{4} = \frac{11}{4}$$

4 parts in a whole

These three pizzas have not been cut up yet.

They have 1 part each, so you can write 3 wholes as the improper fraction $\frac{3}{1}$.

## Try It Out

**1** Write an improper (top-heavy) fraction to describe the shaded area in each diagram.

**(a)**  **(b)** 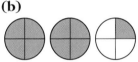 **(c)**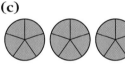

**2** Write your answers to question 1 as mixed numbers.

**3** Convert these mixed numbers to improper fractions.
   **(a)** $1\frac{3}{5}$    **(b)** $2\frac{2}{3}$    **(c)** $3\frac{5}{8}$    **(d)** $9\frac{1}{2}$

## Learn More About It

You can change improper fractions to mixed numbers like this;

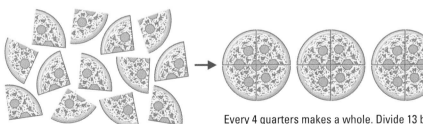

Darren has cut 13 quarters of pizza. You can write this as the improper fraction $\frac{13}{4}$.

Every 4 quarters makes a whole. Divide 13 by 4 to see how many whole pizzas there are.
$13 \div 4 = 3$, remainder 1.
There are 3 whole pizzas and 1 quarter left over.
This can be written as the mixed number $3\frac{1}{4}$.
So $\frac{13}{4} = 3\frac{1}{4}$.

## Try It Out

**H** Convert these improper (top-heavy) fractions to mixed numbers.

| | |
|---|---|
| **Example** | $\frac{17}{3}$ |
| **Working** | $17 \div 3 = 5$ remainder $2$ |
| **Answer** | $5\frac{2}{3}$ |

**1** $\frac{7}{2}$ **2** $\frac{15}{4}$ **3** $\frac{29}{5}$ **4** $\frac{38}{11}$

**5** $\frac{53}{3}$ **6** $\frac{120}{7}$ **7** $\frac{15}{13}$ **8** $\frac{493}{100}$

## Practice

**I** **1** Cancel these improper fractions so they are expressed in their lowest terms, then convert them to mixed numbers.

(a) $\frac{10}{4}$    (b) $\frac{12}{9}$    (c) $\frac{20}{6}$    (d) $\frac{70}{20}$

(e) $\frac{36}{10}$    (f) $\frac{48}{18}$    (g) $\frac{100}{35}$    (h) $\frac{500}{110}$

**2** Convert these improper fractions to mixed numbers, then cancel them to their lowest terms.

| | |
|---|---|
| **Example** | $\frac{100}{45}$ |
| **Working** | $100 \div 45 = 2$ remainder $10$ |
| | $= 2\frac{10}{45} = 2\frac{2}{9}$ |
| **Answer** | $2\frac{2}{9}$ |

(a) $\frac{15}{6}$    (b) $\frac{52}{10}$    (c) $\frac{115}{30}$    (d) $\frac{152}{14}$

(e) $\frac{140}{50}$    (f) $\frac{425}{100}$    (g) $\frac{972}{100}$    (h) $\frac{5245}{1000}$

**J** The mixed number $2\frac{7}{5}$ is wrong because $\frac{7}{5}$ is improper. Write the following mixed numbers correctly.

| | |
|---|---|
| **Example** | $2\frac{7}{5}$ |
| **Working** | Convert $\frac{7}{5}$ to a mixed number: $7 \div 5 = 1$ remainder $2$, so $\frac{7}{5} = 1\frac{2}{5}$. |
| | Add the whole number: $2 + 1\frac{2}{5} = 3\frac{2}{5}$. |
| **Answer** | $3\frac{2}{5}$ |

**1** $1\frac{9}{5}$ **2** $2\frac{14}{3}$ **3** $5\frac{30}{7}$ **4** $10\frac{7}{2}$

**5** $8\frac{15}{10}$ **6** $4\frac{53}{6}$ **7** $5\frac{20}{6}$ **8** $2\frac{50}{12}$

**Finished Early?**
➡ Go to page 396

## Further Practice

**1** Write an improper fraction to describe the shaded area in each diagram. Make sure your answers are cancelled to their lowest terms.

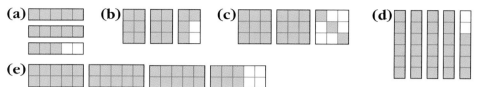

**(a)** **(b)** **(c)** **(d)**

**(e)**

**2** Convert your answers to question 1 to mixed numbers.

Match each mixed number with the improper fraction that has the same value. Write down the matching pairs.

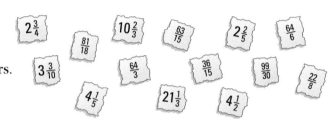

$2\frac{3}{4}$  $10\frac{2}{3}$  $\frac{63}{15}$  $2\frac{2}{5}$  $\frac{64}{6}$

$\frac{81}{18}$

$3\frac{3}{10}$  $\frac{64}{3}$  $\frac{36}{15}$  $\frac{99}{30}$  $\frac{22}{8}$

$4\frac{1}{5}$  $21\frac{1}{3}$  $4\frac{1}{2}$

# Fraction Calculations

> **Finished Early?**
> ➡ Go to page 396

## Learn About It

To add or subtract fractions that have the same denominator, just add their numerators.

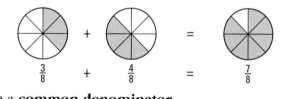

$\frac{3}{8}$ + $\frac{4}{8}$ = $\frac{7}{8}$

If the denominators are different, change to equivalent fractions with a **common denominator**.

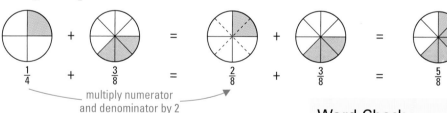

$\frac{1}{4}$ + $\frac{3}{8}$ = $\frac{2}{8}$ + $\frac{3}{8}$ = $\frac{5}{8}$

multiply numerator and denominator by 2

Sometimes you have to change the denominators of both fractions. Multiply them together to find the common denominator.

> **Word Check**
> ................................
> **common denominator**
> same denominator

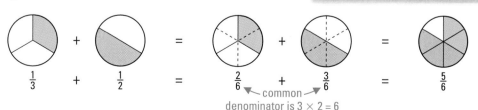

$\frac{1}{3}$ + $\frac{1}{2}$ = $\frac{2}{6}$ + $\frac{3}{6}$ = $\frac{5}{6}$

common denominator is 3 × 2 = 6

## Key Fact

When adding or subtracting fractions with different denominators, change to equivalent fractions so that the fractions have the same (common) denominator.

## Try It Out

 Calculate the following.

**1** First change the smaller denominator to match the bigger one.

(a) $\frac{1}{2} + \frac{1}{6}$     (b) $\frac{1}{4} + \frac{3}{8}$     (c) $\frac{3}{5} - \frac{3}{10}$     (d) $\frac{2}{3} - \frac{2}{9}$

(e) $\frac{1}{16} + \frac{3}{4}$     (f) $\frac{7}{10} - \frac{9}{20}$     (g) $\frac{13}{20} + \frac{7}{40}$     (h) $\frac{6}{7} - \frac{10}{21}$

**2** First multiply the denominators to find the common denominator.

(a) $\frac{3}{4} - \frac{2}{5}$     (b) $\frac{2}{3} + \frac{1}{5}$     (c) $\frac{3}{10} + \frac{1}{4}$     (d) $\frac{5}{6} - \frac{1}{7}$

(e) $\frac{1}{4} + \frac{1}{5}$     (f) $\frac{1}{3} - \frac{2}{7}$     (g) $\frac{9}{11} - \frac{1}{2}$     (h) $3\frac{1}{4} - 1\frac{2}{3}$

## Learn More About It

Naomi adds $\frac{3}{20}$ to $\frac{5}{8}$. She multiplies the denominators, 20 and 8, to find a common denominator, 160. She has to cancel her answer to its lowest terms. This could mean that her common denominator, 160, is too big.

$$\frac{3}{20} + \frac{5}{8}$$

Common denominator = 20 × 8 = 160

$$\frac{24}{160} + \frac{100}{160} = \frac{124}{160} = \frac{31}{40}$$

Look at the denominators of $\frac{3}{20}$ and $\frac{5}{8}$. Both 20 and 8 can be divided by 4, so you can divide the common denominator, 160, by 4, giving 40 as common denominator instead. 4 is the biggest number that divides both 20 and 8, so 40 is the **lowest common denominator**.

### Word Check

**lowest common denominator**
   the smallest denominator you can use to add or subtract fractions

$\frac{3}{20} + \frac{5}{8} = \frac{6}{40} + \frac{25}{40} = \frac{31}{40}$

Always change mixed numbers to improper fractions first, then convert your answer back to a mixed number, if necessary.

| **Example** | $3\frac{1}{4} - 1\frac{3}{8}$ | |
|---|---|---|
| **Working** | $\frac{13}{4} - \frac{11}{8}$ | (*Convert to improper fractions.*) |
| | $= \frac{26}{8} - \frac{11}{8}$ | (*Change to have a common denominator.*) |
| | $= \frac{26-11}{8} = \frac{15}{8}$ | (*Subtract numerators.*) |
| | $= 1\frac{7}{8}$ | (*Convert back to a mixed number.*) |
| **Answer** | $1\frac{7}{8}$ | |

# Try It Out

**1** Calculate the following. First find the lowest common denominator.

(a) $\frac{9}{10} - \frac{3}{8}$    (b) $\frac{4}{9} + \frac{1}{4}$    (c) $\frac{6}{7} - \frac{1}{2}$    (d) $\frac{7}{12} + \frac{3}{8}$

(e) $\frac{3}{10} + \frac{4}{15}$    (f) $\frac{5}{6} - \frac{1}{4}$    (g) $\frac{5}{9} - \frac{5}{12}$    (h) $\frac{7}{8} - \frac{9}{20}$

**2** Calculate the following. First convert the whole numbers and mixed numbers to improper fractions.

(a) $3\frac{1}{5} - 1\frac{3}{10}$    (b) $4\frac{2}{3} + 2\frac{1}{6}$    (c) $5\frac{3}{4} - 2\frac{1}{3}$

(d) $2\frac{1}{4} - 1\frac{5}{6}$    (e) $3 - 1\frac{2}{3}$    (f) $4\frac{5}{8} - 2$

# Learn More About It

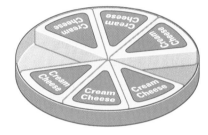

$\frac{6}{8}$ of the cheese portions are left in this box.

The remaining portions are divided into two halves.

Each half is $\frac{3}{8}$, so $\frac{1}{2}$ of $\frac{6}{8}$ is $\frac{3}{8}$.

In maths, **of** means ×. So $\frac{1}{2} \times \frac{6}{8} = \frac{3}{8}$

You can work this out another way.

$$\frac{1}{2} \times \frac{6}{8} = \frac{1 \times 6}{2 \times 8} \quad \textit{(Multiply the numerators.)}$$
$$\textit{(Multiply the denominators.)}$$

$$= \frac{\cancel{6}^{3}}{\cancel{16}_{8}} \quad \textit{(Cancel.)}$$

$$= \frac{3}{8}$$

You could cancel first to make the numbers smaller to multiply.

$$\frac{1}{2} \times \frac{\cancel{6}^{3}}{\cancel{8}_{4}} = \frac{1}{2} \times \frac{3}{4} = \frac{1 \times 3}{2 \times 4} = \frac{3}{8}$$

Here is another way of cancelling. You can cancel any numerator with any denominator when multiplying fractions.

$$\frac{1}{\cancel{2}_{1}} \times \frac{\cancel{6}^{3}}{8} = \frac{1}{1} \times \frac{3}{8} = \frac{1 \times 3}{1 \times 8} = \frac{3}{8}$$

Change mixed numbers to improper fractions, then cancel before multiplying.

$$1\frac{3}{5} \times 3\frac{1}{3} = \frac{8}{\cancel{5}_{1}} \times \frac{\cancel{10}^{2}}{3} = \frac{8 \times 2}{1 \times 3} = \frac{16}{3} = 5\frac{1}{3}$$

Change whole numbers to improper fractions before cancelling and multiplying.

$$3 \times \frac{6}{8} = \frac{3}{1} \times \frac{\cancel{6}^{3}}{\cancel{8}_{4}} = \frac{3 \times 3}{1 \times 4} = \frac{9}{4} = 2\frac{1}{4}$$

write 3 as a fraction

## Key Fact

To multiply fractions:

- change mixed numbers to improper fractions
- change whole numbers to improper fractions
- cancel any numerator with any denominator
- multiply the numerators together
- multiply the denominators together
- change the answer to a mixed number if necessary.

## Try It Out

**1** Multiply the following fractions.  Cancel your answers to their lowest terms.

    **(a)** $\frac{2}{3} \times \frac{1}{4}$      **(b)** $\frac{3}{5} \times \frac{1}{6}$      **(c)** $\frac{3}{4} \times \frac{4}{5}$      **(d)** $\frac{6}{7} \times \frac{3}{8}$

**2** Cancel these fractions first, then multiply them.

    **(a)** $\frac{6}{8} \times \frac{1}{5}$      **(b)** $\frac{3}{7} \times \frac{5}{10}$      **(c)** $\frac{9}{12} \times \frac{20}{50}$      **(d)** $\frac{4}{6} \times \frac{12}{16}$

**3** Multiply the following. Change the mixed numbers to improper fractions first. Write your answers as mixed numbers.

    **(a)** $2\frac{2}{3} \times \frac{5}{6}$      **(b)** $\frac{3}{4} \times 1\frac{3}{5}$      **(c)** $2\frac{1}{2} \times 1\frac{3}{10}$      **(d)** $3\frac{1}{5} \times 1\frac{1}{8}$

**4** Multiply the following. Change your answers to mixed numbers if necessary.

    **(a)** $2 \times \frac{5}{7}$      **(b)** $\frac{2}{3} \times 6$      **(c)** $5 \times \frac{3}{4}$      **(d)** $8 \times \frac{5}{14}$

## Learn More About It

You know that $2 \times 3 = 6$, so $6 \div 3 = 2$.

You know that $2 \times \frac{3}{8} = \frac{6}{8}$, so $\frac{6}{8} \div \frac{3}{8} = 2$.

You can divide fractions a different way, like this:

$$\frac{6}{8} \div \frac{3}{8} = 2$$

change
to × turn
upside down

$$\frac{\overset{2}{\cancel{6}}}{\cancel{8}_1} \times \frac{\overset{1}{\cancel{8}}}{\cancel{3}_1} = 2$$

Change mixed numbers to improper fractions before dividing:

$$2\frac{5}{8} \div 2\frac{1}{3} = \frac{21}{8} \div \frac{7}{3}$$

$$= \frac{\overset{3}{\cancel{21}}}{8} \times \frac{3}{\cancel{7}_1}$$

$$= \frac{9}{8}$$

$$= 1\frac{1}{8}$$

Change whole numbers to improper fractions before dividing.

$$\frac{6}{7} \div 3 = \frac{6}{7} \div \frac{3}{1}$$

$$= \frac{\cancel{6}^2}{7} \times \frac{1}{\cancel{3}_1}$$

$$= \frac{2}{7}$$

## Key Fact

To divide one fraction by another fraction:
- change mixed numbers to improper fractions
- change whole numbers to improper fractions
- change ÷ to × and turn the second fraction upside down
- multiply the fractions as usual
- change the answer to a mixed number, if necessary.

## Try It Out

Work these out. Change your answers to mixed numbers if necessary.

**1** $\frac{3}{4} \div \frac{1}{6}$      **2** $\frac{2}{3} \div \frac{5}{6}$      **3** $\frac{1}{8} \div \frac{3}{4}$      **4** $\frac{3}{10} \div \frac{4}{15}$

**5** $2\frac{1}{4} \div 3\frac{1}{3}$      **6** $1\frac{3}{5} \div 2\frac{2}{5}$      **7** $\frac{3}{8} \div 2$      **8** $2\frac{2}{9} \div 8$

## Practice

Add or subtract fractions to answer the following questions. Write your answers as fractions.

| | |
|---|---|
| **Example** | Isabel bought 3 bars of chocolate. She gave $\frac{3}{4}$ of a bar to Sara and $\frac{2}{3}$ of a bar to Tarun.<br>**(a)** How many bars did she give away altogether?<br>**(b)** How many bars did she have left? |
| **Working** | **(a)** $\frac{3}{4} + \frac{2}{3} = \frac{9}{12} + \frac{8}{12} = \frac{9+8}{12} = \frac{17}{12} = 1\frac{5}{12}$<br>**(b)** $3 - \frac{17}{12}$<br>    $= \frac{3}{1} - \frac{17}{12}$    (*Change 3 to $\frac{3}{1}$.*)<br>    $= \frac{36}{12} - \frac{17}{12}$<br>    $= \frac{36-17}{12}$<br>    $= \frac{19}{12}$<br>    $= 1\frac{7}{12}$ |
| **Answer** | **(a)** Isabel gave away $1\frac{5}{12}$ bars of chocolate.<br>**(b)** She had $1\frac{7}{12}$ chocolate bars left. |

**1** A petrol tank was $\frac{1}{2}$ full at the beginning of a journey. $\frac{2}{5}$ of a tank was used on the journey. What fraction of a full tank was left?

**2** Douglas wrote $2\frac{1}{2}$ pages of history homework and $1\frac{2}{3}$ pages of French homework.
(a) How many pages did he write altogether?
(b) How many more pages of history did he write than of French?

**3** There are 4 hours of recording time on Liam's video tape. He recorded a film lasting $1\frac{2}{3}$ hours and a documentary lasting $\frac{1}{2}$ hour.
(a) How much of the video tape was used up?
(b) How much recording time was left on the tape?

**4** In Britain, $\frac{1}{10}$ of people use skimmed milk. $\frac{3}{5}$ use semi-skimmed milk. The rest use full-cream milk.
(a) What fraction of people use skimmed or semi-skimmed milk?
(b) What fraction do not use semi-skimmed milk?
(c) What fraction use full-cream milk?

**5** Tracy spent $\frac{3}{8}$ of Saturday decorating and $\frac{1}{6}$ playing tennis. She spent the rest of the day relaxing.
(a) What fraction of Saturday did she spend decorating and playing tennis altogether?
(b) What fraction of Saturday did she spend relaxing?

**6** One evening, $\frac{2}{7}$ of a new candle burned down. The next evening $\frac{3}{8}$ burned down.
(a) What fraction of the candle burned down altogether?
(b) What fraction of the candle was left?

**7** $\frac{2}{5}$ of Class 8G got a grade A in a test. $\frac{1}{4}$ got grade B. The rest got grade C.
(a) What fraction of the class got grade A or B?
(b) What fraction did not get grade A?
(c) What fraction got grade C?

**Finished Early?**
➡ Go to page 397

## Further Practice

**R** **1** Copy the table below. Add the red numbers to the blue numbers. Write your answers in the table.

| | $+\frac{7}{8}$ | $+\frac{4}{5}$ | $+1\frac{2}{3}$ | $+\frac{5}{6}$ |
|---|---|---|---|---|
| $1\frac{3}{4}$ | | | | |
| $1\frac{7}{8}$ | | | | |
| $2$ | | | | |
| $2\frac{3}{10}$ | | | | |

**2** Copy the table in question 1 again. This time, subtract the red numbers from the blue numbers. Write your answers in the table.

In each question, two of the three calculations give the same answer.
Write the odd one out in each set.

**1** (a) $\frac{2}{3} \times \frac{1}{4}$     (b) $\frac{5}{8} \div \frac{3}{10}$     (c) $\frac{1}{15} \div \frac{2}{5}$

**2** (a) $\frac{3}{4} \div \frac{2}{5}$     (b) $12\frac{1}{2} \div 2\frac{2}{3}$     (c) $2\frac{1}{4} \times \frac{5}{6}$

**3** (a) $3 \times 2\frac{3}{4}$     (b) $1\frac{2}{5} \times 2\frac{1}{7}$     (c) $2\frac{1}{5} \times 3\frac{3}{4}$

**4** (a) $\frac{17}{3} \div \frac{5}{6}$     (b) $10\frac{1}{2} \div 6$     (c) $4\frac{2}{3} \times \frac{3}{8}$

**5** (a) $\frac{70}{100} \div \frac{3}{20}$     (b) $18\frac{2}{3} \div 4$     (c) $\frac{8}{6} \times 1\frac{1}{4}$

**6** (a) $\frac{6}{8} \div \frac{4}{6}$     (b) $\frac{6}{4} \div \frac{4}{8}$     (c) $\frac{6}{8} \times \frac{6}{4}$

> **Finished Early?**
>  Go to page 397

# Fractions of an Amount

## Learn About It

Owen, Vicky and Jan have 15 conkers each. Paula has none. The others decide to give Paula $\frac{2}{5}$ of their conkers. They each work out $\frac{2}{5}$ of 15 conkers in a different way but they get the same answer.

Owen works out $\frac{2}{5}$ of 15 like this:

first he finds one fifth ($\frac{1}{5}$) by dividing: $15 \div 5 = 3$

then he finds two fifths ($\frac{2}{5}$) by multiplying: $2 \times 3 = 6$

Vicky works out $\frac{2}{5}$ of 15 using fractions:

$$\frac{2}{5} \text{ of } 15 = \frac{2}{5} \times 15 = \frac{2}{\cancel{5}_1} \times \frac{\cancel{15}^3}{1} = \frac{2 \times 3}{1 \times 1} = \frac{6}{1} = 6.$$

Jan changes $\frac{2}{5}$ to a decimal then multiplies by 15:

$\frac{2}{5} = 2 \div 5 = 0.4$

So $\frac{2}{5}$ of $15 = 0.4 \times 15 = 6$

They each give Paula 6 conkers.

## Try It Out

**1** Calculate the following using Owen's method. (Divide first, then multiply.)

   (a) $\frac{3}{4}$ of 12     (b) $\frac{2}{3}$ of 18     (c) $\frac{3}{10}$ of 20     (d) $\frac{5}{6}$ of 24

**2** Calculate the following using Vicky's method. (Use fractions.)

   (a) $\frac{3}{7}$ of 21     (b) $\frac{7}{8}$ of 32     (c) $\frac{9}{10}$ of 30     (d) $\frac{5}{12}$ of 48

**3** Calculate the following using Jan's method. (Change the fractions to decimals, then multiply.)

   (a) $\frac{2}{5}$ of 20     (b) $\frac{5}{8}$ of 16     (c) $\frac{3}{4}$ of 12     (d) $\frac{7}{10}$ of 60

## Practice

Write whether (a), (b) or (c) is the largest amount in each question.

**1** (a) $\frac{5}{8}$ of £20   (b) $\frac{4}{5}$ of £16   (c) $\frac{3}{4}$ of £18

**2** (a) $\frac{7}{20}$ of 500 kg   (b) $\frac{4}{15}$ of 300 kg   (c) $\frac{5}{7}$ of 154 kg

**3** (a) $\frac{3}{64}$ of 480 cm   (b) $\frac{17}{40}$ of 50 cm   (c) $\frac{91}{100}$ of 18 cm

**4** (a) $3\frac{1}{4}$ bottles of wine, each containing 50 cl when full

   (b) $2\frac{2}{3}$ bottles of wine, each containing 72 cl when full

   (c) $1\frac{5}{8}$ bottles of wine, each containing 100 cl when full

**5** (a) $3\frac{1}{5}$ boxes of screws, each containing 40 when full

   (b) $2\frac{2}{3}$ boxes of screws, each containing 60 when full

   (c) $1\frac{3}{10}$ boxes of screws, each containing 120 when full

**6** Which costs the most?

   (a) $2\frac{3}{4}$ kg of rice at £1.60 per kg

   (b) $3\frac{1}{10}$ kg of rice at £1.40 per kg

   (c) $2\frac{5}{6}$ kg of rice at £1.92 per kg

Dr Smelting mixes different amounts of metals together.

He writes each formula on a strip of paper like this:   $60\,kg$ of $\frac{1}{6}Sn$, $\frac{2}{5}Cu$, $\frac{13}{30}Fe$

Sn stands for tin, Cu for copper and Fe for iron.

Calculate the amount of each metal he uses in the following mixtures. Give your answers correct to 3 s.f.

| | |
|---|---|
| **Example** | 60 kg of $\frac{1}{6}$ Sn, $\frac{2}{5}$ Cu, $\frac{13}{30}$ Fe |
| **Working** | Tin = $\frac{1}{6}$ of 60 = 60 ÷ 6 = 10 kg |
| | Copper = $\frac{2}{5}$ of 60 kg = 2 × 60 ÷ 5 = 24 kg |
| | Iron = $\frac{13}{30}$ of 60 kg = 13 × 60 ÷ 30 = 26 kg |
| **Answer** | 10 kg tin, 24 kg copper, 26 kg iron |

**1** 40 kg of $\frac{1}{6}$Sn, $\frac{2}{5}$Cu, $\frac{13}{30}$Fe

**2** 50 kg of $\frac{2}{5}$Sn, $\frac{3}{8}$Cu, $\frac{9}{40}$Fe

**3** 200 kg of $\frac{1}{250}$Sn, $\frac{9}{25}$Cu, $\frac{159}{250}$Fe

**4** 7.2 tonnes of $\frac{1}{4}$Sn, $\frac{2}{7}$Cu, $\frac{13}{28}$Fe

**5** 2.52 tonnes of $\frac{2}{3}$Sn, $\frac{1}{15}$Cu, $\frac{4}{15}$Fe

**6** 0.48 tonnes of $\frac{27}{88}$Sn, $\frac{15}{72}$Cu, $\frac{16}{33}$Fe

**Finished Early?**
Go to page 397

# Further Practice

Calculate these fractions of fractions.

**1** $\frac{2}{3}$ of $\frac{4}{5}$      **2** $\frac{1}{2}$ of $\frac{5}{8}$      **3** $\frac{3}{4}$ of $\frac{6}{10}$      **4** $\frac{5}{8}$ of $\frac{7}{20}$

**5** $\frac{1}{6}$ of $2\frac{1}{4}$      **6** $\frac{7}{8}$ of $4\frac{2}{5}$      **7** $\frac{3}{20}$ of $\frac{12}{15}$      **8** $\frac{9}{10}$ of $\frac{1}{3}$

Answer the following questions by dividing fractions. Show your working.

| | |
|---|---|
| **Example** | Judy's dog eats $\frac{2}{3}$ of a can of Chappy each day. How many days will 4 cans last? |
| **Working** | $4 \div \frac{2}{3}$ |
| | $= \frac{4}{1} \div \frac{2}{3}$     *(Change 4 to $\frac{4}{1}$.)* |
| | $= \frac{4}{1} \times \frac{3}{2}$     *(Change $\div$ to $\times$ and turn $\frac{2}{3}$ upside down.)* |
| | $= \frac{4 \times 3}{1 \times 2}$ |
| | $= \frac{12}{2}$ |
| | $= 6$ |
| **Answer** | 4 cans will last for six days. |

**1** A TV drama lasts $\frac{2}{3}$ of an hour. How many episodes can be recorded on a 3-hour video tape?

**2** George divides $7\frac{2}{5}$ kg of oats equally among 5 bags. How much does each bag contain?

**3** Dean is $12\frac{1}{2}$ years old. Charlotte is $3\frac{3}{4}$ years old. How many times older is Dean than Charlotte?

**4** How many $2\frac{3}{4}$-minute messages will fit onto a 30-minute answering machine tape?

**5** Raj is making shelves $1\frac{1}{5}$ m long.
    **(a)** How many shelves can he make from 10 m of wood?
    **(b)** How much wood will be left over, in centimetres?

> **Finished Early?**
>  Go to page 397

# 14 Percentages

In this chapter you will learn about ...
1. percentages of an amount
2. percentage increase and decrease
3. reverse calculations

## 1 Percentages of an Amount

### Remember?

25 out of 100 squares are blue.

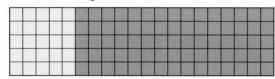

That's $\frac{25}{100}$ as a fraction.

A fraction out of 100 is called a **percentage**.

25% of the rectangle is blue.

| | |
|---|---|
| **Example** | Write 48% as a fraction in its lowest terms. |
| **Working** | $48\% = \dfrac{\overset{12}{\cancel{48}}}{\underset{25}{\cancel{100}}} = \dfrac{12}{25}$ |
| **Answer** | $\frac{12}{25}$ |

| | |
|---|---|
| **Example** | Write 17% as a decimal. |
| **Working** | $17\% = \dfrac{17}{100} = 0.17$   hundredths |
| **Answer** | 0.17 |

| | |
|---|---|
| **Example** | Write $\frac{2}{5}$ as a percentage. |
| **Working** | $\dfrac{2}{5} = \dfrac{2 \times 20}{5 \times 20} = \dfrac{40}{100}$ $= 40\%$ |
| **Answer** | 40% |

| | |
|---|---|
| **Example** | Write 0.04 as a percentage. |
| **Working** | $0.04 = \dfrac{4}{100} = 4\%$   hundredths |
| **Answer** | 4% |

## Try It Out

**1** Write these percentages as fractions in their lowest terms.

    **(a)** 20%       **(b)** 15%        **(c)** 70%       **(d)** 32%

    **(e)** 100%     **(f)** 200%     **(g)** 250%     **(h)** 120%

**2** Write these percentages as decimals.

    **(a)** 38%       **(b)** 17%        **(c)** 60%       **(d)** 5%

**3** Write these fractions as percentages.

    **(a)** $\frac{32}{100}$    **(b)** $\frac{9}{10}$    **(c)** $\frac{21}{50}$    **(d)** $\frac{7}{20}$    **(e)** $\frac{3}{5}$

**4** Write these decimals as percentages.

    **(a)** 0.65     **(b)** 0.14     **(c)** 0.4     **(d)** 0.07

## Learn About It

There was 15% off the price of Smash Band's latest CD in a sale.

Dawn, Rex and Jamila were buying one CD each.

**Dawn's method**

Dawn worked out how much she would save.
She changed 15% to a decimal first.

    15% of £20

$= \frac{15}{100} \times £20$     *(Remember: 15% means $\frac{15}{100}$ and **of** means ×.)*

$= 15 \div 100 \times £20$   *(Divide 15 by 100 to change 15% into a decimal.)*

$= 0.15 \times £20$      *(15% is the same as 0.15)*

$= £3$

**Rex's method**

Rex worked out 15% of £20 like this.
First he divided £20 by 100 to find 1%.
Then he multiplied by 15 to find 15%.

1% of £20 = £20 ÷ 100 = £0.20

So 15% of £20 = 15 × £0.20 = £3

**Jamila's method**

Jamila multiplied the amount by the number of per cent: 15 × £20 = £300.
Then she divided by 100:
£300 ÷ 100 = £3.

### Key Fact

To calculate a percentage (%) of an amount, use one of these methods.

- Convert the percentage to a decimal and multiply by the amount you need to find the percentage of.
- Divide by 100 to find 1%, and multiply by this decimal, then multiply by the number of per cent.
- Multiply by the number of per cent then divide by 100.

# Try It Out

**1** Calculate the following amounts by changing the percentage to a decimal first.

    **(a)** 40% of £45    **(b)** 75% of £36    **(c)** 88% of £75    **(d)** 1% of £9

**2** Calculate the following amounts by dividing by 100 then multiplying by the percentage.

    **(a)** 6% of £150    **(b)** 90% of £25    **(c)** 35% of £10    **(d)** 3% of £40

**3** Calculate the following amounts by multiplying by the number of per cent then dividing by 100.

    **(a)** 80% of £20    **(b)** 60% of £15    **(c)** 40% of £25    **(d)** 25% of £48

    **(e)** 16% of £125    **(f)** 70% of £300    **(g)** 4% of £450    **(h)** 6% of £2000

**4** Martin had to pay 100% of £40. How much did he pay?

# Practice

**1** Calculate the following amounts without using a calculator. Show your working.

    **(a)** 23% of 200 m    **(b)** 60% of £15    **(c)** 8% of 350 g    **(d)** 12% of 225 cl

    **(e)** 10% of £4.60    **(f)** 1% of 7 kg    **(g)** 22% of 15 cm  **(h)** 47% of £80

**2** Use your calculator to find the following amounts.

| | |
|---|---|
| **Example** | $6\frac{1}{4}\%$ of 4000 m |
| **Working** | Change $6\frac{1}{4}\%$ to 6.25%. |
| | Calculate $6.25 \div 100 \times 4000$: |
| |  |
| **Answer** | 250 m |

    **(a)** 34% of £71               **(b)** 60% of 6.23 km

    **(c)** 3.7% of 70 cl            **(d)** 96.3% of 600 m

    **(e)** 29.2% of 4.5 kg         **(f)** 0.4% of 9 litres

    **(g)** 0.01% of 520 000 t     **(h)** $17\frac{1}{2}\%$ of £48

    **(i)** $2\frac{1}{4}\%$ of 96 mm        **(j)** $\frac{3}{4}\%$ of £47 300

**3** Calculate these amounts.

    **(a)** 150% of £20    **(b)** 120% of 35 mm    **(c)** 270% of 900 kg

    **(d)** 105% of £2.60    **(e)** 400% of £134.20    **(f)** $117\frac{1}{2}\%$ of £40

    **(g)** 200% of 6 m    **(h)** 500% of 30 g    **(i)** 1000% of 2 cl

The pie chart shows how people in Birley spend their money on food.
The table shows how much four families spend each week on food.

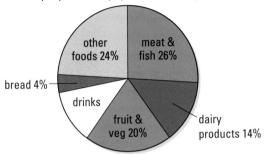

How people in Birley spend their money on food

| Amount spent on food each week | |
|---|---|
| Family | Amount |
| Smith | £48 |
| Yeung | £60 |
| Turner | £52 |
| Patel | £42 |

**1** In a week, how much would you expect …
   **(a)** the Smith family to spend on meat and fish?
   **(b)** the Yeung family to spend on dairy products?
   **(c)** the Turner family to spend on fruit and vegetables?
   **(d)** the Patel family to spend on bread?

**2** What percentage do people spend on drinks in Birley?

**3** In a week, how much altogether would you expect …
   **(a)** the Smith family to spend on bread and drinks?
   **(b)** the Patel family to spend on meat, fish, fruit and vegetables?

**4** How much money would you expect the Yeung family to have left in their weekly budget after buying meat and fish for the week?

**5** How much more would you expect the Turner family to spend on fruit and vegetables than on dairy products in a week?

**6** How much would you expect each of the four families to spend on bread in a week?

**Finished Early?**
➡ Go to page 398

## Further Practice

**E** Calculate the amount of each ingredient in the following packages of food.

**Finished Early?**
➡ Go to page 398

## ❷ Percentage Increase and Decrease

 Learn About It

Jade belongs to the school Stock Market Club. The members meet once a month and pretend to buy shares, which they sell the next month.

Jade bought £200 of ABC shares. They **increased** in value by 12% in one month. She calculated the increase in value like this:

12% of £200 = 12 × £200 ÷ 100 = £2400 ÷ 100
= £24.

So the shares are now worth £200 plus the increase of £24, i.e.
£200 + £24 = £224.

She also bought £120 of Skanda shares.

They **decreased** in value by 5%. She calculated the decrease in value like this:

5% of £120 = 5 × £120 ÷ 100
= £600 ÷ 100
= £6.

The shares are now worth £120 less the decrease of £6, i.e. £114.

### Stockmarket Press

| | | | |
|---|---|---|---|
| ABC | £2.30 | Net Links | £2.85 |
| Air Med. | £6.72 | News Int. | £1.09 |
| Booth's | £7.14 | NTV | £8.27 |
| BPS | £3.43 | Metals | £1.07 |
| Campos | £1.34 | OP Group | £1.09 |
| Chronicle | £2.80 | Pacifics | £3.20 |
| CDR | £3.56 | Powell's | £3.26 |
| Derwent | £5.40 | Orantico | £2 |

### Word Check

**increase** get bigger; go up

**decrease** get smaller; go down

## Try It Out

**1** Calculate the value of these shares.
   **(a)** £160 of Frog Tech shares increase by 10%.
   **(b)** £240 of Brite Metal shares decrease by 10%.
   **(c)** £6000 of Fast Food shares increase by 5%.
   **(d)** £12 000 of Mota Homes shares decrease by 20%.

**2** Calculate the following.
   **(a)** Sam's take-home pay when 20% income tax is **deducted** from £340 wages.
   **(b)** The cost of a refrigerator at £230 plus a 5% delivery charge.
   **(c)** The amount left after Cameron drinks 70% of a 330 ml can of cola.
   **(d)** The cost of a £4.80 book reduced by 10% in a sale.
   **(e)** £600 in a bank account, with 6% interest.

## Learn More About It

Jade bought £250 of Plastek shares. They increased in value by 15%. Jade's teacher showed her a quick way of increasing an amount by a percentage.
The original value is 100% of £250.
The increase in value is 15% of £250.
So the increased value is 115% of £250.
$115\% = \frac{115}{100} = 1.15$.
Jade calculated the increased value like this:
115% of £250 = 1.15 × £250 = £287.50.

## Try It Out

Calculate the value of these shares.

| **Example** | £500 of Online shares increase by 29%. |
|---|---|
| **Working** | 100% + 29% = 129% = 1.29<br>1.29 × £500 = £645 |
| **Answer** | £645 |

| **Example** | £300 of TNT shares decrease by 18%. |
|---|---|
| **Working** | 100% − 18% = 82% = 0.82<br>0.82 × £300 = £246 |
| **Answer** | £246 |

**1** £200 of Wonderworld shares increase by 14%.
**2** £600 of Fabrik shares decrease by 21%.
**3** £5300 of Store Pack shares increase by 47%.
**4** £480 of Transcom shares decrease by 10%.
**5** £15 000 of Bio Food shares increase by 7%.
**6** £90 000 of BN shares decrease by 2%.

## Practice

**H** Calculate each new share price, correct to the nearest penny.

**1** Boron Plus shares increased from £1.85 by 12%.

**2** Carson Educational shares decreased from £29.42 by 6%.

**3** TM Chemicals shares increased from 72p by 23%.

**4** Orbit Communication shares decreased from 38p by 4%.

**5** PDQ International shares increased from £6.16 by 47%.

**6** Digital Retail Co. shares decreased from £3.21 by 2%.

**I** The map shows how house prices changed from last year to this year.

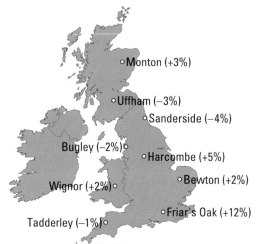

| House Prices | | |
|---|---|---|
| | **Last year** | **This year** (to nearest £1000 |
| Bewton | £93 000 | |
| Bugley | £33 600 | |
| Friar's Oak | £120 000 | |
| Harcombe | £80 000 | |
| Monton | £75 900 | |
| Sanderside | £39 600 | |
| Tadderley | £74 000 | |
| Uffham | £69 000 | |
| Wignor | £82 250 | |

Monton (+3%)
Uffham (−3%)
Sanderside (−4%)
Bugley (−2%)
Harcombe (+5%)
Wignor (+2%)
Bewton (+2%)
Friar's Oak (+12%)
Tadderley (−1%)

Copy and complete the table, calculating the average price of a house this year to the nearest £1000.

> **Finished Early?**
> Go to page 398

## Further Practice

**J** Add VAT (Value Added Tax) to the following prices. VAT is $17\frac{1}{2}$%.

| **Example** | £120 |
|---|---|
| **Working** | $100\% + 17\frac{1}{2}\% = 117.5\% = 1.175$ <br> $1.175 \times £120 = £141$ |
| **Answer** | £141 |

**1** £40    **2** £100    **3** £48    **4** £9

**5** £6.40    **6** £600    **7** £2.40

**8** £158    **9** £40 000    **10** £590

> **Finished Early?**
> Go to page 398

# Reverse Calculations

## Learn About It

A shopkeeper reduces the price of a £60 radio by 15% in a sale.

She calculates the sale price like this:

£60 × 0.85 = £51 (because 100% – 15% = 85% = 0.85)

A customer reverses the calculation
to find the pre-sale price:

£51 ÷ 0.85 = £60

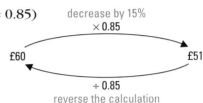

decrease by 15%
× 0.85

£60        £51

÷ 0.85
reverse the calculation

## Try It Out

**1** Find the pre-VAT price of these items. Give your answers to the nearest penny.

| | |
|---|---|
| **Example** | A table costs £303.15 including VAT at $17\frac{1}{2}$%. Find the price before VAT was added. |
| **Working** | 100% + $17\frac{1}{2}$% = 117.5% = 1.175 <br> £303.15 ÷ 1.175 = £258 |
| **Answer** | £258 |

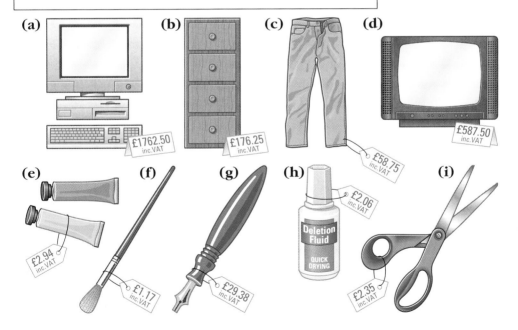

(a) £1762.50 inc.VAT

(b) £176.25 inc.VAT

(c) £58.75 inc.VAT

(d) £587.50 inc.VAT

(e) £2.94 inc.VAT

(f) £1.17 inc.VAT

(g) £29.38 inc.VAT

(h) £2.06 inc.VAT   Deletion Fluid QUICK DRYING

(i) £2.35 inc.VAT

## Key Fact

To find the pre-VAT (at $17\frac{1}{2}$%) price of an item, divide by 1.175.

**2** The owners of a clothes shop decide to decrease their prices by 20% during a sale. The sale prices of the following items are marked. Calculate the original selling prices.

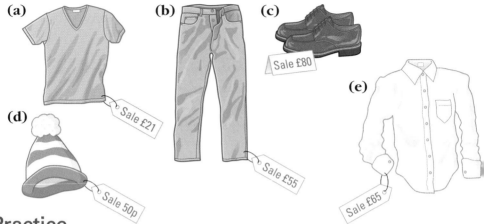

(a)

(b)

(c) Sale £80

(d) Sale £21

Sale 50p

Sale £55

(e) Sale £65

## Practice

This table shows how prices of some items changed between one year and the next.

| Fuel | | Food and drink | | Entertainment | |
|---|---|---|---|---|---|
| Diesel | + 2% | Wine | + 7% | CDs | + 9% |
| Leaded petrol | + 3% | Chocolates | + 12% | Computer games | − 5% |
| Unleaded petrol | − 4% | Fizzy drink | + 1% | | |

Here are the prices of various items after the changes.
Find the previous year's prices to the nearest penny.

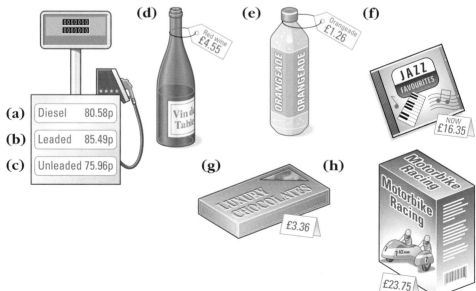

(d) Red wine £4.55

(e) Orangeade £1.26

(f)

(a) Diesel   80.58p

(b) Leaded   85.49p

(c) Unleaded 75.96p

JAZZ FAVOURITES   NOW £16.35

(g) LUXURY CHOCOLATES   £3.36

(h) Motorbike Racing   £23.75

**1** In 1911 the UK population was 42 000 000. This was an increase of 9% on the previous census in 1901. What was the population in 1901, rounded to the nearest whole number?

**2** The 1991 census showed a decrease of 0.5% since the 1981 census. The population in 1991 was 55 500 000. Find the population in 1981, rounded to the nearest whole number.

**3** Susie gives 2% of her salary to OXFAM. It is deducted from her wages before she gets them. She takes home £550 per month. How much would she take home if she didn't contribute to OXFAM?

**4** Find the population of the following countries in 1970.

| Country | Population in 1990 (millions) | % increase since 1970 |
|---|---|---|
| Netherlands | 14.82 | 14% |
| USA | 246 | 20% |
| Italy | 57.2 | 6% |
| Sweden | 8.2 | 0.5% |
| Australia | 15 | 25% |
| Dominican Republic | 7 | 57% |
| Turkey | 54 | 50% |

**Finished Early?**
Go to page 399

## Further Practice

In a local election the votes, **to the nearest hundred**, were as follows.

| Party | Votes | % change from previous election |
|---|---|---|
| Labour | 15 200 | + 2% |
| Conservative | 12 500 | − 3% |
| Liberal Democrat | 5 800 | − 12% |
| Green | 300 | + 10% |
| Monster Raving Loony | 100 | + 400% |

Find the votes, **to the nearest hundred**, for each party in the previous election.

**Finished Early?**
Go to page 399

# Unit 7 *Fractional Parts*

## Summary of Chapters 13 and 14

- To get an equivalent fraction, multiply (or divide) the numerator and denominator of a fraction by the same number.

$$\frac{2}{3} \overset{\times 4}{=} \frac{8}{12} \qquad \frac{8}{12} \overset{\div 2}{=} \frac{4}{6} \overset{\div 2}{=} \frac{2}{3} \qquad \frac{8}{12} = \frac{2}{3} \qquad \text{cancel to lowest terms}$$

- $2\frac{1}{4}$ is a mixed number.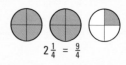
  $\frac{9}{4}$ is an improper or top-heavy fraction.
  Whole numbers can be written as
  improper fractions, e.g. $3 = \frac{3}{1}$.

  $$2\frac{1}{4} = \frac{9}{4}$$

- To change a fraction to a decimal, divide, e.g. $\frac{3}{4} = 3 \div 4 = 0.75$.
- To add or subtract fractions with different denominators, change them to equivalent fractions with the same (common) denominator, e.g.
  $\frac{1}{4} + \frac{3}{8} = \frac{2}{8} + \frac{3}{8} = \frac{5}{8}$.
- Change mixed numbers to improper fractions before calculating with them.
- Cancel fractions before multiplying, e.g.
  $\frac{5}{12} \times \frac{8}{15} = \frac{1 \times 2}{3 \times 3} = \frac{2}{9}$.
- To divide by a fraction, change $\div$ to $\times$ and turn the fraction upside down,
  e.g. $\frac{5}{8} \div \frac{2}{3} = \frac{5}{8} \times \frac{3}{2} = \frac{15}{16}$.
- To find a fraction of an amount, divide by the denominator and multiply by the numerator:
  $\frac{2}{5}$ of 20 kg = $20 \div 5 \times 2 = 4 \times 2 = 8$ kg
  or $\frac{2}{5}$ of 20 kg = $2 \times 20 \div 5 = 40 \div 5 = 8$ kg
  or $\frac{2}{5}$ of 20 kg = $0.4 \times 20 = 8$ kg (change $\frac{2}{5}$ to a decimal).
- To change a percentage to a decimal, divide the number of per cent by
  100, e.g. 75% = $\frac{75}{100}$ = 0.75.
  To change a decimal to a percentage, multiply by 100, e.g.
  0.75 = 0.75 × 100% = 75%.
  To change a fraction to a percentage, change it to a decimal first, e.g.
  $\frac{3}{4}$ = 3 ÷ 4 = 0.75 = 75%.
- To calculate a percentage of an amount, multiply by the number of per cent and divide by 100, e.g.
  7% of £30 = 7 × £30 ÷ 100 = £210 ÷ 100 = £2.10.
- A quick way to increase £20 by 25% is to multiply: 1.25 × £20 = £25.
- To reverse a percentage increase or decrease, divide: £25 ÷ 1.25 = £20.

# Brush Up Your Number 8

## Dividing Whole Numbers

### Learn About It

Dividing is the **opposite** or **inverse** of multiplying.

| | |
|---|---|
| **Example** | $24 \div 3 = 8$ because $8 \times 3 = 24$. |
| | $25 \div 3 = 8$ remainder 1, or $8\frac{1}{3}$. |

To **divide** by 10, 100 or 1000, move the digits to the **right** 1, 2 or 3 places.
Put in a decimal point if you have to.

To divide by 1 s.f. numbers, use tables **and** move digits.

| | |
|---|---|
| **Example** | $6 \div 3 = 2$, so $60 \div 3 = 20$, $600 \div 3 = 200$, $600 \div 30 = 20$, etc. |
| | $24 \div 4 = 6$, so $240 \div 4 = 60$, $2400 \div 4 = 600$, |
| | $2400 \div 40 = 60$, etc. |

To divide larger numbers, use short or long division.

**Examples** $714 \div 3$

$$3 \overline{)7^1 1^2 4} \quad \begin{array}{r} 2\ 3\ 8 \end{array}$$

$1288 \div 23$

$$23 \overline{)1288} \quad \begin{array}{r} 56 \end{array}$$
$$\underline{115}\downarrow$$
$$138$$
$$\underline{138}$$
$$0$$

### Try It Out

Work out the answers.

**1** (a) $35 \div 7$     (b) $256 \div 4$     (c) $972 \div 6$
    (d) $1445 \div 5$     (e) $42\,624 \div 8$

**2** (a) $510 \div 10$     (b) $1200 \div 100$     (c) $23\,500 \div 10$
    (d) $703\,000 \div 100$     (e) $2\,500\,000 \div 1000$

**3** (a) $420 \div 6$     (b) $400 \div 8$     (c) $3000 \div 50$
    (d) $8000 \div 200$     (e) $36\,000 \div 40$

**4** (a) $480 \div 16$     (b) $1958 \div 22$     (c) $4598 \div 38$
    (d) $399 \div 57$     (e) $18\,952 \div 92$

## Practice

**B** **1** Jamal's keyboard can play 512 different sounds, divided into **banks**. There are 16 sounds in one bank. How many banks of sounds are there?

**2** A CD lasts, on average, for about 70 minutes. Mandy has 132 CDs.
  **(a)** How many minutes of music is this altogether?
  **(b)** How many hours of music is this?
  **(c)** Mandy decides to listen to **all** her CDs. She spends 8 hours each day listening. How many days does it take her?

**3** A number under 1000 is **prime** if you get a remainder when you divide by all of these numbers:

2   3   5   7   11   13   17   19   23   29   31

Test these numbers to see if they are prime. Write down the prime numbers.
  **(a)** 123      **(b)** 599      **(c)** 989      **(d)** 967      **(e)** 341

**4** Copy and complete this diagram.

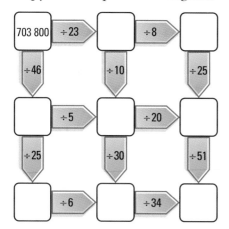

**Finished Early?**
 Go to page 400

# 15 Averages

In this chapter you will learn about ...
1. mode and median
2. mean and range
3. grouped data
4. comparing sets of data

## Mode and Median

### Remember?

Sets of **data** have different kinds of average. **Mode** and **median** are two of them.

#### The Mode

Seven friends looked in their pockets to see how many £1 coins they had.

| Angharad | Ben | Chloë | Davinder | Eve | Frank | Gary |
|----------|-----|-------|----------|-----|-------|------|
| £4 | £3 | £2 | £2 | £4 | £2 | £3 |

The table on the right shows how the data looks when it is better organised.

The amount that appears most often is £2.
More people had £2 than any other amount.
This is the **mode** of the data. You can also call it the **modal amount**.

| Amount | Frequency |
|--------|-----------|
| £2 | 3 |
| £3 | 2 |
| £4 | 2 |

#### The Median

Write the amounts of money in order.

£2, £2, £2, £3, £3, £4, £4

The middle amount in the list, when it is written in order, is the **median**.
You can also call it the **median amount**.

### Word Check

**data** information or facts about something

**frequency** how many times something occurs

**mode** the value of the data item with the highest frequency

**median** the value of the middle item, when the data is written in order

## Try It Out

 **1** Write down the mode of each set of numbers.

(a) 4, 6, 5, 4, 8, 6, 4

(b) 200, 100, 200

(c) 26, 22, 23, 27, 27

(d) 8.5, 8.7, 9, 8.6, 8.7, 9.1, 9, 8.7, 8.5

(e) 1, 100, 1, 1, 1, 100, 100, 1, 100, 1, 1, 1, 100, 100, 100

**2** Write each set of numbers from question 1 in order, from smallest to largest. Write down the median of each set.

## Learn About It

This is a table of the number of pets owned by pupils in 8P.
1 and 2 have the same frequency. They are **both** modes.

| Number of pets | 0 | 1 | 2 | 3 | 4 |
|---|---|---|---|---|---|
| Frequency | 5 | 8 | 8 | 4 | 3 |

Look at this set of numbers:
100, 400, 300, 500, 200.
There is just one of each number. You could say that there are five modes, or you could say that there isn't a mode. Either of these answers is correct.

The pupils in 8P weighed themselves.

Their masses in kilograms are in this table.

This data needs to be better organised. If you just make a table of the different masses, there will be a lot of different values. It will be hard to see a pattern.

| 45 | 49 | 33 | 36 | 44 | 52 | 35 | 57 | 39 |
|---|---|---|---|---|---|---|---|---|
| 49 | 38 | 44 | 55 | 32 | 48 | 42 | 39 | 51 |
| 49 | 49 | 46 | 32 | 39 | 50 | 45 | 44 | 34 |

You need to put the data into groups. These groups are sometimes called **classes** or **class intervals**. This does not have anything to do with a 'class' you might be in at school.

 The classes must not overlap.

**1** Copy and complete this tally/frequency table.

| Mass (kg) | Tally | Frequency |
|---|---|---|
| 31–35 | | |
| 36–40 | | |
| 41–45 | | |
| 46–50 | | |
| 51–55 | | |
| 56–60 | | |

The class with the highest frequency is called the **modal class**. It is the **mode** of data that has been put into groups.

**2** Copy and complete this statement about the masses of the pupils in 8P:
'The modal class is ___-___'.

You can have more than one modal class. In 8Q, the pupils' masses are:

| Mass (kg) | Frequency |
|-----------|-----------|
| 31–35 | 3 |
| 36–40 | 5 |
| 41–45 | 8 |
| 46–50 | 8 |
| 51–55 | 2 |
| 56–60 | 2 |

> **Word Check**
>
> **class** grouped data
>
> **modal class** the class which has the highest frequency

There are two modal classes, 41–45 kg and 46–50 kg.

## Try It Out

Find the mode of each set of numbers below. You do not need to put them into groups.

**1**

| 10 | 6 | 10 | 8 | 6 | 6 | 10 |
|----|---|----|---|---|---|----|

**2**

| 27 | 28 | 22 | 26 | 28 |
|----|----|----|----|----|
| 26 | 25 | 28 | 29 | 20 |
| 27 | 24 | 21 | 26 | 23 |

**3**

| 28 | 23 | 22 | 25 | 21 | 24 | 30 | 29 |
|----|----|----|----|----|----|----|----|

**4**

| 103 | 113 | 107 | 118 | 107 |
|-----|-----|-----|-----|-----|
| 115 | 117 | 117 | 111 | 118 |
| 109 | 118 | 104 | 108 | 102 |
| 107 | 117 | 103 | 103 | 111 |

When the pupils in 8P were still in Year 7, they measured themselves. On the right are their heights, in centimetres.

| 170 | 144 | 162 | 139 | 150 | 161 | 136 |
|-----|-----|-----|-----|-----|-----|-----|
| 149 | 161 | 136 | 162 | 163 | 154 | 148 |
| 164 | 154 | 150 | 163 | 167 | 166 | 159 |
| 166 | 164 | 158 | 171 | 144 | 160 | 140 |

**1** Using the data on the right, copy and complete the tally/frequency table below. You need to work out the missing groups.

**2** What is the modal class?

| Height (cm) | Tally | Frequency |
|-------------|-------|-----------|
| 136–140 | | |
| 141–145 | | |
| | | |
| 171–175 | | |

# Learn More About It

Sometimes you need to do a simple calculation to find the median.

Look at these numbers. They are already written in order. There isn't a middle number.

The middle position is between 7 and 8, so you have to find the number **halfway between**. The median is 7.5.

Sometimes, the two middle numbers are the same.

This makes it even easier. The median is 13!

There is a simple rule for finding out where the median is in a list:

Number of data items [ +1 ] ⟶ [ ÷2 ] position of median.

---

| **Example** | Find the position of the median of 29 numbers. |
|---|---|
| **Working** | 29 + 1 = 30 |
| | 30 ÷ 2 = 15 |
| **Answer** | The median is the fifteenth number in the list. |

median

---

| **Example** | Find the position of the median of 12 numbers. |
|---|---|
| **Working** | 12 + 1 = 13 |
| | 13 ÷ 2 = 6.5 |
| **Answer** | The median is halfway between the sixth and seventh numbers in the list. |

median

This rule is useful when you have a large amount of data.

8Q counted the number of people in each car passing the school one morning.

| Number of people in a car | 1 | 2 | 3 | 4 | 5 | Total |
|---|---|---|---|---|---|---|
| Number of cars | 36 | 24 | 11 | 5 | 1 | 77 |

To find the median number of people in the cars, you could write out a list of 36 **1**s, 24 **2**s, 11 **3**s, etc. but this takes a lot of time. It is easier to use the rule and **pretend** you have a list. There are 77 cars, so there are 77 numbers:

77 + 1 = 78.

78 ÷ 2 = 39, so the median is the thirty-ninth number.

The first 36 numbers in the 'list' are **1**s. To get to the thirty-ninth number you need to go three more places along the 'list'. That takes you into the **2**s.

So the median number is 2 people per car.

| Number of people in a car | 1 | 2 | 3 | 4 | 5 | Total |
|---|---|---|---|---|---|---|
| Number of cars | 36 | 24 | 11 | 5 | 1 | 77 |

↑

the thirty-ninth
number is in
this group

## Try It Out

Find the median of each set of numbers.

**1**

| 38 | 33 | 32 | 35 | 31 | 34 | 40 | 29 |
|---|---|---|---|---|---|---|---|

**2**

| 11 | 14 | 12 | 12 | 18 | 10 | 11 | 8 | 13 | 14 |
|---|---|---|---|---|---|---|---|---|---|

**3**

| 6 | 8 | 6 | 5 | 5 | 7 | 6 | 5 |
|---|---|---|---|---|---|---|---|

**4**

| 84 | 94 | 88 | 99 | 88 | 90 | 99 | 85 | 89 | 83 |
|---|---|---|---|---|---|---|---|---|---|
| 96 | 98 | 98 | 92 | 99 | 88 | 98 | 84 | 84 | 92 |

**E** Charlie works at a chocolate factory. His job is to check that the boxes contain the right number of sweets. Today he is checking boxes of Mint Stix. He counts the Mint Stix in 50 boxes.

| Number per box | 47 | 48 | 49 | 50 | 51 |
|---|---|---|---|---|---|
| Number of boxes | 2 | 10 | 18 | 12 | 8 |

    **(a)** There are 50 boxes. What position in the list is the median?
    **(b)** Find the median number of Mint Stix per box.
    **(c)** There are supposed to be 50 Mint Stix in a box. Should Charlie say there are the right number in a box, too many or too few?

## Practice

**F 1** Bimla and Toby compared their maths test scores through the year. This is what they scored.

| Test | 1 | 2 | 3 | 4 | 5 | 6 | 7 | 8 | 9 |
|---|---|---|---|---|---|---|---|---|---|
| Bimla | 10 | 19 | 20 | 11 | 10 | 17 | 10 | 18 | 15 |
| Toby | 9 | 11 | 12 | 8 | 13 | 10 | 12 | 12 | 11 |

    **(a)** Calculate the mode for each person.
    **(b)** Calculate the median for each person.
    **(c)** Both Bimla and Toby said, 'I did better than you.'
        Who was right? Why?

**2** Shelley works for the traffic police. She recorded the speeds of 40 vehicles that passed her. These are the results, in miles per hour.

**Speeds of vehicles (mph)**

| | | | | | | | | | |
|---|---|---|---|---|---|---|---|---|---|
| 60 | 62 | 73 | 72 | 95 | 35 | 75 | 68 | 80 | 77 |
| 71 | 78 | 53 | 68 | 72 | 72 | 62 | 73 | 82 | 57 |
| 75 | 76 | 70 | 29 | 73 | 44 | 71 | 63 | 38 | 72 |
| 75 | 46 | 80 | 65 | 58 | 70 | 54 | 47 | 68 | 80 |

    **(a)** Put the results into a table like the one on the right.

| Speed (mph) | Tally | Frequency |
|---|---|---|
| 0–20 | | |
| 21–30 | | |
| 81–100 | | |

    **(b)** What is the modal class?
    **(c)** What kind of road do you think this was?
    **(d)** Do you think the drivers of the cars could see Shelley?

**3** 100 travellers were asked how long they had to wait for a bus.

The bar graph shows their answers.
**(a)** What was the modal time?
**(b)** Use the information from the bar graph to draw up a frequency table.
**(c)** What position is the median?
**(d)** What was the median waiting time?

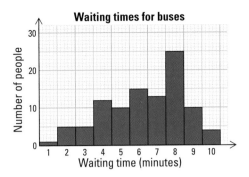

Waiting times for buses

Number of people

Waiting time (minutes)

Finished Early?
Go to page 400

## Further Practice

**1** Find the mode and median of each set of numbers.

**(a)**

| 5 | 8 | 7 | 5 | 4 | 5 | 3 | 7 | 2 | 7 |
|---|---|---|---|---|---|---|---|---|---|

**(b)**

| 0 | 2 | 2 | 0 | 1 | 3 | 3 | 1 |
|---|---|---|---|---|---|---|---|

**(c)**

| 24 | 32 | 25 | 24 | 27 | 15 | 20 | 30 | 36 | 50 | 12 | 50 |
|----|----|----|----|----|----|----|----|----|----|----|----|

**(d)**

| 54 | 53 | 55 | 45 | 60 | 21 |
|----|----|----|----|----|----|
| 32 | 50 | 54 | 60 | 35 | 68 |
| 44 | 68 | 66 | 33 | 32 | 54 |
| 35 | 60 | 20 | 45 | 71 | 40 |

**2** The pupils in 8S did a survey to find out how many hours of TV they watched in an evening.

The pictogram shows the results.
**(a)** Draw a frequency table for this data.
**(b)** What was the modal number of hours?
**(c)** What is the position of the median?
**(d)** What is the median number of hours?

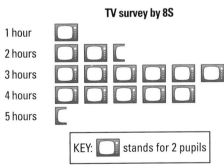

TV survey by 8S

1 hour
2 hours
3 hours
4 hours
5 hours

KEY: stands for 2 pupils

Finished Early?
Go to page 400

# T ❷ Mean and Range

## Remember?

### The Mean

When people say 'average', they are usually talking about the **mean**.

To calculate the mean of a set of data:
- work out the total of all the data values
- divide this by the number of data items.

| **Example** | Find the mean of these numbers. |
|---|---|

| 5 | 6 | 4 | 2 | 4 | 5 | 3 | 8 | 2 | 3 |
|---|---|---|---|---|---|---|---|---|---|

**Working**   The total is 42. There are 10 numbers.
$42 \div 10 = 4.2$.

**Answer**   4.2

Notice that the mean does not have to be one of the numbers in the list.

### The Range

The **range** of a set of numbers tells you how spread out they are.

It is the difference between the largest and the smallest.

| **Example** | Find the range of these numbers. |
|---|---|

| 5 | 6 | 4 | 2 | 4 | 5 | 3 | 8 | 2 | 3 |
|---|---|---|---|---|---|---|---|---|---|

**Working**   largest = 8, smallest = 2
$8 - 2 = 6$

**Answer**   6

## Try It Out

Find the mean and range of each set of numbers.

**1**

| 13 | 16 | 14 | 14 | 10 | 12 | 13 | 10 | 15 | 16 |

**2**

| 28 | 23 | 22 | 25 | 21 | 24 | 32 | 29 |

**3**

| 27 | 29 | 22 | 26 | 28 |
| 26 | 25 | 28 | 29 | 20 |
| 27 | 24 | 21 | 26 | 23 |

**4**

| 103 | 113 | 107 | 113 | 107 |
| 115 | 117 | 117 | 111 | 118 |
| 109 | 118 | 104 | 108 | 102 |
| 107 | 117 | 103 | 103 | 111 |

## Learn About It

When you have data in a frequency table, you need to do some extra calculations to work out the **mean**. This table shows the number of paper clips in 10 boxes.

| Number of paper clips in a box | Number of boxes | Number of paper clips |
|---|---|---|
| 18 | 1 | 18 × 1 = 18 |
| 19 | 5 | 19 × 5 = 95 |
| 20 | 3 | 20 × 3 = 60 |
| 22 | 1 | 22 × 1 = 22 |
| **Total** | 10 | 195 |

**Word Check**

**mean** the average data value

**range** the 'spread' of the data; the difference between the lowest and highest data values

The mean number of clips in a box is:
195 (total number of paper clips) ÷ 10 (number of boxes) = 19.5.

## Try It Out

At Weston Farm they keep ducks. Some of the ducks lay an egg every day, but most do not.
Copy and complete the table below.

| Eggs laid each week | 0 | 1 | 2 | 3 | 4 | 5 | 6 | 7 | Total |
|---|---|---|---|---|---|---|---|---|---|
| Number of ducks | 1 | 0 | 1 | 4 | 7 | 8 | 7 | 8 | |
| Number of eggs | | | | | | | | | |

What is the mean number of eggs laid by a duck in a week?

# Learn More About It

Sometimes you need to work out what one or more value needs to be to achieve a particular mean.

| **Example** | These are John's maths test marks. They are all out of 10. |
|---|---|

| Test 1 | Test 2 | Test 3 | Test 4 | Test 5 |
|---|---|---|---|---|
| 6 | 5 | 6 | 7 | ? |

|  |  |
|---|---|
|  | John has not taken Test 5 yet. He needs an average score of 7 over the five tests to equal Meera's average. Can he do it? |
| **Working** | John's average score in four tests is $24 \div 4 = 6$. <br> To have an average score of 7 in five tests, he needs a total of $7 \times 5 = 35$ marks. He has 24 marks so far, so he needs 11 more, but the test is only out of 10! |
| **Answer** | He can't do it. |

## Key Fact

To find the data value needed to make a given mean:
**1** work out the total so far, by adding all the data values
**2** work out the total you need (new mean value × number of data items)
**3** subtract the first total from the second; this is the extra data value.

Sometimes you need to work out what one or more value needs to be to achieve a particular range.

| **Example** | These are Meera's first three marks. |
|---|---|

| Test 1 | Test 2 | Test 3 | Test 4 | Test 5 |
|---|---|---|---|---|
| 10 | 8 | 9 | ? | ? |

|  |  |
|---|---|
|  | Her mean mark for all five tests was 7. The range of her marks was 6. What did she score on Tests 4 and 5? |
| **Working** | Her total for tests 1, 2 and 3 was 27. <br> Her mean mark for all five tests was 7. That means her total for the five tests is 35 marks. <br> So she must get 8 marks altogether on Tests 4 and 5. <br> She could do this by getting 0 and 8, 1 and 7, 2 and 6, 3 and 5 or 4 and 4. <br> However, any mark below 4 will make the range more than 6. |
| **Answer** | 4 marks each |

# Try It Out

**1 (a)** Write two numbers with a mean of 10 and a range of 4.
**(b)** Write two numbers with a mean of 10 and a range of 10.
**(c)** Write three numbers with a mean of 10 and a range of 6.
**(d)** Write four numbers with a mean of 10 and a range of 4.
**(e)** Write five numbers with a mean of 10 and a range of 5.

**2** Matthew got these marks out of 10 on three tests.

| Test 1 | Test 2 | Test 3 | Test 4 | Test 5 |
|--------|--------|--------|--------|--------|
| 5 | 7 | 6 | ? | ? |

**(a)** What is his total so far?
**(b)** What is his mean mark for the three tests?
**(c)** What does he need to score on Test 4 to have a mean mark of 7 for the four tests?
**(d)** Matthew gets just what he needs on Test 4 to make his mean mark 7. What does he need to score on Test 5 to make his mean mark 8?
**(e)** Matthew does not get what he needs on Test 5 to have a mean mark of 8. His mark makes the range 7. What did he score on Test 5?

# Practice

**1** Safebury's food store carried out a survey of their customers.
They asked people whether they shopped for food every week or every month.
**(a)** The weekly shoppers were asked how much they spent on food each week, to the nearest £10. These are the results.

| Amount per week (£) | 10 | 20 | 30 | 40 | 50 | 60 | 70 | 80 | 90 | 100 |
|---|---|---|---|---|---|---|---|---|---|---|
| Number of customers | 2 | 5 | 12 | 35 | 20 | 8 | 3 | 2 | 0 | 0 |

Draw a frequency table. Calculate the mean amount spent per week.
**(b)** The monthly shoppers were asked how much they spent on food each month, to the nearest £20. These are the results.

| Amount per month (£) | 20 | 40 | 60 | 80 | 100 | 120 | 140 | 160 | 180 | 200 |
|---|---|---|---|---|---|---|---|---|---|---|
| Number of customers | 0 | 1 | 2 | 5 | 5 | 10 | 27 | 29 | 14 | 5 |

Draw a frequency table. Calculate the mean amount spent per month.
**(c)** Safebury's want to know who spends more on average, the weekly or the monthly shoppers.
Work out the mean spending per year for each group. Who spends more?

*Hint: multiply the weekly figure by 52. Multiply the monthly figure by 12.*

**2** Three students are comparing their exam marks.

|  | Paper 1 (%) | Paper 2 (%) | Paper 3 (%) | Paper 4 (%) | Paper 5 (%) |
|---|---|---|---|---|---|
| **Alison** | 41 | 58 | 61 | 52 | ? |
| **Maggie** | 65 | 72 | 73 | 66 | ? |
| **Nina** | 81 | 74 | 46 | ? | ? |

Nina was ill just before Paper 4 and has not taken it yet.

Each student's mean mark over all five papers is used to calculate the grade.

The table shows the marks they need to get each grade.

| Grade A (%) | Grade B (%) | Grade C (%) |
|---|---|---|
| 75 | 65 | 55 |

(a) How many marks does Alison need on Paper 5 to get Grade C?

(b) How many marks does she need to get Grade B?

(c) How many marks does Maggie need on Paper 5 to get Grade B?

(d) How many marks does she need to get Grade A?

(e) How many marks does Nina need on Papers 4 and 5 together to get Grade A?

(f) Nina got just enough marks to get Grade B. The range of all her marks was 40%. What were her scores on the last two papers?

**3** A sample of names from the telephone directory was checked. This table records how long the surnames were.

| Letters in surname | 3 | 4 | 5 | 6 | 7 | 8 | 9 | 10 | 11 |
|---|---|---|---|---|---|---|---|---|---|
| Frequency | 5 | 30 | 101 | 131 | 108 | 64 | 34 | 22 | 5 |

(a) What is the mean length of the surnames?

(b) What is the modal length?

(c) What is the median length?

> **Finished Early?**
> ➯ Go to page 401

## Further Practice

**1** This table shows whether a number of trains on the PasTran network were late and by how much.

(a) Copy and complete the table.

(b) What is the mean number of minutes by which the trains were late?

| Minutes late | 0 | 1 | 2 | 3 | 4 | 5 | 10 | Total |
|---|---|---|---|---|---|---|---|---|
| Number of trains | 14 | 13 | 8 | 4 | 6 | 10 | 5 | |
| Number of minutes | | | | | | | | |

**2** Iain sells double glazing by phone.
He has to sell £500 worth of windows a week, on average. That is his **quota**.
His boss checks his sales every six weeks.

| Week 1 | Week 2 | Week 3 | Week 4 | Week 5 | Week 6 |
|--------|--------|--------|--------|--------|--------|
| £650 | £325 | £440 | £720 | £555 | ? |

(a) How much does Iain need to sell in Week 6 to meet his quota for the six weeks?

(b) What is the range of the figures for Weeks 1-5?

(c) Iain makes his quota for the six weeks.
The range of his figures is now £500.
How much did he sell in Week 6?

> **Finished Early?**
> ➡ Go to page 401

# Grouped Data

## Learn About It

This table shows the shoe sizes of 1000 people.

To find the mean shoe size, work out the total of all the shoe sizes, then divide by the number of people.

The mean shoe size is
7963 ÷ 1000 = 7.963.

| Shoe size | Frequency | Size × frequency |
|-----------|-----------|------------------|
| 5 | 91 | 455 |
| 6 | 128 | 768 |
| 7 | 212 | 1484 |
| 8 | 185 | 1480 |
| 9 | 159 | 1431 |
| 10 | 130 | 1300 |
| 11 | 95 | 1045 |
| **Total** | **1000** | **7963** |

**1** Copy this table. It shows the ages of the same 1000 people. You need two blank columns, as shown.

To work out the mean age of these people, you need to find the total of all their ages. You can't do it! This is because the data has been put into **classes** or groups. You don't know the exact ages.

| Age | Frequency | | |
|-----|-----------|--|--|
| 11–20 | 102 | | |
| 21–30 | 266 | | |
| 31–40 | 251 | | |
| 41–50 | 185 | | |
| 51–60 | 100 | | |
| 61–70 | 74 | | |
| 71–80 | 22 | | |
| **Total** | **1000** | | |

## Word Check

class or class interval a group of values for data

The best you can do is to **estimate** the mean age. To do this, assume that everyone's age is in the **middle** of their class. The range of the first class is from 11 to 20 years old. To work out the middle value, calculate $(11 + 20) \div 2 = 31 \div 2 = 15.5$, so assume that everyone in the first class is 15.5 years old. This is called the **middle value** of the class. You can shorten it to **MV**.

**2** Write **middle value** as the heading of the third column of your table. Put 15.5 into the first row, then work out the rest of the middle values.

Now you can estimate the total age for each class. If you assume that everyone in the first class is 15.5 years old, the total age will be $15.5 \times 102 = 1581$ years. Head the last column **MV × frequency** and write 1581 in the first row.

**3** Work out the rest of the totals in this column.

You are trying to estimate the mean age of all the people in the table. To do this, add up all the numbers in the last column.

**4** Write the total in the correct space. Now divide by 1000 to estimate the mean age. If you have not made a mistake, you should get 37.75 years. Underneath the table, write Estimated mean = 37.75 years. This is within the range of the ages, so it's reasonable.

Make sure you don't divide by the number of classes. In the last example, this would make the mean age $37\,750 \div 7 \approx 513$ years! This can't be right – it's far outside the range of the data. Always divide by the **total frequency**.

## Word Check

**middle value** halfway between the smallest and largest values in a class

## Key Fact

To estimate the mean of a grouped set of data:

- work out the **middle value** of each class
- multiply each middle value by the **frequency** for that class
- add up these numbers to estimate the **total**
- divide by the **total frequency**.

## Try It Out

This table shows the speeds of 200 cars passing a road checkpoint.

Estimate the mean speed of the cars.

| Speed (km/h) | Frequency | Middle value | MV × frequency |
|---|---|---|---|
| 31–40 | 14 | 35.5 | |
| 41–50 | 30 | | |
| 51–60 | 52 | | |
| 61–70 | 71 | | |
| 71–80 | 33 | | |
| **Total** | | | |

## Learn More About It

When data is grouped into classes, you have to estimate the **range** as well. The table of ages in Learn About It on page 189 contains these classes:

11-20     21-30     31-40     41-50     51-60     61-70     71-80

It's possible that the youngest person is 20 and the oldest is 71. That would make the range 71 − 20 = 51. This is called the **minimum range**.

The youngest person could be 11 and the oldest could be 80. That would make the range 80 − 11 = 69. This is called the **maximum range**.

A sensible estimate for the range is halfway between these two values, so it is $(51 + 69) \div 2 = 60$.

### Word Check

**range** the difference between the biggest value and the smallest value in a set of data

## Try It Out

Work out the minimum, maximum and estimated range for the question in Try It Out **M** above.

## Practice

**1** SADA supermarkets check their products regularly. One week, Don checks the mass of Weetcrunch cereal packets. The mass given on the packet is 500 g. The table shows Don's findings.

(a) Estimate the mean mass of a packet.
(b) Estimate the range of masses.
(c) Don has to write a report about his findings. Should he write that the mean and range are satisfactory? Give reasons for your answer.

| Mass (g) | Frequency |
|---|---|
| 481–490 | 2 |
| 491–500 | 5 |
| 501–510 | 12 |
| 511–520 | 27 |
| 521–530 | 4 |

**2** The annual salaries paid to the employees of SADA supermarkets are shown in this table.

(a) Estimate the mean annual salary.

(b) Estimate the range of the salaries.

(c) Luke earns £11 000 a year. Is he above or below the average.

| Annual salary (£) | Number of employees |
|---|---|
| 1–5000 | 23 |
| 5001–10 000 | 62 |
| 10 001–15 000 | 32 |
| 15 001–20 000 | 25 |
| 20 001–30 000 | 6 |
| 30 001–50 000 | 2 |

 The classes aren't all the same size, so be careful working out the middle values.

**3** Yasmin often plays her favourite computer game. The table shows the rating the computer gives her for each score.

One weekend, she played all the levels. Her ratings were:

| Rating | Score (points) |
|---|---|
| **A**wesome | 10 001–20 000 |
| **B**rilliant | 5 001–10 000 |
| **C**ompetent | 1 001–5 000 |
| **D**ire | 0–1 000 |

| B | C | B | B | A | B | B | D | B | B |
|---|---|---|---|---|---|---|---|---|---|
| B | B | B | A | D | B | A | B | B | B |
| C | B | B | B | B | B | B | A | A | B |

(a) Estimate the range of Yasmin's scores.

(b) Estimate her mean score.

(c) What rating would you give her for the weekend's playing?

**4** Doctor Snapper did an experiment to find out how quickly people blink when they see a bright flash of light. She used the flashgun from a camera and recorded the time it took people to close their eyes.

(a) Estimate the mean blink time.

(b) Estimate the range of the times.

(c) Doctor Snapper timed herself. Her blinking time was 0.45 seconds. Is this quicker or slower than the mean?

| Time (seconds) | Frequency |
|---|---|
| 0.01–0.1 | 1 |
| 0.11–0.2 | 3 |
| 0.21–0.3 | 10 |
| 0.31–0.4 | 15 |
| 0.41–0.5 | 12 |
| 0.51–0.6 | 6 |
| 0.61–0.7 | 2 |
| 0.71–1.0 | 1 |

**Finished Early?**

▷ Go to page 402

# Further Practice

**1** The table shows the masses of 50 pupils.

   **(a)** Copy and complete the table to estimate the total mass.

   **(b)** Estimate the mean mass of the pupils.

   **(c)** Estimate the range of their masses.

| Mass (kg) | Frequency | Middle value | MV × frequency |
|---|---|---|---|
| 31–40 | 4 | 35.5 | |
| 41–50 | 12 | | |
| 51–60 | 21 | | |
| 61–70 | 8 | | |
| 71–80 | 5 | | |
| **Total** | **50** | | |

**2** Mr Chauke checks his register at the end of the school year. There are 30 pupils in his tutor group. He writes down the number of days the pupils were absent.

   **(a)** Copy and complete the table to estimate the total number of days absent.

| Number of days absent | Frequency | Middle value | MV × frequency |
|---|---|---|---|
| 0 | 1 | 0 | |
| 1–5 | 10 | 3 | |
| 6–10 | 10 | | |
| 11–20 | 7 | | |
| 21–50 | 2 | | |
| **Total** | | | |

The classes aren't all the same size, so be careful working out the middle values.

   **(b)** Estimate the mean number of days absent.

   **(c)** Estimate the range.

   **(d)** Samantha was absent on 10 days. Would you say she was average? Give a reason for your answer.

> **Finished Early?**
> ⇨ Go to page 402

# T 4 Comparing Sets of Data

## Learn About It

These are the last 20 throws (in metres)
made by a shot putter.

| A. Putter | 14 | 15 | 15 | 14 | 13 |
|-----------|----|----|----|----|----|
|           | 17 | 13 | 15 | 17 | 12 |
|           | 12 | 17 | 18 | 14 | 14 |
|           | 11 | 15 | 15 | 13 | 16 |

These are the last 20 throws made by another athlete.

| B. Chucker | 17 | 20 | 15 | 15 | 18 | 13 | 15 | 12 | 22 | 11 |
|------------|----|----|----|----|----|----|----|----|----|----|
|            | 14 | 20 | 20 | 15 | 16 | 9  | 19 | 20 | 13 | 16 |

The table below is called a **comparison table**. It lets you **compare** the results
for the two athletes.

|            | Mean | Best | Worst | Range |
|------------|------|------|-------|-------|
| A. Putter  | 14.5 | 18   | 11    | 7     |
| B. Chucker | 16   | 22   | 9     | 13    |

You can see that Chucker's mean is better than Putter's. However, Chucker is
not as **consistent** as Putter. That means the length of his throws varies a lot
more. The **range** is bigger. Chucker's best throw is longer than Putter's, but
Chucker's worst throw is shorter.

If you were choosing one of the athletes to be
in a team, you would probably choose Putter,
who is more consistent. Just having the best
throw does not make you the best choice.

> ### Word Check
> **comparison table** a table
>   comparing the results of
>   two sets of data
> **consistent** staying about
>   the same; reliable

## Try It Out

Q These are the last 20 times (in seconds) made by two 400-metre runners.

| C. Runner | 53.6 | 58.2 | 56.2 | 53.8 | 56.9 | 56.3 | 55.8 | 55.1 | 53.1 | 53.1 |
|-----------|------|------|------|------|------|------|------|------|------|------|
|           | 54.9 | 53.5 | 54.2 | 54.5 | 54.6 | 56.3 | 54.1 | 55.1 | 55.7 | 55.0 |

| D. Asher | 55.8 | 55.6 | 57.2 | 56.8 | 56.2 | 56.6 | 57.2 | 56.0 | 56.6 | 56.8 |
|----------|------|------|------|------|------|------|------|------|------|------|
|          | 57.0 | 56.2 | 56.4 | 55.6 | 55.6 | 56.4 | 55.2 | 56.4 | 57.2 | 57.2 |

**1** Copy and complete this comparison table. Write your working underneath.

| | Mean | Fastest | Slowest | Range |
|---|---|---|---|---|
| **C. Runner** | | | | |
| **D. Asher** | | | | |

**2** **(a)** Who has the fastest time?     **(b)** Whose mean time is the faster?
   **(c)** Who has the slowest time?     **(d)** Who is the more consistent runner?

# Practice

A long ruler

**1** This is an experiment to test your **reflexes** (how quickly you react to something).

Suppose you decide to be first to be tested – the **subject**.

Another person – the **tester** – holds up the ruler at the top. The zero mark has to be at the bottom.

You hold your finger and thumb round the bottom of the ruler, but not touching it. The zero mark should be level with the top edge of your forefinger.

When the tester lets go of the ruler, grab it as quickly as you can between thumb and forefinger.

Write down how many centimetres the ruler drops. This should be the mark on the scale that's level with the top edge of your forefinger. Be as accurate as you can. If you miss the ruler, have another go. Do this **20 times**. Subject and tester should swap every five goes so that neither gets too used to it. Record each person's results.

> *Hints for the tester:*
> *Don't look at the subject when you drop the ruler. Your eyes can give away when you're going to let go. Vary the length of time you wait before you drop the ruler. Don't get into a 'rhythm'.*

**2** When you've finished testing …
   **(a)** write your results neatly in a list or table
   **(b)** work out your mean drop distance.

**3** Draw a comparison table to compare your results with your partner's.

**4** **(a)** Who had the smaller mean?
   **(b)** Who was more consistent?
   **(c)** Who do you think had the better reflexes?
   **(d)** If you can, find out who had the best reflexes in your class.

> **Finished Early?**
> ➡ Go to page 403

**NUMBER SKILLS** Calculate means and ranges of sets of numbers     **195**

# Further Practice

 **1** Mr Ghir sells two kinds of pen in his shop, Write-Rite and Linemaster. People were always asking him which was better, so he decided to find out. He tested 10 of each kind of pen, drawing a long line with each pen until it ran out of ink.
This table shows the lengths of the 20 lines in metres, rounded to the nearest 10 metres.

| Write-Rite | 1220 | 1170 | 1200 | 1180 | 1230 | 1180 | 1230 | 1150 | 1230 | 1210 |
|---|---|---|---|---|---|---|---|---|---|---|
| Linemaster | 1200 | 1220 | 1190 | 1220 | 1140 | 1300 | 1290 | 1370 | 1430 | 1140 |

(a) Copy and complete this comparison table. Write your working underneath.

| | Mean | Longest | Shortest | Range |
|---|---|---|---|---|
| Write-Rite | | | | |
| Linemaster | | | | |

(b) Which kind of pen lasted longer, on average?
(c) Which kind of pen was more consistent?
(d) Should Mr Ghir recommend Write-Rite or Linemaster pens to his customers? Give your reasons.

**2** A magazine tested two types of battery, PowerPlus and Xtralife, to see which lasted longer. These pictograms show the results.

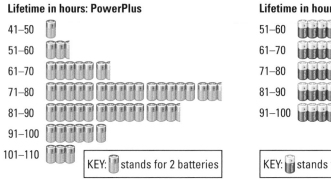

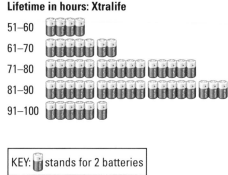

 This data is grouped.

(a) Draw a frequency table for PowerPlus batteries. Remember to include columns for the middle values and for multiplying.
(b) **Estimate** the mean lifetime and the range of a PowerPlus battery.
(c) Draw a frequency table for Xtralife batteries.
(d) **Estimate** the mean lifetime and the range of an Xtralife battery.
(e) Draw a comparison table.
(f) Which do you think are the better batteries? Why?

**3** SADA supermarkets like to check on how things sell when they are advertised on TV.
They knew there would be adverts for Weetcrunch cereal one Friday night, so they recorded sales of Weetcrunch for the week before and the week after that day.
This is what they sold in the week before the adverts.

|  | Sat. | Sun. | Mon. | Tue. | Wed. | Thu. | Fri. |
|---|---|---|---|---|---|---|---|
| Packets sold | 26 | 15 | 25 | 15 | 27 | 28 | 46 |

This is what they sold in the week after.

|  | Sat. | Sun. | Mon. | Tue. | Wed. | Thu. | Fri. |
|---|---|---|---|---|---|---|---|
| Packets sold | 21 | 44 | 17 | 15 | 44 | 35 | 41 |

(a) Work out the mean sales for the first week.
(b) Work out the mean sales for the second week.
(c) Draw a comparison table.
(d) Do you think the adverts had any effect on the sales of Weetcrunch? Give reasons for your answers.

**Finished Early?**
 Go to page 403

# 16 Statistical Diagrams

In this chapter you will learn about …
- **1** scatter diagrams
- **2** correlation

## T **1** Scatter Diagrams

### Remember?

#### Using scales

Check how many gaps or **divisions** there are between the main marks on a scale.

There may be 2, 4, 5 or 10. Make sure you know how many units each gap covers.

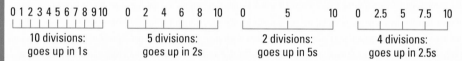

| 0 1 2 3 4 5 6 7 8 9 10 | 0  2  4  6  8  10 | 0        5        10 | 0  2.5  5  7.5  10 |
|:---:|:---:|:---:|:---:|
| 10 divisions: goes up in 1s | 5 divisions: goes up in 2s | 2 divisions: goes up in 5s | 4 divisions: goes up in 2.5s |

#### Plotting and reading coordinates

When plotting coordinates, the first number is on the **horizontal** or **x-axis**. The second number is on the **vertical** or **y-axis**.

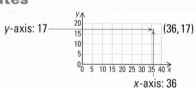

y-axis: 17

x-axis: 36

(36, 17)

---

### Word Check

**scale** a line marked with numbers at equal intervals

**divisions** parts of a scale, shown by marks

**coordinates** pairs of numbers in brackets, used to show the position of a point on a grid or graph

**axis** a line on a graph on which the scale is marked

# Try It Out

2 mm graph paper

**1** Write down the coordinates of each point marked with a letter on this graph.

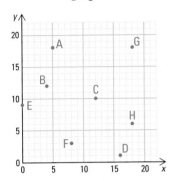

**2** Draw a set of axes labelled from –5 to +5.

Plot each set of coordinates and join them up in order, with straight lines. Each set makes a simple shape.
**(a)** $(1, 1) \rightarrow (1, 4) \rightarrow (4, 1) \rightarrow (1, 1)$
**(b)** $(0, 0) \rightarrow (3, 0) \rightarrow (3, -4) \rightarrow (0, -4) \rightarrow (0, 0)$
**(c)** $(0, 2) \rightarrow (-3, 5) \rightarrow (-5, -2) \rightarrow (-2, -5) \rightarrow (0, 2)$

**3** Write down the numbers shown by the arrows.

**(a)**

**(b)**

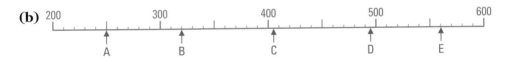

**(c)**

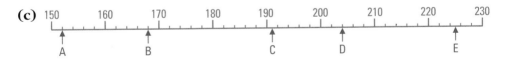

**(d)**

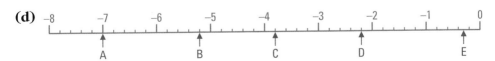

## Learn About It

A **scatter diagram** is used to investigate whether there is a link between two sets of data. You plot a point for each data item.

You **must not** join up the points. They are **scattered**.

Suppose you think that people who have big hands also have big feet. That would mean your handspan and the length of your foot are linked.

Draw a scatter diagram like this.

Suppose your handspan is 15 cm and your foot is 22 cm long. You plot that point, as shown.

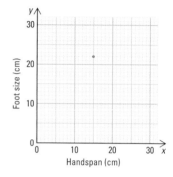

Plot one point on the scatter diagram for each person's measurements. When you have plotted all the measurements, it might look like the diagram on the right.

There is a circle around one of the points. This shows that there were **two** people with these measurements.

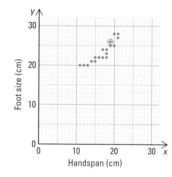

### Remember?

Sometimes it is better **not** to start the axes at 0.

Do this when the points might all be crammed into a small part of the graph.

Use to show you have done this.

### Word Check

**plot** mark a point on a graph

# Try It Out

2 mm graph paper

This table shows exam results for class 8M.

| Year 7 (%) | 65 | 32 | 68 | 54 | 81 | 44 | 59 | 62 | 75 | 72 | 17 | 85 | 34 | 56 | 56 | 70 | 55 | 61 | 77 | 60 |
| Year 8 (%) | 67 | 45 | 56 | 50 | 75 | 60 | 60 | 54 | 69 | 72 | 25 | 88 | 40 | 58 | 48 | 75 | 58 | 57 | 74 | 70 |

The top row shows their scores last year, in their Year 7 maths exam.
The bottom row shows their results this year. Plot the data on a scatter diagram.

Use a scale of 1 cm to 5% and label the axes from 0 to 100%.

Label the horizontal axis 'Year 7 exam scores' and the vertical axis 'Year 8 exam scores'.

## Word Check

**range** the difference between the smallest and largest numbers on a scale or axis

# Practice

2 mm graph paper

**1** This table shows 8M's handspans and foot sizes, in centimetres.

| Handspan | 14 | 13 | 21 | 17 | 18 | 20 | 16 | 16 | 15 | 18 | 19 | 21 | 15 | 18 | 16 | 18 | 15 | 16 | 14 | 19 |
| Foot size | 21 | 21 | 29 | 23 | 24 | 28 | 22 | 23 | 22 | 27 | 28 | 30 | 22 | 26 | 21 | 28 | 21 | 24 | 23 | 27 |

Plot a scatter diagram. Use a scale of 1 cm to 2 cm.

**2** This table shows the number of rainy and sunny days for each month in a year.

| Month | Jan. | Feb. | Mar. | Apr. | May | Jun. | Jul. | Aug. | Sep. | Oct. | Nov. | Dec. |
|---|---|---|---|---|---|---|---|---|---|---|---|---|
| Rainy days | 10 | 15 | 18 | 10 | 4 | 10 | 1 | 0 | 5 | 5 | 10 | 14 |
| Sunny days | 6 | 4 | 8 | 10 | 18 | 16 | 20 | 25 | 19 | 16 | 14 | 12 |

Plot a scatter diagram. Use a scale of 1 cm to 5 days.

**3** In an experiment, Jon makes a pendulum using string and an eraser.
He writes down the length of the string. He times 100 swings, then divides
by 100 to find the time for one swing. This table shows his results.

| Length of string (m) | 0.1 | 0.25 | 0.33 | 0.46 | 0.51 | 0.6 | 0.74 | 0.79 | 0.85 | 0.98 |
|---|---|---|---|---|---|---|---|---|---|---|
| Time for one swing(s) | 0.70 | 1.09 | 1.08 | 1.37 | 1.52 | 1.61 | 1.67 | 1.74 | 1.86 | 1.92 |

Plot a scatter diagram. Label the horizontal axis 'Length of string (m)', with a scale of 2 cm to 0.1 m. Label the vertical axis 'Time for one swing (s)', with a scale of 1 cm to 0.1 s.

## Finished Early?

⇨ Go to page 404

# Further Practice

2 mm graph paper

**D** The kiosk in the park sells ice-creams and cold drinks.
One year, they recorded the maximum temperature each day. They also
recorded what they sold.

This table shows what they sold on the **warmest** day of each month.

| Month | Jan. | Feb. | Mar. | Apr. | May | Jun. | Jul. | Aug. | Sep. | Oct. | Nov. | Dec. |
|---|---|---|---|---|---|---|---|---|---|---|---|---|
| Max. temp (°C) | 2 | 8 | 12 | 16 | 18 | 20 | 25 | 30 | 23 | 17 | 10 | 7 |
| Ice-creams sold | 0 | 2 | 4 | 10 | 22 | 32 | 50 | 54 | 28 | 6 | 3 | 0 |
| Cold drinks sold | 10 | 15 | 25 | 25 | 30 | 41 | 36 | 21 | 29 | 15 | 10 | 12 |

**1** Plot a scatter diagram to show the relationship between temperature and
the number of ice-creams sold.

Label the horizontal axis 'temperature (°C)' from 0 to 30, with a scale of 1 cm
to 5 °C. Label the vertical axis 'Ice-creams sold' from 0 to 60, with a scale of
1 cm to 5 ice-creams.

**2** Plot a similar scatter diagram to show the relationship between temperature
and the number of cold drinks sold.

> **Finished Early?**
> ⇨ Go to page 404

**P** **2** # Correlation

## Learn About It

If there is a link between two different
things, it will show up on a scatter diagram.
The mathematical word is **correlation**. The
two things are said to be **correlated**.

This scatter diagram shows the heights
and armspans of pupils in Year 8 at
Mount School.

The taller pupils have bigger armspans.
The shorter pupils have smaller armspans.
As one thing goes up, the other one goes up.

Height and armspan are **correlated**.

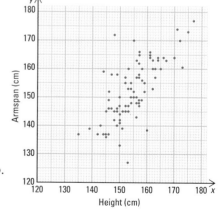

**(a)** What do you notice about the top left-
hand corner of the diagram?

**(b)** What do you notice about the bottom right-hand corner?

**(c)** Do you think any of the measurements are wrong?
Which ones? Write down the coordinates.

There are different kinds of correlation. The height–armspan data is an example of **positive correlation**. Height and armspan are **positively correlated**. As one variable goes up, the other one goes up.

Sometimes, as one variable goes up, the other one goes **down**. For instance, as the weather improves and temperatures rise, heating costs drop. This is called **negative correlation**. The variables are **negatively correlated**.

Correlation can also be **perfect**, **strong** or **weak**. Each type gives a different kind of diagram.

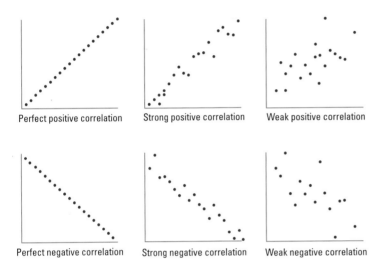

Perfect positive correlation   Strong positive correlation   Weak positive correlation

Perfect negative correlation   Strong negative correlation   Weak negative correlation

**Perfect** correlation means the link is so strong that there is actually a mathematical **rule** connecting the two things.

**No** correlation means that points are scattered randomly around. There is no link.

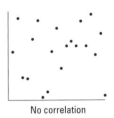

No correlation

## Word Check

correlation a connection or link between two sets of data

correlated connected or linked

# Try It Out

**E** Look at these scatter diagrams. Identify what type of correlation each one shows.

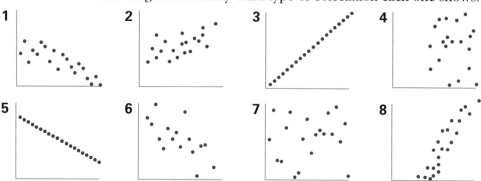

# Learn More About It

When a scatter diagram shows correlation, you can use it to make predictions. You can draw a line on the diagram that matches the way the points are placed. This is called a **line of best fit**.

The line needs to have the right slope.

It needs to go through the middle of the points, so that there are roughly the same number of points on either side of the line.

It's quite easy to see when the **slope** is right, but not so easy to know when the line is too **high** or too **low**. There is a rule you can use to get it in the right place.

Look at this data about the heights and widths of ten trees.

| Width (m) | 25 | 31 | 28 | 19 | 14 | 23 | 17 | 22 | 27 | 17 |
| Height (m) | 40 | 42 | 38 | 29 | 17 | 32 | 21 | 32 | 38 | 27 |

The scatter diagram looks like the first diagram.

The mean width of the trees is 223 ÷ 10 = 22.3 m.

The mean height is 316 ÷ 10 = 31.6 m.

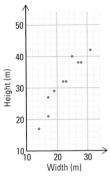

The point given by these values (22.3, 31.6) is now plotted, as on the second diagram.

It is called the **mean point**.

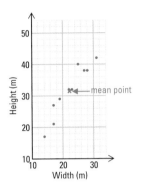

The line of best fit should pass through the mean point, as in the third diagram.

If you don't have enough information to calculate the mean point, draw the line of best fit 'by eye'.

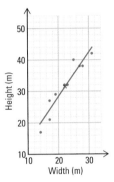

## Word Check

**line of best fit** the line all the points would lie on if the correlation were perfect

**mean point** the point with coordinates that are the means of the two types of data plotted on the scatter diagram

You can use the line of best fit to make predictions. For example, if you want to know the value on the *y*-axis that corresponds to a particular value on the *x*-axis, follow a line up from the point on the *x*-axis to the line of best fit, then move across to the *y*-axis.

find point on the axis

read up to the line

follow across to the axis

# Try It Out

**F** This table shows the number of millimetres of rain that fell at two weather stations from January to September one year.

| Month | Jan. | Feb. | Mar. | Apr. | May | Jun. | Jul. | Aug. | Sep. |
|---|---|---|---|---|---|---|---|---|---|
| Rainfall at Windy Crag (mm) | 52 | 48 | 61 | 50 | 32 | 29 | 44 | 40 | 31 |
| Rainfall at Forest Hill (mm) | 46 | 42 | 54 | 44 | 29 | 28 | 39 | 36 | 30 |

On the right is the scatter diagram of this data. The line of best fit has been drawn. Use it to answer the following questions.

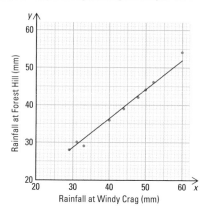

**1** What kind of correlation is there between the rainfall at the two stations?

**2** Estimate the rainfall at Forest Hill in months in which the following amounts fell at Windy Crag.

    **(a)** 42 mm    **(b)** 58 mm    **(c)** 36 mm

**3** Estimate the rainfall at Windy Crag in months in which the following amounts fell at Forest Hill.

    **(a)** 47 mm    **(b)** 37 mm    **(c)** 41 mm

# Practice

2 mm A4 graph paper

**G** **1** An exam was one hour long. 20 pupils were asked to write down how much time they had to spare after completing the exam paper. This table shows the times, with their marks.

| Time left (min.) | 18 | 0 | 4 | 0 | 8 | 12 | 20 | 5 | 35 | 25 | 0 | 10 | 29 | 32 | 2 | 15 | 40 | 0 | 9 | 45 |
|---|---|---|---|---|---|---|---|---|---|---|---|---|---|---|---|---|---|---|---|---|
| Mark (%) | 43 | 75 | 73 | 82 | 67 | 74 | 46 | 64 | 35 | 48 | 70 | 62 | 38 | 40 | 85 | 55 | 30 | 61 | 55 | 25 |

    **(a)** Plot a scatter diagram.
        Label the horizontal axis 'Time left (min.)' with a scale of 1 cm to 5 min.
        Label the vertical axis 'Exam mark (%)' with a scale of 1 cm to 5%.
    **(b)** What kind of correlation is there?
    **(c)** Draw the line of best fit by eye. Do not do any calculations.
    **(d)** Estimate the mark for someone who had …
        **(i)** 13 minutes left        **(ii)** 38 minutes left.
    **(e)** Estimate the time spent doing the exam if the mark was …
        **(i)** 42%        **(ii)** 60%.

**2** A weather balloon was sent up into the atmosphere. It recorded its height in kilometres and the air pressure in millibars (mb).
This table shows the results.

| Height (km) | 0 | 0.7 | 1 | 1.4 | 2.8 | 5.5 | 7.7 | 8 | 8.5 | 8.9 | 9.2 | 9.8 |
|---|---|---|---|---|---|---|---|---|---|---|---|---|
| Pressure (mb) | 990 | 960 | 970 | 870 | 870 | 670 | 540 | 500 | 460 | 470 | 400 | 440 |

(a) Plot a scatter diagram.
   Label the horizontal axis 'Height (km)' with a scale of 2 cm to 1 km.
   Label the vertical axis 'Pressure (mb)' with a scale of 2 cm to 100 mb.
(b) What kind of correlation is there?
(c) Calculate the mean height and pressure to 3 s.f. Plot the mean point.
(d) Draw the line of best fit through the point.
(e) Estimate the pressure at heights of …
   (i) 4 km         (ii) 7 km         (iii) 2.5 km
(f) Estimate the height when the pressure was …
   (i) 900 mb       (ii) 600 mb       (iii) 750 mb.

> **Finished Early?**
> ➡ Go to page 404

# Further Practice

2 mm A4 graph paper

This table shows the results of two maths tests, taken at Christmas and Easter.

| Christmas (30) | 25 | 27 | 18 | 20 | 11 | 13 | 20 | 6 | 15 | 14 | 21 | 14 | 12 | 9 | 25 |
|---|---|---|---|---|---|---|---|---|---|---|---|---|---|---|---|
| Easter (50) | 40 | 45 | 35 | 32 | 24 | 15 | 33 | 12 | 28 | 31 | 42 | 22 | 20 | 12 | 38 |

**1** Plot a scatter diagram. The scale should be 1 cm to 5 marks.

**2** What kind of correlation is there?

**3** Calculate the mean marks for Christmas and Easter to 1 d.p. Plot the mean point.

**4** Draw the line of best fit through the point.

**5** Estimate the Easter mark for a pupil whose Christmas mark was …
   (a) 17/30         (b) 23/30         (c) 10/30.

**6** Estimate the Christmas mark for a pupil whose Easter mark was …
   (a) 17/50         (b) 44/50         (c) 4/50.
   (d) Do you think the graph is right about (c)? Say why.

> **Finished Early?**
> ➡ Go to page 404

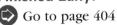

# Unit 8 *Statistics*

## Summary of Chapters 15 and 16

- The **frequency** of a data item is the number of times it occurs in a list. Sometimes you need to put the data into groups, called **classes** or **class intervals**. The classes must not overlap.

- The **mode** is the data item that has the biggest frequency. The **modal class** is the **mode** of data that has been put into groups. You can have more than one mode or modal class.

- The value in the middle of an ordered list is the **median**. If you have an even number of data items, there isn't a middle one. The median is **halfway** between the two middle items.

- The **mean** of a set of data is the total of all the data values divided by the number of data items.

- If you have data in groups or classes, you need to assume that all the data items are in the middle of their classes, so you use the **middle value**. This way, you can **estimate** the total and the mean.

- The **range** of a set of numbers is the difference between the largest and the smallest values.

- A **scatter diagram** is used to investigate whether there is a link between two sets of data. If a link exists, the amounts on the scatter diagram are **correlated**.

- Types of correlation:
  **positive correlation:** as one thing goes up, so does the other
  **negative correlation:** as one thing goes up, the other goes down
  **uncorrelated:** no link.

- The **line of best fit** follows the points as closely as possible. It has to pass through the **mean point**. The coordinates of this point are the means of the two types of data plotted on the scatter diagram.

# Brush Up Your Number 9

## Reverse Calculations

### Learn About It

**Inverse** operations reverse a calculation.

$12 \times 4 = 48$ and so $48 \div 4 = 12$.

The operations must be done in the correct order. An *approximate* formula for a temperature in degrees Fahrenheit (°F) in terms of degrees Celsius (°C) is $F = 2C + 32$.

So 20 °C in °F is    20 $\boxed{\times 2}$ 40 $\boxed{+ 32}$ 72.

Starting with 72 °F, the reverse of this is:

20 $\boxed{\div 2}$ 40 $\boxed{- 32}$ 72.

You can also write this as:

72 $\boxed{- 32}$ 40 $\boxed{\div 2}$ 20.

> **Word Check**
>
> **approximate** nearly correct, but not exact
>
> **inverse** opposite

### Try It Out

Write down the inverse operations for these calculations, using number machines.

**1** 12 $\boxed{+ 5}$ 17

**2** 24 $\boxed{- 6}$ 18

**3** 8 $\boxed{\times 2}$ 16

**4** 36 $\boxed{\div 3}$ 12

**5** 6 $\boxed{+ 2}$ 8 $\boxed{+ 5}$ 13

**6** 9 $\boxed{\times 2}$ 18 $\boxed{- 6}$ 12

**7** 10 $\boxed{\times 3}$ 30 $\boxed{- 6}$ 24

**8** 14 $\boxed{+ 11}$ 25 $\boxed{\div 5}$ 5

---

## Key Fact

Subtraction is the inverse of addition.
Division is the inverse of multiplication.

---

### Practice

Use inverse operations to find the numbers fed into these machines.

| **Example** | ? $\boxed{+ 5}$ → $\boxed{\times 3}$ 36 |
|---|---|
| **Working** | 7 $\boxed{- 5}$ 12 $\boxed{\div 3}$ 36 |
| **Answer** | 7 |

**1** ? $\boxed{+7}$ 15

**2** ? $\boxed{-13}$ 16

**3** ? $\boxed{+16}$ 31

**4** ? $\boxed{-12}$ 24

**5** ? $\boxed{\times 3}$ 27

**6** ? $\boxed{\times 12}$ 96

**7** ? $\boxed{\div 8}$ 6

**8** ? $\boxed{+9}$ ➤ $\boxed{\times 2}$ 30

**9** ? $\boxed{\times 4}$ ➤ $\boxed{+8}$ 36

**10** ? $\boxed{\times 5}$ ➤ $\boxed{+5}$ 50

**11** ? $\boxed{\div 3}$ ➤ $\boxed{+20}$ 25

**12** ? $\boxed{+17}$ ➤ $\boxed{\div 5}$ 7

**C** An *accurate* formula for finding the temperature in degrees Fahrenheit (°F) given the temperature in degrees Celsius (°C) is $F = \frac{9}{5}C + 32$. Find the temperature in Fahrenheit given the following Celsius temperatures and then use inverse operations to check your calculations.

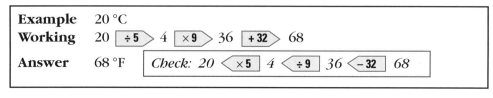

**Example** 20 °C
**Working** 20 $\boxed{\div 5}$ 4 $\boxed{\times 9}$ 36 $\boxed{+32}$ 68
**Answer** 68 °F   *Check:* 20 $\boxed{\times 5}$ 4 $\boxed{\div 9}$ 36 $\boxed{-32}$ 68

**1** 30 °C

**2** 35 °C

**3** 45 °C

**4** 15 °C

**5** 50 °C

**6** 80 °C

**D** Use inverse operations to find the numbers fed into these machines.

**1** ? $\boxed{+11}$ 26

**2** ? $\boxed{+14}$ 21

**3** ? $\boxed{-18}$ 4

**4** ? $\boxed{-9}$ 21

**5** ? $\boxed{\times 4}$ 48

**6** ? $\boxed{\times 7}$ 63

**7** ? $\boxed{\div 6}$ 7

**8** ? $\boxed{+11}$ ➤ $\boxed{\times 3}$ 45

**9** ? $\boxed{\times 3}$ ➤ $\boxed{+9}$ 30

**10** ? $\boxed{\times 3}$ ➤ $\boxed{+4}$ 40

**11** ? $\boxed{\div 5}$ ➤ $\boxed{+34}$ 38

**12** ? $\boxed{+18}$ ➤ $\boxed{\div 5}$ 8

**13** ? $\boxed{+3}$ ➤ $\boxed{\times 4}$ 32

**14** ? $\boxed{+9}$ ➤ $\boxed{\times 5}$ 75

**15** ? $\boxed{+6}$ ➤ $\boxed{\times 5}$ 70

**16** ? $\boxed{-7}$ ➤ $\boxed{\times 6}$ 72

**17** ? $\boxed{\times 6}$ ➤ $\boxed{\div 8}$ 3

**18** ? $\boxed{+27}$ ➤ $\boxed{\times 2}$ 70

**19** ? $\boxed{\div 3}$ ➤ $\boxed{\times 9}$ 72

**20** ? $\boxed{\times 13}$ ➤ $\boxed{+18}$ 83

**Finished Early?**
➡ Go to page 405

# 17 Multiples and Factors

In this chapter you will learn about ...
1. multiples
2. factors

## Multiples

## Learn About It

Hundred grid

A number can have many multiples.
6 has multiples 6, 12, 18, 24, etc.
You can see some multiples of 6 shaded
red on this hundred grid.

| 1 | 2 | 3 | 4 | 5 | 6 | 7 | 8 | 9 | 10 |
|---|---|---|---|---|---|---|---|---|---|
| 11 | 12 | 13 | 14 | 15 | 16 | 17 | 18 | 19 | 20 |
| 21 | 22 | 23 | 24 | 25 | 26 | 27 | 28 | 29 | 30 |
| 31 | 32 | 33 | 34 | 35 | 36 | 37 | 38 | 39 | 40 |
| 41 | 42 | 43 | 44 | 45 | 46 | 47 | 48 | 49 | 50 |
| 51 | 52 | 53 | 54 | 55 | 56 | 57 | 58 | 59 | 60 |
| 61 | 62 | 63 | 64 | 65 | 66 | 67 | 68 | 69 | 70 |
| 71 | 72 | 73 | 74 | 75 | 76 | 77 | 78 | 79 | 80 |
| 81 | 82 | 83 | 84 | 85 | 86 | 87 | 88 | 89 | 90 |
| 91 | 92 | 93 | 94 | 95 | 96 | 97 | 98 | 99 | 100 |

1. Cross out all the multiples of 6 on a
   hundred grid like this. 12̸

2. Cross out all the multiples of 8 on the same
   grid like this 1̸6. Use a different colour if
   possible. The numbers crossed out twice are multiples of 6 *and* 8. They are
   called **common multiples**.

3. Common multiples are multiples of two or more numbers. Write down the
   common multiples of 6 and 8 up to 100. The lowest number in this list is
   called the **lowest common multiple** (often shortened to **l.c.m.**) of 6 and
   8. Write down the lowest common multiple of 6 and 8.

4. You can work out multiples without using a hundred grid. Find multiples of
   6 by multiplying 6 by 1, 2, 3, 4, etc. up to 20. Now multiply 8 by 1, 2, 3, 4, etc.
   up to 20. Compare your two lists. The numbers in both lists are the
   common multiples and the smallest of these is the lowest common multiple.

## Try It Out

Hundred grid

A) On a hundred grid, shade in the multiples of both numbers in each pair below.
Use a different colour for each number and stick your grid in your book. Write
down **(a)** the common multiples, **(b)** the lowest common multiple for each
pair of numbers.

**1** 4, 10   **2** 6, 9   **3** 3, 7   **4** 12, 8   **5** 4, 9

## Word Check

**multiple of a number** a number produced by multiplying the number by any number

**common multiple** a number that is a multiple of two or more numbers

**lowest common multiple (l.c.m.)** the smallest number that is a common multiple of two or more numbers

# Practice

**B** In each question, write down:

(a) the first three multiples of each number

(b) two common multiples

(c) the lowest common multiple.

| | | | |
|---|---|---|---|
| **1** 12, 15 | **2** 10, 25 | **3** 14, 10 | **4** 18, 24 |
| **5** 36, 48 | **6** 28, 60 | **7** 120, 72 | **8** 64, 100 |

**C** When adding or subtracting fractions, you choose as a common denominator the l.c.m. of the denominators. Write down the lowest common denominators for these calculations.

**1** $\frac{}{12} + \frac{}{8}$  **2** $\frac{}{15} + \frac{}{24}$  **3** $\frac{}{16} + \frac{}{20}$  **4** $\frac{}{8} - \frac{}{20}$

**5** $\frac{}{16} - \frac{}{12}$  **6** $\frac{}{24} + \frac{}{16}$  **7** $\frac{}{30} + \frac{}{12}$  **8** $\frac{}{72} + \frac{}{80}$

**9** $\frac{}{16} - \frac{}{56}$  **10** $\frac{}{36} + \frac{}{48} + \frac{}{12}$  **11** $\frac{}{18} + \frac{}{24} - \frac{}{30}$  **12** $\frac{}{20} - \frac{}{42} + \frac{}{14}$

**D** Find the l.c.m. of each group of numbers below.

| **Example** | 6, 8, 16 |
|---|---|
| **Working** | Multiples of 6 up to 100 are 6, 12, 18, 24, 30, 36, 42, **48**, 54, 60, 66, 72, 78, 84, 90, **96**. |
| | Multiples of 8 up to 100 are 8, 16, 24, 32, 40, **48**, 56, 64, 72, 80, 88, **96**. |
| | Multiples of 16 up to 100 are 16, 32, **48**, 64, 80, **96**, 112, 128. |
| **Answer** | 48 |

| | | |
|---|---|---|
| **1** 3, 4, 5 | **2** 2, 5, 6 | **3** 3, 10, 12 |
| **4** 8, 30, 48 | **5** 9, 24, 60 | **6** 2, 3, 5, 7, 9 |

**Finished Early?**
➡ Go to page 405

# Further Practice

For each diagram below:
- **(a)** list the numbers in the outer circle that are multiples of *all* the numbers in the inner circle
- **(b)** write down the lowest common multiple of the numbers in the inner circle; this may not be one of the numbers in the outer circle.

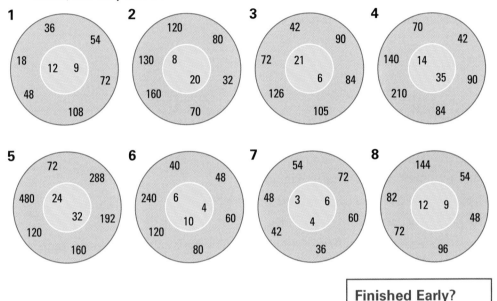

**1**
Inner: 12, 9
Outer: 36, 54, 18, 72, 48, 108

**2**
Inner: 8, 20, 32
Outer: 120, 80, 130, 160, 70

**3**
Inner: 21, 6
Outer: 42, 90, 72, 84, 126, 105

**4**
Inner: 14, 35
Outer: 70, 42, 140, 90, 210, 84

**5**
Inner: 24, 32
Outer: 72, 288, 480, 192, 120, 160

**6**
Inner: 6, 4, 10
Outer: 40, 48, 240, 60, 120, 80

**7**
Inner: 3, 6, 4
Outer: 54, 72, 48, 60, 42, 36

**8**
Inner: 12, 9
Outer: 144, 54, 82, 48, 72, 96

> **Finished Early?**
> ➡ Go to page 405

# ❷ Factors

## Remember?

A **factor** is a whole number that divides exactly into another whole number. 1 and the number itself are always factors.

1, 2, 4 and 8 are factors of 8.

You can show factors on a **factor diagram**.

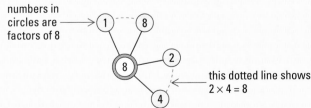

numbers in circles are → factors of 8

this dotted line shows
$2 \times 4 = 8$

## Try It Out

**F** Draw factor diagrams for the following numbers.

**1** 12        **2** 15        **3** 18        **4** 20

**5** 14        **6** 30        **7** 22        **8** 25

## Learn About It

These diagrams show the factors of 12 and 18.

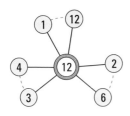 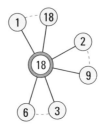

Some numbers occur in both diagrams.

The factors of 12 are $1, 2, 3, 4, 6, 12$.

The factors of 18 are $1, 2, 3, 6, 9, 18$.

The red numbers are factors of 12 and 18. They are called **common factors**.

6 is the largest of the common factors. It is called the **highest common factor (h.c.f.)**. The highest common factor of two or more numbers is the largest whole number that will divide exactly into both numbers.

## Try It Out

**G** For each pair of numbers below
   **(a)** draw a factor diagram for each number
   **(b)** list their common factors
   **(c)** write down the highest common factor.

**1** 8, 12        **2** 10, 15        **3** 16, 20        **4** 18, 24

**5** 12, 30       **6** 24, 32       **7** 27, 36       **8** 15, 33

### Word Check

**factor of a number** a whole number that divides into it exactly

**common factor** a number that is a factor of two or more numbers

**highest common factor (h.c.f.)** the largest common factor of two or more numbers

## Practice

**H** For each set of numbers below, list the factors of each number and write down the highest common factor.

**1** 35, 45       **2** 36, 60       **3** 45, 72

**4** 48, 64       **5** 24, 32, 72       **6** 27, 54, 45

**7** 60, 84, 120       **8** 60, 90, 150, 225       **9** 45, 60, 72

**10** 36, 56, 63       **11** 40, 60, 72, 90       **12** 80, 96, 100, 120

**I** You cancel fractions into their lowest terms by dividing the numerator and denominator by the same number. Write down the number you would divide into the top and bottom of each fraction to cancel it to its lowest terms.

**1** $\frac{8}{12}$       **2** $\frac{16}{40}$       **3** $\frac{12}{15}$       **4** $\frac{18}{24}$

**5** $\frac{27}{36}$       **6** $\frac{48}{64}$       **7** $\frac{72}{144}$       **8** $\frac{42}{150}$

**9** $\frac{56}{80}$       **10** $\frac{63}{90}$       **11** $\frac{84}{120}$       **12** $\frac{45}{165}$

> **Finished Early?**
> ➡ Go to page 405

## Further Practice

**J** For each diagram below:
**(a)** list the numbers in the outer circle which are common factors of all the numbers in the inner circle
**(b)** write down the highest common factor of the numbers in the inner circle.

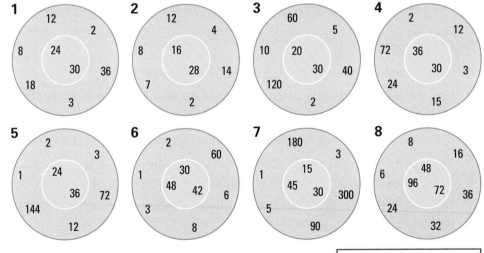

> **Finished Early?**
> ➡ Go to page 405

# 18 Patterns and Sequences

In this chapter you will learn about ...
1. what's next?
2. finding the formula
3. quadratic sequences

## ⊤ ❶ What's Next?

### Remember?

A **sequence** is a list of numbers in order. The numbers are called the **terms** of the sequence. Look at the sequence $2, 4, 6, 8, 10$ ...

| postion in sequence | 1st | 2nd | 3rd | 4th | 5th |
|---|---|---|---|---|---|

terms of the sequence  2 ↘+2 4 ↘+2 6 ↘+2 8 ↘+2 10

There is a pattern to the sequence. You add 2 each time. So the sixth term is 12, the seventh term is 14 ....

## Try It Out

1. Find the third, fifth and sixth terms of the sequence $1, 3, 5, 7, 9$ ...
2. Find the fourth, sixth and seventh terms of the sequence $1, 4, 7, 10, 13, 16$ ...
3. Find the second, fourth and sixth terms of the sequence $2, 6, 10, 14, 18$ ...
4. Find the third, fifth and sixth terms of the sequence $5, 7, 9, 11, 13$ ...
5. Find the fourth, sixth and seventh terms of the sequence $2, 5, 8, 11, 14$ ...
6. Find the third, fourth and sixth terms of the sequence $16, 14, 12, 10, 8$ ...
7. Find the third, fifth and sixth terms of the sequence $48, 45, 42, 39$ ...
8. Find the fourth, fifth and seventh terms of the sequence $30, 26, 22, 18$ ...
9. Find the fifth, sixth and eighth terms of the sequence $1, 6, 11, 16$ ...
10. Find the sixth, seventh and eighth terms of the sequence $3, 12, 21, 30$ ...

## Learn About It

Any set of numbers that grows or shrinks according to a rule is called a **sequence**.

The **even numbers** make a sequence: $2, 4, 6, 8, \ldots$

You start at 2, and add 2 every time.

Each number in a sequence is one of its **terms**. The first term in this sequence is 2.

The **odd numbers** make a sequence: $1, 3, 5, 7, \ldots$

The 10th term in the sequence is 19.

Sequences do not have to be made by adding a number each time.

The **square numbers** are $1^2, 2^2, 3^2, 4^2, \ldots = 1, 4, 9, 16, \ldots$

The $10^{\text{th}}$ term is $10^2 = 100$.

The **cube numbers** are $1^3, 2^3, 3^3, 4^3, \ldots = 1, 8, 27, 81, \ldots$

The $7^{\text{th}}$ term is $7^3 = 343$.

These dot patterns make the sequence of **triangular numbers**: $1, 3, 6, 10 \ldots$
To find the $5^{\text{th}}$ term you add 5 on to make 15.

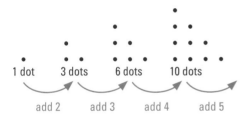

The sequence $1, 1, 2, 3, 5, 8, 13, \ldots$ is called the **Fibonacci sequence**. To make it, add the last two terms to get the next one.

$1 + 1 = 2$

$\qquad 1 + 2 = 3$

$\qquad\qquad 2 + 3 = 5$

$\qquad\qquad\qquad 3 + 5 = 8$

$\qquad\qquad\qquad\qquad 5 + 8 = 13 \ldots$ etc.

### Word Check

**sequence** a set of numbers that follow a rule

**term** a number in a sequence

**rule** how to work out any number in a sequence

**position** the location of a term in a sequence

## Try It Out

**B** The numbers of dots in each group of patterns make a sequence. Write down the first six terms of each sequence. Draw more patterns if this helps you.

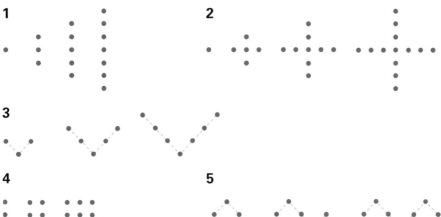

## Practice

**C** In each of the following questions you are given a pattern made with matchsticks. The patterns make sequences of numbers. For each sequence:

**(a)** write down the first six terms of the sequence (Draw the patterns if this helps.)

**(b)** write down a rule for working out the next term of the sequence

**(c)** write down the 20$^{th}$ term of the sequence

**(d)** name the sequence if it has a special name.

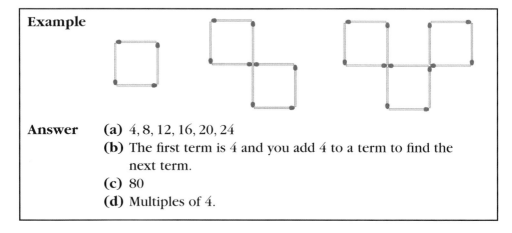

**Example**

**Answer**
**(a)** 4, 8, 12, 16, 20, 24
**(b)** The first term is 4 and you add 4 to a term to find the next term.
**(c)** 80
**(d)** Multiples of 4.

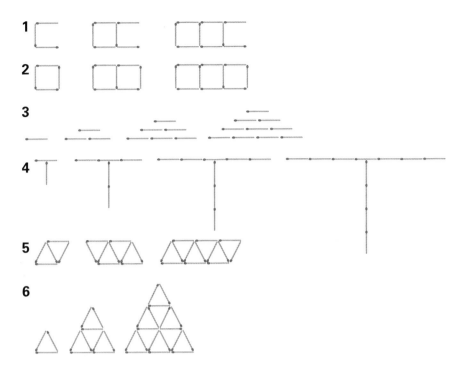

**1**

**2**

**3**

**4**

**5**

**6**

Write down the first six terms in each of the sequences described below.

**1** The first term is 1. To find the next term, add 3.

**2** The first term is 2. To find the next term, add 2.

**3** The first term is 1. To find the next term, multiply by 3.

**4** The first term is 4 and the next term is 3 times the previous term.

**5** The first two terms are both 1. You add the last two terms to find the next term.

**6** The first term is 32. To find the next term, subtract 2.

## Further Practice

Copy these sequences and fill in the missing numbers.

**1** 2, 4, _, _,10, 12, 14, 16

**2** 3, 5, _, _, 11, 13, 15, 17

**3** 1, _, 9, 16, 25, 36

**4** 2, 4, 8, _, _, 64, 128

**5** 3, _, _, 15, 19, 23, 27

**6** 3, 6, 9, _, _, _, 21, 24

**7** 2, 6, _, 54, 162, 486

**8** 1, 1, 2, 3, 5, 8, _, _, 34

**F** For each of these sequences, write down:
(a) the first eight terms
(b) the rule to find the next term.

**1** 2, 4, 6, 8 ...       **2** 3, 5, 7, 9 ...       **3** 4, 7, 10, 13 ...

**4** 1, 4, 16, 64 ...       **5** 2, 7, 12, 17 ...

**6** 1, 3, 9, 27 ...       **7** 4, 9, 14, 19 ...

**8** 40, 36, 32, 28 ...       **9** 4000, 2000, 1000, 500 ...

> **Finished Early?**
> ➡ Go to page 406

# T ❷ Finding the Formula

## Learn About It

A **sequence** is a set of numbers that follow a rule. The numbers in the sequence are called **terms**. The letter $n$ is normally used for the **position** in the sequence.

You can use a formula to **generate** a sequence. This sequence uses the formula $T = 4n - 1$.

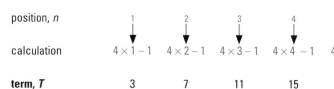

| position, $n$ | 1 | 2 | 3 | 4 | 5 |
|---|---|---|---|---|---|
| calculation | $4 \times 1 - 1$ | $4 \times 2 - 1$ | $4 \times 3 - 1$ | $4 \times 4 - 1$ | $4 \times 5 - 1$ |
| **term, $T$** | 3 | 7 | 11 | 15 | 19 |

For every $T$erm, multiply the position $n$umber by 4, then subtract 1.

 The formula does not contain '+ 4' anywhere. That just tells you how to get from one term to the next.

You can calculate terms anywhere in the sequence easily.

| **Example** | What is the 100th term of the sequence? |
|---|---|
| **Working** | $n = 100$. Substitute this into the formula. |
| | $T = 4n - 1$ |
| | $\quad = 4 \times 100 - 1$ |
| | $\quad = 399$ |
| **Answer** | The 100th term is 399. |

This is much easier than writing down 100 terms!

You can show the terms of a sequence on a graph.

Use the horizontal axis for $n$ and the vertical axis for $T$.

The first term is 3, so plot $(1, 3)$. The second term is 7, so plot $(2, 7)$, etc.

The graph looks like this.

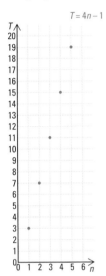

$T = 4n - 1$

### Word Check

**formula** the rule that describes the sequence

**generate** make terms using the formula

## Try It Out

Generate the first five terms of the sequences given by these formulae.

Plot a graph to illustrate each sequence.

**1** $T = 2n$                    **2** $T = 2n - 5$

**3** $T = 5n + 1$               **4** $T = 10n - 3$

**5** $T = -n + 10$             **6** $T = 6 - 2n$

# Learn More About It

3, 6, 9, 12, 15 ...

To find the formula for this sequence, look at the **differences** between terms. Draw a **differences table** to help you.

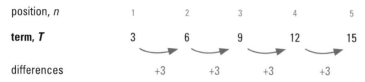

| position, *n* | 1 | 2 | 3 | 4 | 5 |
|---|---|---|---|---|---|
| term, *T* | 3 | 6 | 9 | 12 | 15 |
| differences | | +3 | +3 | +3 | +3 |

The differences are all +3. Every time the position number goes up by 1, the term goes up by 3. This means that the value of the terms increases 3 times as fast as the value of the positions. So the rule must use ×3.

Try $T = 3n$. Substitute values for $n$ and see if they match the sequence.

$n = 1$ means $T = 3 \times 1 = 3$ ✓

$n = 4$ means $T = 3 \times 4 = 12$ ✓

5, 7, 9, 11, 13 ...

In this sequence, the differences are all +2.

> ## Word Check
>
> **difference**  the amount you have to add on to get the next term
>
> **differences table**  a clear way of setting out the positions, terms and differences

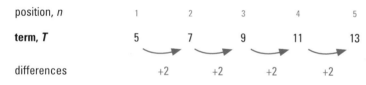

| position, *n* | 1 | 2 | 3 | 4 | 5 |
|---|---|---|---|---|---|
| term, *T* | 5 | 7 | 9 | 11 | 13 |
| differences | | +2 | +2 | +2 | +2 |

The rule must use ×2, but $T = 2n$ doesn't work. The differences are correct but this sequence doesn't start at 5. Something needs to be added. The difference between the first term of the sequence we want and the first term of $T = 2n$ is 3.

Try $T = 2n + 3$.

$n = 2$ means $T = 2 \times 2 + 3 = 7$ ✓

$n = 3$ means $T = 2 \times 3 + 3 = 9$ ✓

16, 13, 10, 7, 4 ...

Sequences where the terms decrease have **negative** differences.

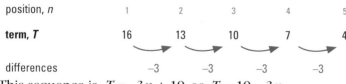

| position, *n* | 1 | 2 | 3 | 4 | 5 |
|---|---|---|---|---|---|
| term, *T* | 16 | 13 | 10 | 7 | 4 |
| differences | | −3 | −3 | −3 | −3 |

This sequence is $T = -3n + 19$, or $T = 19 - 3n$.

# Try It Out

For each sequence:

(a) draw a differences table

(b) find the formula

(c) calculate the 20th term.

**1** 4, 7, 10, 13, 16 …

**2** 2, 8, 14, 20, 26 …

**3** 7, 6, 5, 4, 3 …

**4** 21, 18, 15, 12, 9 …

**5** 1.5, 2, 2.5, 3, 3.5 …

**6** 2.25, 2, 1.75, 1.5, 1.25 …

# Practice

Each set of squares generates a sequence. For each question:

(a) write down the terms given by the diagrams

(b) draw a differences table

(c) find the formula

(d) calculate the 50th term.

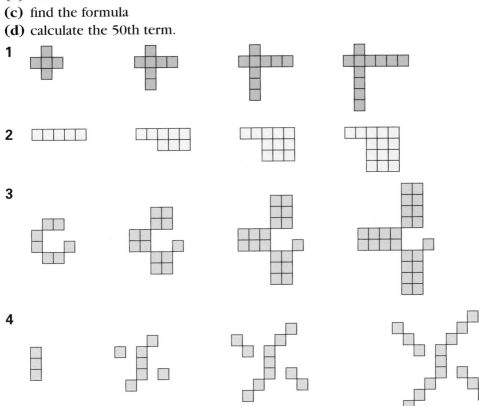

**1**

**2**

**3**

**4**

**J** Each of these graphs was generated by a sequence. For each question:

(a) write down the terms given by the graphs

(b) draw a differences table

(c) find the formula

(d) calculate the $100^{th}$ term.

**1**
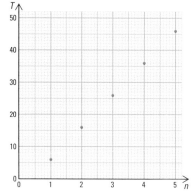

**2**
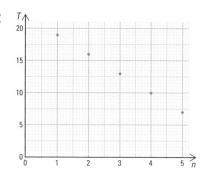

**3**
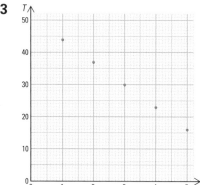

**4**
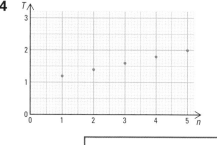

**Finished Early?**
➡ Go to page 406

## Further Practice

**K** Generate the first five terms of the sequences given by these formulae.
Plot a graph to illustrate each sequence.

**1** $T = 7n$       **2** $T = n - 5$       **3** $T = 3n + 2$

**4** $T = 8n - 1$       **5** $T = 10 - 3n$

For each sequence:

**(a)** draw a differences table

**(b)** find the formula

**(c)** calculate the 10<sup>th</sup> term.

**1** $7, 8, 9, 10, 11 \ldots$       **2** $8, 14, 20, 26, 32 \ldots$

**3** $3, 3.3, 3.6, 3.9, 4.2 \ldots$     **4** $110, 90, 70, 50, 30 \ldots$

**5** $2.5, 4.5, 6.5, 8.5, 10.5 \ldots$

> **Finished Early?**
> ⏵ Go to page 406

# Quadratic Sequences

## Learn About It

The formula for a **quadratic** sequence contains $n^2$.

These are all examples of quadratic sequences.

$T = n^2 + 3n + 1$:       $5, 11, 19, 29, 41 \ldots$

$T = n^2 - 4$:       $-3, 0, 5, 12, 21 \ldots$

$T = 5n^2$:       $5, 20, 45, 80, 125 \ldots$

$T = -3n^2 + 6n$:       $3, 0, -9, -24, -45 \ldots$

The sequence of **square numbers** $(1, 4, 9, 16, 25 \ldots)$ has terms given by $T = n^2$.

The differences table needs two rows:

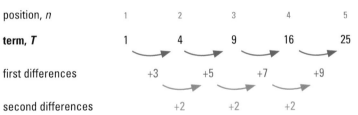

When the second difference row is all $+2$, this means that the formula begins with $n^2$.

$11, 14, 19, 26, 35 \ldots$

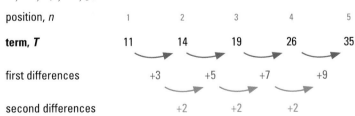

The formula must contain $n^2$, but $T = n^2$ doesn't work. The differences are correct, but this sequence doesn't start at 11. Something needs to be added. Try $T = n^2 + 10$.

$n = 2$ means $T = 2^2 + 10 = 14$ ✓      $n = 3$ means $T = 3^2 + 10 = 19$ ✓

$3, 8, 15, 24, 35 \ldots$

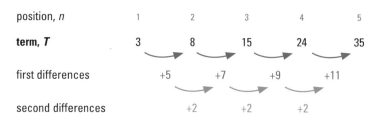

| position, $n$ | 1 | 2 | 3 | 4 | 5 |
|---|---|---|---|---|---|
| term, $T$ | 3 | 8 | 15 | 24 | 35 |
| first differences | | +5 | +7 | +9 | +11 |
| second differences | | | +2 | +2 | +2 |

The formula must contain $n^2$, but $T = n^2$ doesn't work. Try $T = n^2 + 2$.

$n = 1$ means $T = 1^2 + 2 = 3$ ✓

$n = 4$ means $T = 4^2 + 2 = 18$ ✗

So this formula doesn't work. There must be more to it. You need to remove the $n^2$ part of the formula so you can look at what's left, the **residue**. To do this, subtract $n^2$ from the terms of the formula.

| position, $n$ | 1 | 2 | 3 | 4 | 5 |
|---|---|---|---|---|---|
| term, $T$ | 3 | 8 | 15 | 24 | 35 |
| $n^2$, to be subtracted | 1 | 4 | 9 | 16 | 25 |
| residue, $T - n^2$ | 2 | 4 | 6 | 8 | 10 |

The residue is a sequence given by $2n$.

So $T - n^2 = 2n$.

Adding $n^2$ to both sides gives $T = n^2 + 2n$.

$n = 1$ means $T = 1^2 + 2 \times 1 = 3$ ✓

$n = 4$ means $T = 4^2 + 2 \times 4 = 24$ ✓

## Word Check

**quadratic sequence**  sequence with terms involving $n^2$.

**second differences**  the differences between the numbers in the first differences row.

**residue**  the part of the formula left when $n^2$ has been taken away

## Try It Out

For each sequence:

(a) use the difference method to find the formula

(b) calculate the $10^{th}$ term.

**1** $2, 5, 10, 17, 26 \ldots$    **2** $-4, -1, 4, 11, 20 \ldots$    **3** $2, 6, 12, 20, 30 \ldots$

**4** $4, 9, 16, 25, 36 \ldots$    **5** $0, 0, 2, 6, 12, 20 \ldots$

## Learn More About It

$3, 12, 27, 48, 75 \ldots$ is a quadratic sequence.

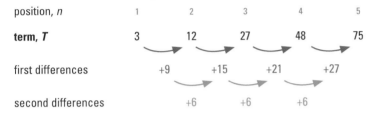

The second differences are all $+6$. This is 3 times as much as the differences for $T = n^2$. Try $T = 3n^2$.

$n = 1$ means $T = 3 \times 1^2 = 3$ ✓

$n = 5$ means $T = 3 \times 5^2 = 75$ ✓

$4, 7, 14, 25, 40 \ldots$

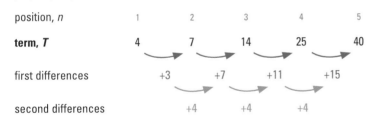

The second differences are all $+4$. The formula must contain $2n^2$, but $T = 2n^2$ doesn't work. Get rid of the $2n^2$ part to find the residue. Subtract $2n^2$ from the terms of the formula.

| position, $n$ | 1 | 2 | 3 | 4 | 5 |
|---|---|---|---|---|---|
| term, $T$ | 4 | 7 | 14 | 25 | 40 |
| $2n^2$, to be subtracted | 2 | 8 | 18 | 32 | 50 |
| residue, $T - 2n^2$ | 2 | −1 | −4 | −7 | −10 |

The residue is also a sequence, given by $-3n + 5$.

So $T - 2n^2 = -3n + 5$.

Adding $n^2$ to both sides gives $T = 2n^2 - 3n + 5$.

## Key Fact

Halve the number in the second differences row to find the number of $n^2$ in the formula.

## Try It Out

For each sequence:

(a) use the difference method to find the formula
(b) calculate the 15$^{th}$ term.

**1** 5, 20, 45, 80, 125 ...    **2** 5, 12, 23, 38, 57 ...    **3** 5, 14, 27, 44, 65 ...

**4** 5, 19, 41, 71, 109 ...    **5** 5, 3, -1, -7, -15 ...

## Practice

For each sequence:

(a) use the difference method to find the formula
(b) calculate the 50$^{th}$ term.

**1** 1, 10, 23, 40, 61 ...    **2** 2, 6, 14, 26, 42 ...    **3** -5, 10, 35, 70, 115 ...

**4** 5, 15, 31, 53, 81 ...    **5** -8, -12, -12, -8, 0 ...    **6** 10, 34, 74, 130, 202 ...

**7** 3, 3, 1, -3, -9 ...    **8** 4, 6.5, 10, 14.5, 20 ...

Each set of dots generates a sequence. For each question:

(a) write down the terms given by the diagrams
(b) draw a differences table
(c) find the formula
(d) calculate the 20$^{th}$ term.

**1**

**2**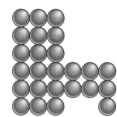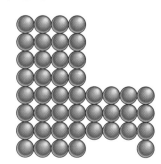

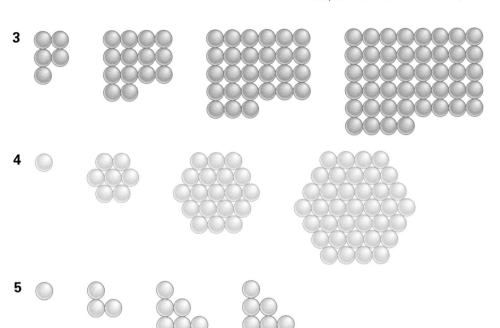

**3**

**4**

**5**

**Finished Early?**
➡ Go to page 406

## Further Practice

For each sequence:

**(a)** use the difference method to find the formula

**(b)** calculate the $100^{th}$ term.

**1** $-3, 4, 15, 30, 49 \ldots$

**2** $-1, 3, 9, 17, 27 \ldots$

**3** $2, 8, 18, 32, 50 \ldots$

**4** $2, 10, 24, 44, 70 \ldots$

**5** $2, 6, 12, 20, 30 \ldots$

**6** $2, 2, 0, -4, -10 \ldots$

**7** $0, 25, 70, 135, 220 \ldots$

**8** $-2.5, 0, 5.5, 14, 25.5 \ldots$

**Finished Early?**
➡ Go to page 406

# Unit 9 *Number Relationships*

## Summary of Chapters 17 and 18

- $3, 6, 9, 12 \ldots$ are all **multiples** of 3.
  When a number is found in the multiple list of two or more numbers, it is called a **common multiple**. $12, 24, 36 \ldots$ are common multiples of 4 and 6. The smallest number like this is called the **lowest common multiple** (l.c.m.). So 12 is the l.c.m. of 4 and 6.

- $1, 2, 3, 4, 6$ and 8 are all **factors** of 12.
  When a number appears the factor list of two or more numbers, it is called a **common factor**. $1, 2, 3$ and 6 are common factors of 24 and 30. The largest number like this is called the **highest common factor** (h.c.f.). So the h.c.f. of 24 and 30 is 6.

- A **sequence** is a list of numbers that follows a rule.
  Some important sequences:.
  
  | | |
  |---|---|
  | Even numbers | $2, 4, 6, 8, 10 \ldots$ |
  | Odd numbers | $1, 3, 5, 7, 9 \ldots$ |
  | Square numbers | $1, 4, 9, 16, 25 \ldots$ |
  | Cube numbers | $1, 8, 27, 64, 125 \ldots$ |
  | Triangular numbers | $1, 3, 6, 10, 15 \ldots$ |
  | Fibonacci sequence | $1, 1, 2, 3, 5, 8 \ldots$ |

- You can find a term from its position in the sequence if you know the **formula** for the sequence. To find the formula, use a **differences table**.

- **Simple** sequences have formulae such as $T = 2n + 3$, $T = 4n - 1$, $T = 5 - n$. Simple sequences make straight lines of data points on a graph.

- **Quadratic** sequences have $n^2$ in the formula. Halve the number in the second differences row to find the number of $n^2$ in the formula. Subtract the terms this generates to find the simple **residue** and complete the formula.
  Quadratic sequences have formulae such as $T = n^2 + 2n - 1$, $T = 4n^2 - 1$, $T = -2n^2 + 5n$.

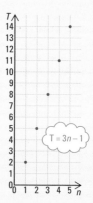

$T = 3n - 1$

# Brush Up Your Number 10

## Place Value Calculations

### Learn About It

Multiplying by 10, 100, 1000, etc. moves digits to the left.
You fill empty columns with zeros.

| | × 10 | × 100 | × 1000 | × 1 000 000 |
|---|---|---|---|---|
| **250** | 2500 | 25 000 | 250 000 | 250 000 000 |
| **2.5** | 25 | 250 | 2500 | 2 500 000 |
| **0.025** | 0.25 | 2.5 | 25 | 25 000 |

Dividing by 10, 100, 1000, etc. moves digits to the right.
You fill empty columns with zeros.

| | ÷ 10 | ÷ 100 | ÷ 1000 | ÷ 1 000 000 |
|---|---|---|---|---|
| **377 000** | 37 700 | 3770 | 377 | 0.377 |
| **3770** | 377 | 37.7 | 3.77 | 0.003 77 |
| **37.7** | 3.77 | 0.377 | 0.0377 | 0.000 037 7 |

### Try It Out

Work out the four output numbers for each question.

| | Input numbers | Machine | Output numbers |
|---|---|---|---|
| 1 | 6, 4100, 8.1, 0.05 | × 10 | |
| 2 | 55, 20 600, 0.03, 7.6 | × 100 | |
| 3 | 7600, 340, 0.2, 10.66 | ÷ 100 | |
| 4 | 4, 4.5, 4.55, 4.5555 | × 1000 | |
| 5 | 350, 35, 27.2, 0.088 | ÷ 10 | |
| 6 | 9000, 12 000, 350, 2.6 | ÷ 1000 | |
| 7 | 3, 650, 1.52, 0.000 05 | × 1 000 000 | |

### Learn More About It

When you multiply by a decimal, you are multiplying by a fraction.

$4 \times 0.1 = 4 \times \frac{1}{10} = 4 \div 10 = 0.4$

$2.5 \times 0.01 = 2.5 \times \frac{1}{100} = 2.5 \div 100 = 0.025$

When you divide by a decimal, you are dividing by a fraction.

$3.7 \div 0.1 = 3.7 \div \frac{1}{10}$

Remember, you have to invert and multiply.

$3.7 \div \frac{1}{10} = 3.7 \times \frac{10}{1} = 3.7 \times 10 = 37$

This makes sense. When you work out $3.7 \div 0.1$, you are asking how many 0.1s it takes to make 3.7. The answer has to be 37!

| **Example** | $0.4 \times 0.3$ |
|---|---|
| **Working** | $4 \times 3 = 12$ |
| | $4 \times 0.3 = 1.2$ |
| **Answer** | 0.12 |

| **Example** | $0.32 \div 0.8$ |
|---|---|
| **Working** | $32 \div 8 = 4$ |
| | $32 \div 0.8 = 40$ |
| **Answer** | 0.4 |

## Try It Out

**B** Work out the four output numbers for each question.

| | Input numbers | Machine | Output numbers |
|---|---|---|---|
| **1** | 3, 0.5, 250, 1.6 | × 0.1 | |
| **2** | 50, 6, 0.2, 0.07 | × 0.3 | |
| **3** | 1, 1.2, 12, 0.12 | × 0.01 | |
| **4** | 3.6, 3, 360, 0.04 | ÷ 20 | |
| **5** | 2, 5, 20, 700 | × 0.05 | |
| **6** | 9, 27, 5.4, 999 | ÷ 0.9 | |
| **7** | 3, 30, 12, 0.004 | × 600 | |

## Practice

**C** Work out the missing numbers and operations.

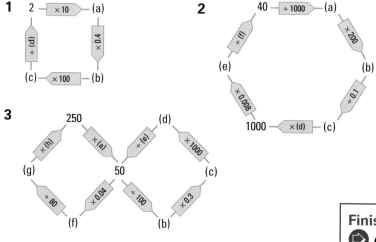

**Finished Early?**
⇨ Go to page 407

# Length, Mass and Capacity

In this chapter you will learn about ...
1. metric units
2. accuracy of measurements
3. calculations

## Metric Units

### Remember?

The basic unit for measuring length is the **metre** (m).
A tall adult is about 2 m tall.

100 **centimetres** (cm) = 1 m         10 mm = 1 cm

1000 **millimetres** (mm) = 1 m        1 **kilometre** (km) = 1000 m

When you weigh something, you are actually finding its **mass**.
The basic unit of mass is the **gram** (g).

1 **kilogram** (kg) = 1000 g            1000 kg = 1 **tonne** (t)

A bag of sugar has a mass of         A small car has a mass of about
about 1 kg.                          1 tonne.

The volume of liquid a container can hold is called its **capacity**.
Capacity is measured in **litres** (*l*).

100 **centilitres** (cl) = 1 litre

1000 **millilitres** (ml) = 1 litre

10 ml = 1 cl

## Learn About It

When you want to draw a straight line:
- with a ruler, draw a base line slightly longer than the one you want
- make a neat mark near one end
- measure from this mark and make a mark at the correct distance.

When you use scales to weigh something:
- check what units the scales show
- make sure you know what a single small division on the scale means
- round off the answer if you have to.

When you use a balance to weigh something:
- check what each weight is
- very carefully balance the weights and the thing you are weighing
- round off the answer if you have to.

## Try It Out

**A** Follow these instructions carefully.

**1** Draw a straight base line at least 20 cm long.

**2** Mark a point within 1 cm of the left-hand end of the line. Label this point O.

**3** Mark points at the following distances from O and label them as shown.

| Label | P | Q | R | S | T |
|---|---|---|---|---|---|
| Distance from O (cm) | 6.8 | 7.5 | 10.8 | 15.3 | 18 |

Your line should look like this (bigger, of course!).

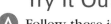

**4** Now draw the following circles.

| Centre | P | Q | R |
|---|---|---|---|
| Radius (cm) | 2.7 | 5 | 3.3 |

Your diagram should now look like this.

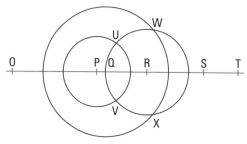

**5** Label the points U, V, W and X, as shown, and measure the distance between each pair of points on your diagram.
  (**a**) OU      (**b**) SV
  (**c**) TW      (**d**) OX
  (**e**) UV      (**f**) WX

# Learn More About It

You often need to change a length from one unit into another.
You need to know how many of the smaller units make the bigger unit.
If you are changing to **smaller** units, **multiply**. If you are changing to **bigger** units, **divide**.

| **Example** | Change 12.3 km to metres. |
|---|---|
| **Working** | There are 1000 m in 1 km. $12.3 \times 1000 = 12\,300$ |
| **Answer** | 12 300 m |

| **Example** | Change 156 cm to metres. |
|---|---|
| **Working** | There are 100 cm in 1 m. $156 \div 100 = 1.56$ |
| **Answer** | 1.56 m |

| **Example** | What is 1.24 tonnes in kilograms? |
|---|---|
| **Working** | There are 1000 kg in 1 tonne. $1.24 \times 1000 = 1240$ |
| **Answer** | 1240 kg |

| **Example** | What is 200 ml in centilitres? |
|---|---|
| **Working** | There are 10 ml in 1 cl. $200 \div 10 = 20$ |
| **Answer** | 20 cl |

# Try It Out

Copy each statement, putting the correct operation in the number machine.

| **Example** | ? > changes cm to mm. |
|---|---|
| **Answer** | × 10 > changes cm to mm. |

1  ? > changes *l* to cl.

2  ? > changes mm to cm.

3  ? > changes m to km.

4  ? > changes cm to m.

5  ? > changes *l* to ml.

6  ? > changes km to m.

7  ? > changes ml to cl.

8  ? > changes mm to km.

9  ? > changes kg to t.

10  ? > changes m to km.

11  ? > changes t to kg.

12  ? > changes t to g.

**C** In the tables below, each row represents the same quantity, expressed in four different units. Copy and complete the tables.

**1**

| mm | cm | m | km |
|---|---|---|---|
| 2000 | 200 | 2 | 0.002 |
|  | 6 |  |  |
|  |  |  | 5 |
| 8 |  |  |  |
|  | 48 |  |  |
| 235 |  |  |  |
|  |  | 2.6 |  |

**2**

| g | kg | t |
|---|---|---|
|  | 3 |  |
|  | 200 |  |
|  |  | 5 |
| 8 |  |  |
| 95 |  |  |
|  | 15 |  |
|  |  | 0.43 |
| 120 |  |  |
|  | 8.6 |  |

**3**

| ml | cl | l |
|---|---|---|
| 3000 |  |  |
|  |  | 2 |
|  | 45 |  |
|  |  | 12.55 |
| 25 |  |  |
|  |  | 80 |

## Learn More About It

When you **estimate** a length, mass or capacity:
- make sure you use a sensible unit
- use something with a length/mass/capacity you know, for comparison.

Here are the capacities of some everyday things for comparison.

| teaspoon | coffee mug | cola bottle | oil bottle | bucket | bath |
|---|---|---|---|---|---|
| 5 ml | 250 ml | 1 *l* | 5 litres | 15 litres | 300 litres |

NUMBER SKILLS **Round numbers to a specified accuracy, multiply/divide by a power of 10**

## Try It Out

**1** Copy and complete the following sentences, using **mm**, **cm**, **m** or **km**, or a number.

(a) An adult is about 2 _____ tall.

(b) The Moon is 3460 _____ across.

(c) A newspaper page is about 30 _____ wide.

(d) A compact disc is about 120 _____ wide.

(e) A house is about _____ m tall.

(f) This book is about _____ m thick.

**2** Copy and complete the following sentences, using **g**, **kg** or **t** (tonnes).

(a) An adult has a mass of about 70 _____.

(b) A teacup has a mass of about 160 _____.

(c) The mass of a small van is about 2 _____.

(d) A compact disc has a mass of 16 _____.

(e) A brick has a mass of about 2800 _____.

**3** Copy and complete the following sentences, using **ml**, **cl** or **l**, or a number.

(a) A car's petrol tank contains about 50 _____.

(b) A fish-bowl contains about 4000 _____.

(c) A kitchen sink holds about 12 _____.

(d) A yoghurt pot holds about _____ ml.

(e) A drink can holds about _____ ml.

## Practice

*Hint: change them all to the same unit first.*

Each cloud contains a set of lengths or capacities. Write each set in order, from smallest to largest.

**1**

12 cm  12 mm  2 mm  1.2 mm  1.5 cm  15 cm

**2**
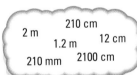
2 m  210 cm  1.2 m  12 cm  210 mm  2100 cm

**3**
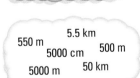
550 m  5.5 km  5000 cm  500 m  5000 m  50 km

**4**
0.3 m  33 cm  3.35 cm  30 mm  0.033 m  0.3 cm

**5**
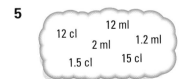
12 cl  12 ml  2 ml  1.2 ml  1.5 cl  15 cl

**6**
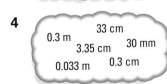
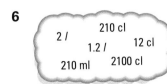
2 l  210 cl  1.2 l  12 cl  210 ml  2100 cl

**F** **1** Copy and complete the following sentences.
   **(a)** The world's tallest building is 45200 _____ tall.
   **(b)** Martyn's handspan is 0.2 _____.
   **(c)** A hen's egg is about 60 _____ long.
   **(d)** A car is about _____ m long.
   **(e)** A pigeon is about _____ cm from beak to tail.
   **(f)** A ruler is about _____ mm thick.

**2** Copy and complete the following sentences.
   **(a)** A bottle of wine holds about 700 _____.
   **(b)** A cup of tea is about 18 _____.
   **(c)** Having a shower uses about _____ *l* of water.
   **(d)** A big spoon holds about _____ cl.
   **(e)** A swimming pool holds about _____ *l*.

**Finished Early?**
Go to page 407

## Further Practice

**G** **1** Copy and complete the following sentences.
   **(a)** A carriage on a train is about _____ m long.
   **(b)** A piece of A4 paper is about _____ cm wide.
   **(c)** A CD case is about _____ mm thick.
   **(d)** The distance between my home and the nearest shopping centre is about _____ km.

**2** Estimate the weights of the following objects.
   **(a)** a frog
   **(b)** a 2 litre carton of milk
   **(c)** a heavy book, such as an encyclopaedia
   **(d)** a television set
   **(e)** a skateboard
   **(f)** a football

**1** Each row shows the same length, expressed in four different units. Copy and complete the table.

| mm | cm | m | km |
|---|---|---|---|
| | 120 | | |
| 300 | | | |
| | | 8 | |
| | | | 4.5 |
| | | 21.5 | |
| | 9.3 | | |

**2 (a)** Put these masses into order, from lightest to heaviest.

1.5 kg, 30 g, 550 g, 250 kg, 0.25 kg, 0.3 tonnes, 2000 g, 350 kg

**(b)** Put these capacities into order, from biggest to smallest.

4 *l*, 30 cl, 40 ml, 0.34 *l*, 4.3 ml, 30.4 ml, 43 *l*, 0.34 cl

> **Finished Early?**
> ➡ Go to page 407

# Accuracy of Measurements

## Remember?

**Rounding**

To round to the nearest whole number, look at the first decimal place. If it is 5, 6, 7, 8 or 9, round **up** to the next whole number. Otherwise, round **down**.

**Examples**   4.6 〉R (1)〉 5        7.15 〉R (1)〉 7

To round to 1 d.p. (decimal place), look at the second decimal place. If it is 5, 6, 7, 8 or 9, round **up** to the next tenth. Otherwise round down.

**Examples**   2.02 〉R (1 d.p.)〉 2.0      5.291 〉R (1 d.p.)〉 5.3

**Inequalities**

$x \geqslant 5.5$ (greater than or equal to)

$x \leqslant 2.8$ (less than or equal to)

$x > 4$ (greater than)

$x < 0.2$ (less than)

$2 \leqslant x < 7$ (range of numbers)

## Try It Out

**1** Copy and complete the table below. Round the number in your calculator display as required.

| Calculation | Answer in calculator display | Rounded to nearest whole number | Rounded to 1 d.p. | Rounded to 2 d.p. |
|---|---|---|---|---|
| **(a)** $3.6 \times 4.21$ | | | | |
| **(b)** $11 \div 16$ | | | | |
| **(c)** $24 \div 7$ | | | | |
| **(d)** $0.215 \times 0.35$ | | | | |
| **(e)** $5.1^4$ | | | | |
| **(f)** $\sqrt{10}$ | | | | |

**2** Write an inequality to describe each number. Use the letter $x$.

**(a)**

**(b)**

**(c)**

**(d)**

**(e)**

**(f)**

**(g)**

**(h)**

**NUMBER SKILLS  Round numbers to a specified accuracy, order decimals**

## Learn About It

You can never measure anything completely accurately. Suppose someone tells you that this pencil is 8 mm wide, to the nearest millimetre. 'To the nearest millimetre' is the **accuracy** of the measurement.

The smallest it could be is 7.5 mm. Any less than this, and it would round **down** to 7 mm. This is called the **lower bound** of the measurement.

It cannot be as wide as 8.5 mm, as this would round **up** to 9 mm. But anything below this still rounds to 8 mm. It can be *very* close to 8.5 mm: 8.49 mm, 8.499 999 …. mm. 8.5 mm is called the **upper bound** of the measurement.

This number line shows the range of widths the pencil might be.

Using $w$ to stand for the width, you can write this as an inequality:
$7.5$ mm $\leqslant w < 8.5$ mm.

If the width is 8 mm **correct to 1 d.p.** (nearest tenth of a millimetre), then
$7.95$ mm $\leqslant w < 8.05$ mm.

If the width is 8 mm, correct to 2 d.p. (nearest hundredth of a mm), then
$7.995$ mm $\leqslant w < 8.005$ mm.

### Key Fact

When a measurement is correct to a number of d.p., the upper and lower bounds use an extra d.p.

### Word Check
**lower bound** the smallest value a measurement can be

**upper bound** the cut-off point before the measurement rounds up – the measurement must be less than this

**accuracy** how exact the measurement is

## Try It Out

**1** The length of a bus is given as 9 m. Write down the lower and upper bounds if the length is correct to:
  **(a)** the nearest metre    **(b)** 1 d.p.    **(c)** 2 d.p.

**2** The diameter of a ball is 7.2 cm. Write down the lower and upper bounds if the diameter is correct to:
  **(a)** 1 d.p.    **(b)** 2 d.p.

**K** In each question below, a measurement is given.
(a) Write down the lower bound.
(b) Write down the upper bound.
(c) Write an inequality for the measurement, using your answers to (a) and (b).

**1** blue whale
length *(l)* = 26 m to nearest metre

**2** backpack
mass *(m)* = 14 kg to 1 d.p.

**3** pencil
length *(l)* = 15.3 cm to 1 d.p.

**4** space shuttle
mass *(m)* = 78.1 tonnes to 1 d.p.

**5** boy
height *(h)* = 1.57 m to 2 d.p.

**6** wine bottle
capacity *(C)* = 0.7 1 to 2 d.p.

**7** computer chip
width *(w)* = 12 mm to 1 d.p.

## Learn More About It

When you calculate using numbers that aren't completely accurate, you end up with a range of answers.

Suppose that $p = 6$ and $q = 2$, and that these values have been rounded to the nearest whole number. Then $5.5 \leqslant p < 6.5$ and $1.5 \leqslant q < 2.5$.

This table shows what can happen when you add $p$ and $q$ together.

$7 \leqslant p + q < 9$.

The lower bound (LB) is 7 and the upper bound (UB) is 9.

|  |  | **p** | |
|---|---|---|---|
| **p + q** | | **LB** 5.5 | **UB** 6.5 |
| **q** | **LB** 1.5 | 7 | 8 |
| | **UB** 2.5 | 8 | 9 |

The tables below show what happens with other operations.

|  |  | **p** | |
|---|---|---|---|
| **p − q** | | **LB** 5.5 | **UB** 6.5 |
| **q** | **LB** 1.5 | 4 | 5 |
| | **UB** 2.5 | 3 | 4 |

$3 < p - q < 5$

|  |  | **p** | |
|---|---|---|---|
| **p × q** | | **LB** 5.5 | **UB** 6.5 |
| **q** | **LB** 1.5 | 8.25 | 9.75 |
| | **UB** 2.5 | 13.75 | 16.25 |

$8.25 \leqslant pq < 16.25$

|  |  | **p** | |
|---|---|---|---|
| **p ÷ q** | | **LB** 5.5 | **UB** 6.5 |
| **q** | **LB** 1.5 | 3.6667 | 4.3333 |
| | **UB** 2.5 | 2.2 | 2.6 |

$2.2 < p \div q < 4.3333$

These answers have been rounded to 4 d.p. where necessary. The lower bound for $p - q$ and $p \div q$ needs a < sign, not a ≤. This is because the upper bound of $q$ is used to work them out, and $q$ can never be equal to its upper bound.

## Try It Out

Work out the lower and upper bounds of each expression if $x = 9$ and $y = 3$, correct to the nearest whole number. Use tables like those on the previous page.

**1** (a) $x + y$
(b) $x - y$
(c) $x \times y$
(d) $x \div y$ (Round answers to 4 d.p. where necessary.)

**2** Repeat question 1 with $x$ and $y$ having the same values, but correct to 1 d.p.

## Practice

**1** Here are four 1 cm metal cubes.

| Iron | Silver | Lead | Gold |
|---|---|---|---|
| **7.86 g** | **10.5 g** | **11.34 g** | **19.3 g** |
| (to 2 d.p.) | (to 1 d.p.) | (to 2 d.p.) | (to 1 d.p.) |

Work out the lower and upper bounds of the mass of:

(a)

(b)

(c)

Find the lower and upper bounds of the **difference** in mass between each pair of cubes.

(d)  and

(e)  and

(f)  and

**2** Remember, to work out the area of a rectangle, you multiply the length by the width. Find the lower and upper bounds of the areas that the following rectangles can have. The accuracy of the measurements is given inside each rectangle.

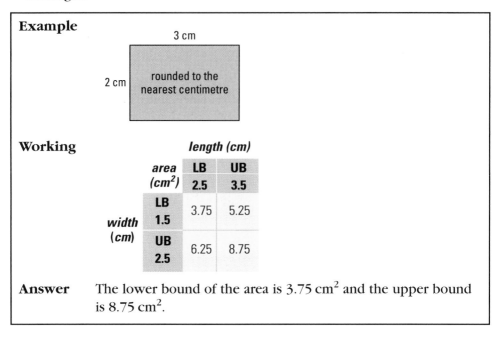

**Example**

3 cm

2 cm | rounded to the nearest centimetre

**Working**

|  | | length (cm) | |
|---|---|---|---|
| area (cm²) | | **LB** 2.5 | **UB** 3.5 |
| width (cm) | **LB** 1.5 | 3.75 | 5.25 |
| | **UB** 2.5 | 6.25 | 8.75 |

**Answer**    The lower bound of the area is 3.75 cm² and the upper bound is 8.75 cm².

**(a)**

9 cm

2 cm | rounded to the nearest centimetre

**(c)**

7 cm

11 cm | rounded to 1 d.p.

**(b)**

6.4 cm

6.4 cm | rounded to 1 d.p.

**(d)**

400 m

150 m | rounded to the nearest 10 metres

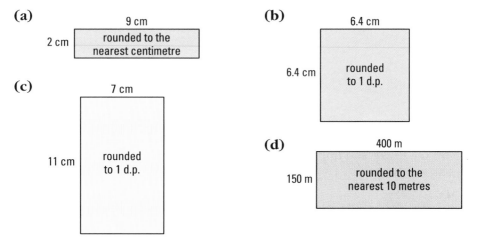

**3** Sim Street is exactly 500 m long. The Council decided that the safe distance between cars driving along the street is 8 m, to the nearest metre. The average length of a car, to 1 d.p., is 3.5 m.

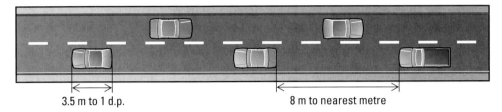

3.5 m to 1 d.p.                8 m to nearest metre

(a) What are the lower and upper bounds for the average car length?
(b) What are the lower and upper bounds for the safe distance between cars?
(c) What are the lower and upper bounds for the length of street taken up by 1 car (add the answers from (a) and (b))?
(d) If everyone keeps to the safe distance, what is the maximum number of cars that could be on Sim Street?

**4** $A = 25$ to the nearest whole number
$B = 400$ to the nearest ten
$u = 5.0$ to 1 d.p.
$v = 1.60$ to 2 d.p.

Find the lower and upper bounds for these expressions. Show all your working.

(a) $A + B$    (b) $u - v$    (c) $uv$    (d) $\frac{B}{A}$

(e) $u^2$    (f) $\sqrt{B}$

> **Finished Early?**
> ➭ Go to page 408

## Further Practice

In each question below, a measurement is given.
(a) Write down the lower bound for its value.
(b) Write down the upper bound for its value.
(c) Write an inequality using the answers to (a) and (b).

**1** $x = 6$ cm to the nearest centimetre    **2** $b = 12$ m to the nearest metre
**3** $C = 2.7$ litres to 1 d.p.    **4** $t = 8.5$ seconds to 1 d.p.
**5** $d = 45°$ to the nearest degree    **6** $m = 14.41$ kg to 2 d.p.
**7** $a = 2400$ km to the nearest 10 km    **8** $w = 90$ cl to the nearest centilitre
**9** $q = 0.064$ mm to 3 d.p.    **10** $Q = 0.064$ mm to 4 d.p.

◉ Work out the lower and upper bounds for each expression if $m = 12$ and $n = 4$, correct to the nearest whole number.

**1** (a) $m + n$

   (b) $m - n$

   (c) $m \times n$

   (d) $m \div n$ (round answers to 4 d.p. where necessary)

**2** Repeat question 1 with $m$ and $n$ having the same values, but correct to 1 d.p.

> **Finished Early?**
> ➡ Go to page 408

**P ❸ Calculations**

## Learn About It

When you are doing questions on length, mass and capacity:

- think about what operations $(+, -, \times, \div)$ you will use
- make sure you have used the information correctly
- ask yourself if the answer is sensible.

Some questions need to be done in two stages.

---

**Example**   A new street is 100 m long. There will be 5 street lamps, spaced equally along it. How far apart are the lamps?

The answer is **not** 100 m ÷ 5!

**Working**

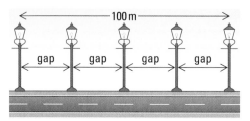

There are 5 lamps, but that means 5 – 1 = 4 **gaps**.
So they will be 100 ÷ 4 = 25 m apart.

**Answer**   25 m

---

This mass question also needs to be worked out in stages.

| | |
|---|---|
| **Example** | Andrea, Bushra and Carol have to carry some equipment. This is their list: |
| | Radio (3 kg), first-aid kit (10 kg), tent (20 kg), cooking gear (5 kg), food (5 kg), maps (1 kg), water (4 kg), 3 sleeping bags (2 kg each) |
| | Who should carry what, so the weight is shared fairly? |
| **Working** | First, work out what **all** the equipment weighs: |
| | $3 + 10 + 20 + 5 + 5 + 1 + 4 + (3 \times 2) = 54$ kg |
| | If they all carried the same weight, this would be $54 \div 3 = 18$ kg. This will not work, because the tent weighs 20 kg. Suppose Andrea carries the tent. That leaves $54 - 20 = 34$ kg between Bushra and Carol. Half of 34 kg is 17 kg, so they should each carry this weight. If Bushra carries the first-aid kit, radio and water, that is $10 + 3 + 4 = 17$ kg. Carol can carry the rest. There is more than one possible answer, for example, Bushra could have carried the radio, food, maps, water and 2 sleeping bags. |
| **Possible answer** | |
| | Andrea: tent (20 kg) = **20 kg** |
| | Bushra: first-aid kit (10 kg), 2 sleeping bags (4 kg), radio (3 kg) = **17 kg** |
| | Carol: cooking gear (5 kg), food (5 kg), water (4 kg), 1 sleeping bag (2 kg), maps (1 kg) = **17 kg** |

## Try It Out

1 Copy and complete this table. Write your working under the table.

| | Length of street | Number of lamps | Distance between lamps |
|---|---|---|---|
| **(a)** | 100 m | 3 | |
| **(b)** | 300 m | 7 | |
| **(c)** | 150 m | 5 | |
| **(d)** | 1.2 km | 21 | |
| **(e)** | 4 km | 126 | |

2 Divide this equipment among 5 people so that the weight is shared fairly.

2 tents (20 kg each), 5 sleeping bags (2 kg each), 2 water containers (4 kg each), 2 food packs (4 kg each), radio (3 kg), first-aid kit (10 kg), cooking gear (5 kg), maps (1 kg), telescope (5 kg)

# Learn More About It

Sometimes you need to change your answer to a more suitable unit.

| | |
|---|---|
| **Example** | A toy company packs dice into boxes. The dice are 2 cm cubes and each has a mass of 8 g.<br>The boxes are 40 cm × 30 cm × 24 cm and have a mass of 200 g each. What is the mass of a full box of dice? |
| **Working** | First you need to know how many dice fit in a box.<br>The volume of a box is 40 cm × 30 cm × 24 cm = 28 800 cm$^3$.<br>The volume of a dice is 2 cm × 2 cm × 2 cm = 8 cm$^3$. So the number of dice which can fit into the box is 28 800 ÷ 8 = 3600.<br>Mass of dice = 8 × 3600 = 28 800 g.<br>Now add the mass of the box. 28 800 + 200 = 30 000 g. |
| **Answer** | 30 000 g = 30 kg |

Sometimes an answer needs to be simplified, depending on the accuracy needed. You might need to **round off** your answer.

| | |
|---|---|
| **Example** | Class 8G laid pennies in a line for charity. The pennies added up to £55.51.<br>A penny is 2.05 cm wide. How long was the line of pennies? |
| **Working** | £55.51 = 5551 pence, so there were 5551 pennies.<br>5551 × 2.05 = 11 379.55 cm = 113.7955 m.<br>An answer to the nearest metre would be more useful. |
| **Answer** | 114 m (to the nearest metre) |

When you do capacity calculations, the same rules apply as with length, mass, area and volume:
- use a sensible size of unit for the answer
- round the answer if you have to.

| | | |
|---|---|---|
| **Example** | Jackie wants to share out a 1-litre bottle of lemonade fairly among herself and 6 friends. How much will they each get to drink? | |
| **Working** | There are 7 people.<br>1 litre ÷ 7 = 0.142 857 14 litre each<br>= 142.857 14 ml each. | *(Change to a better unit.)* |
| **Answer** | 143 ml (to the nearest ml) | *(Use a sensible accuracy.)* |

# Try It Out

**1** Work out the mass of each box when it is full of 2-cm dice each weighing 8 g.
  **(a)** size: 10 cm × 12 cm × 12 cm; mass: 100 g
  **(b)** size: 18 cm × 16 cm × 24 cm; mass: 150 g
  **(c)** size: 50 cm × 50 cm × 40 cm; mass: 1.2 kg
  **(d)** Box (c) is also used for jumbo dice. They are 5-cm cubes and have a mass of 110 g each. What is the mass of the box when it is full of jumbo dice?

**2 (a)** A penny is 2.05 cm wide. Work out the lengths of lines of pennies worth these amounts. Give your answers to the nearest metre.
     **(i)** £21        **(ii)** £32.50            **(iii)** £102.07
  **(b)** 5p coins are 1.75 cm wide. How long is a line of 5p coins worth £25.30?

**1** A fizzy drink can contains 330 ml.
  Samantha buys a 12-pack of cans at the supermarket.
  How much drink is there altogether, in litres?

**2** This ice-cube tray needs 300 ml
  of water to fill it.

  Approximately how much water is in
  each ice cube?

**3** Tim is making punch for a party.

  He uses two 70 cl bottles of grape juice, 1.5 litres of lemonade
  and 400 ml of fruit cordial.
  **(a)** How much punch does this make?
  **(b)** The glasses he uses to serve the punch hold 200 ml each. How many glasses can he fill? Is there any punch left over?

**4** Tim empties $2\frac{1}{2}$ trays of ice cubes into his punch.
  **(a)** How much extra volume do they add?
  **(b)** What is the total volume of the punch now?

## Practice

**(S)** **1** Skeletech construction sets use strips with holes in them. There is always a hole 1 cm from each end.
Here is a piece of Skeletech.

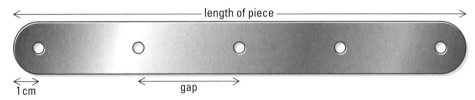

Work out the hole spacing on each of these pieces.

| Piece | A | B | C | D | E | F | G | H |
|---|---|---|---|---|---|---|---|---|
| Length (cm) | 6 | 8 | 10 | 16 | 20 | 26 | 30 | 42 |
| Holes | 2 | 2 | 3 | 3 | 4 | 4 | 5 | 6 |

**2** Each piece of Skeletech is made of metal. A 10-cm strip of the metal has a mass of 30 g. A half-circle end has a mass of 2 g. Every hole punched out reduces the mass by 0.5 g.

Follow the example below to work out the mass of pieces B to H from question 1.

---

**Example** Piece A

**Working** 1 cm of the strip has a mass of 3 g.
Piece A is 4 cm of straight strip plus 2 ends.
So before the holes are punched it has a mass of
$4 \times 3 + 2 \times 2 = 12 + 4 = 16$ g.
2 holes are punched. This reduces the mass by
$2 \times 0.5 = 1$ g.
$16 - 1 = 15$

**Answer** 15 g

---

**3** A boxed set of Skeletech contains these pieces:

| A | B | C | D | E | F | G | H |
|---|---|---|---|---|---|---|---|
| 10 | 10 | 8 | 5 | 5 | 3 | 2 | 1 |

There are also 40 connectors to join the pieces together. These have a mass of 5 g each. The box has a mass of 150 g. Work out the mass of the boxed set.

**4** Boxed sets of Skeletech are packed into cartons at the factory. Each carton has a mass of 500 g.

**Box of Skeletech**

5 cm →

50 cm          30 cm

**Carton**

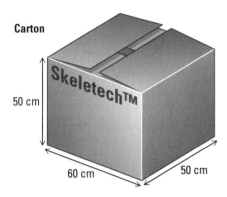

50 cm

60 cm          50 cm

**(a)** How many boxes fit into a carton?

**(b)** What is the mass of a fully packed carton?

**(c)** 36 cartons fit into a lorry. 18 cartons fit onto a pallet. A pallet has a mass of 8 kg. What mass is the lorry carrying when fully loaded?

**5 (a)** If all the pieces in a Skeletech set were laid end to end, how far would they stretch?

**(b)** If all the pieces in a lorry were laid end to end, how far would they stretch?

> **Finished Early?**
> ⇨ Go to page 408

## Further Practice

A4 graph paper (long side vertical)

**1** A hardware shop sells cable by the metre. These are the prices.

| Cable | Telephone | Mains | Speaker |
|---|---|---|---|
| Price per metre | 45p | 70p | £1.25 |

Draw a graph of length and price.

The horizontal axis should be labelled 'Length (m)' and have a scale of 2 cm to 1 m. The vertical axis should be labelled 'Price (£)' and have a scale of 2 cm to £1. Your graph should have three straight lines on it.

**2** The shop will also sell cable by weight.

| Cable | Telephone | Mains | Speaker |
|---|---|---|---|
| Price per kilogram | £18 | £7 | £25 |

Draw a graph of weight and price.

The horizontal axis should be labelled 'Weight (g)' and have a scale of 2 cm to 100 g. It should extend from 0 to 1000 g. The vertical axis should be labelled 'Price (£)' and have a scale of 1 cm to £1. It should extend from 0 to £20. Your graph should have three straight lines on it.

**3** Using your graphs from questions 1 and 2, or by calculating, work out what a metre of each cable weighs.

> **Finished Early?**
> ⇨ Go to page 408

# 20 Time

In this chapter you will learn about ...
1. time calculations
2. timetables
3. speed

## ① Time Calculations

### Remember?

Units of time work in a different way from other units. This is because there are 60 seconds in a minute, 60 minutes in an hour and 24 hours in a day. They are not just counted in tens, hundreds or thousands.
So 2 minutes and 45 seconds is **not** the same as 2.45 minutes!

### Learn About It

To add and subtract times, you can work in separate units.

| | |
|---|---|
| **Example** | Add 3 hours, 46 minutes and 32 seconds to 11 hours, 27 minutes and 51 seconds. |

**Working**

| *h* | *m* | *s* | |
|---|---|---|---|
| 3 | 46 | 32 | |
| 11 | 27 | 51 | |
| 14 | 73 | 83 | |

| 14 | 74 | 23 | Change 83 seconds into 1 minute and 23 seconds. |
|---|---|---|---|
| 15 | 14 | 23 | Change 74 minutes into 1 hour and 14 minutes. |

**Answer**    15 hours, 14 minutes and 23 seconds

Or you can change all the units to the smallest type in the question.

| | |
|---|---|
| **Example** | 3 hours 46 minutes 32 seconds + 11 hours 27 minutes 51 seconds |
| **Working** | 3 hours 46 minutes 32 seconds = $3 \times 3600 + 46 \times 60 + 32$ |
| | = 13 592 seconds |
| | 11 hours 27 minutes 51 seconds = $11 \times 3600 + 27 \times 60 + 51$ |
| | = 41 271 seconds |
| | 13 592 + 41 271 = 54 863 seconds |
| | 54 863 seconds ÷ 60 = 914 remainder 23 |
| | = 914 minutes 23 seconds |
| | 914 ÷ 60 = 15 remainder 14 = 15 hours 14 minutes |
| **Answer** | 15 hours 14 minutes 23 seconds |

## Try It Out

This table shows how the world record for the marathon race has changed in the past century.

| Year | Time (h:m:s) | Year | Time (h:m:s) |
|---|---|---|---|
| 1896 | 3:03:05 | 1958 | 2:15:17 |
| 1908 | 2:55:19 | 1969 | 2:08:34 |
| 1920 | 2:32:35 | 1981 | 2:08:18 |
| 1935 | 2:26:42 | 1988 | 2:06:50 |
| 1947 | 2:25:39 | 1998 | 2:06:05 |

**1** Between which years did the record change least?

**2** Between which years did the record change most?

**3** How much faster did the marathon become between 1896 and 1998?

**4** Frank ran the London marathon last year. His time was the same as the 1908 record and the 1920 record added together. What was his time?

**5** Copy the tables above, rounding all the times to the nearest minute.

## Learn More About It

Multiplying time can be done in separate units.

| | |
|---|---|
| **Example** | A machine takes 2 minutes and 35 seconds to make a toy boat. How long does it take to make 2 dozen boats? |
| **Working** | 2 dozen = $2 \times 12 = 24$ boats |
| | 2 minutes $\times 24 = 48$ minutes |
| | 35 seconds $\times 24 = 840$ seconds = 14 minutes exactly |
| | 48 minutes + 14 minutes = 62 minutes = 1 hour 2 minutes |
| **Answer** | 1 hour 2 minutes |

Dividing time has to be done by changing to the same unit.

| | |
|---|---|
| **Example** | A machine makes 100 boxes in 21 minutes and 40 seconds. How long does it take to make one box? |
| **Working** | 21 minutes 40 seconds = 21 × 60 + 40 = 1300 seconds<br>1300 seconds ÷ 100 = 13 seconds |
| **Answer** | 13 seconds |

## Try It Out

**B** **1** Javed's CD collection is very strange. All the tracks on each CD last exactly the same time. Work out how long each of these CDs last.

| Title | Track length (m:s) | Number of tracks |
|---|---|---|
| (It's) All the Same to Me | 9:15 | 8 |
| Spin Sector | 13:31 | 5 |
| Nice and Even Does It | 5:58 | 12 |
| Time and Time Again | 5:44 | 10 |
| Divided We Fall | 9:54 | 7 |

**2** Five pupils in 8H held a snail race. The prize went to the owner of the fastest snail.

Work out how long each snail took to cover 1 metre.

Write the names of the snails in order, from fastest to slowest.

| Name of snail | Distance covered | Time (h:m:s) |
|---|---|---|
| Lightning | 2 m | 0:15:12 |
| The Flash | 5 m | 0:38:15 |
| Linford | 12 m | 1:24:00 |
| Bluebird | 7 m | 0:51:06 |
| Turbo | 6 m | 0:38:30 |

# Practice

**1** These are the times taken by some women in a triathlon race.

| Name | Swim 1 km (m:s) | Cycle 35 km (h:m:s) | Run 10 km (h:m:s) | Total (h:m:s) |
|---|---|---|---|---|
| Jessica Fraser | 12:11 | 1:20:05 | 43:15 | |
| Kate O'Connor | 14:03 | 1:18:04 | 46:16 | |
| Ruth Coates | 15:34 | 1:06:17 | 48:57 | |
| Jane Harrison | 16:22 | 1:13:37 | 51:05 | |
| Jenn Powell | 16:49 | 1:25:26 | 55:51 | |
| Roxanne MacLaurin | 16:56 | 1:12:19 | 1:00:15 | |
| Jude d'Entremont | 17:38 | 1:04:09 | 52:49 | |
| Melanie Wallace | 21:33 | 1:38:29 | 1:00:41 | |

(a) Copy and complete the table. Write your working underneath.
(b) Write the names of the athletes in order of their total times, fastest to slowest.

**2** Roland estimates that he spends 55 minutes travelling to and from school each day. Last school year, he did this 193 times. How long did he spend travelling altogether? Write your answer in days, hours and minutes.

**3** Remember that to find the **mean** of a set of times, you add up all the times, then divide by the number of times.
(a) Yana travels a long way to visit her family. She records the lengths of six journeys:
2 h 12 m, 2 h 15 m, 1 h 48 m, 2 h 25 m, 4 h 4 m, 2 h 10 m.
Work out:
(i) the total length of her journeys
(ii) the mean length of her journeys.
(b) Five music students are going to play pieces at a concert. These are the lengths of the pieces:
7 m 15 s, 4 m 35 s, 5 m 21 s, 4 m, 8 m 44 s.
Work out:
(i) the total length of the pieces
(ii) the mean length of the pieces.

**Finished Early?**
Go to page 409

# Further Practice

**D** Here is a section from a TV guide.

| Channel 3 | | Channel 4 | |
|---|---|---|---|
| 6.00 | Local News | 6.00 | Animal Documentary |
| 6.25 | News and Weather | 7.00 | Channel 4 News |
| 7.00 | Emmerdale | 7.55 | Video Snapshot |
| 7.30 | Coronation Street | 8.00 | Brookside |
| 8.00 | The Big Match | 8.30 | The Film Show |
| 9.45 | *Drama:* Police Story | 9.00 | *Drama:* Paramedic! |
| 11.05 | Late News | 10.00 | Life in the City |
| 11.20 | Local News and Weather | 10.30 | *Film:* Romeo and Juliet |
| 11.25 | Athletics Highlights | 12.05 | Weather Watch |
| −1.15 | | −12.15 | |

**1** Write down how long each programme lasts.

**2** Cynthia has to go out, so she wants to record *Emmerdale*, *Coronation Street* and *Brookside*.
   **(a)** How long do these programmes last altogether?
   **(b)** Cynthia has a 180 minute tape. She has already recorded a film on it that lasts 1 hour and 40 minutes. Can she fit the soaps onto it?
   **(c)** If the answer to **(b)** was **yes**, how much spare tape is there?
   If the answer was **no**, how much of *Brookside* will she miss?

**3** Jake wants to record *Police Story* and *Romeo and Juliet*. By how much do these programmes overlap?

> **Finished Early?**
> ➡ Go to page 409

---

**P ❷ Timetables**

> ## Remember?
> Times are written using either the 12-hour or the 24-hour clock.
>
> | 12-hour clock | 9am | 12 noon | 2pm | 11pm | 12 midnight |
> |---|---|---|---|---|---|
> | 24-hour clock | 09:00 | 12:00 | 14:00 | 23:00 | 00:00 |

# Learn About It

A **timetable** is used when a lot of time information has to be shown. This is a bus timetable.

| LINCOLN-SWANPOOL-BIRCHWOOD | | | | | | | | *Service 99* |
|---|---|---|---|---|---|---|---|---|
| **Monday to Saturday only** | | | | | | | | |
| | S | NS | | | | | | S |
| Lincoln City Bus Station | 0715 | 0745 | | :45 | | 1945 | 2015 |
| The Junction | — | 0755 | then | :55 | | 1955 | — |
| Swanpool Almond Avenue | 0730 | 0800 | at | :00 | | 2000 | 2030 |
| Birchwood The Wildlife Inn | 0732 | 0802 | these | :02 | | 2002 | 2032 |
| Birchwood The Neighbourhood Centre | 0740 | 0810 | minutes | :10 | until | 2010 | 2040 |
| Birchwood The Wildlife Inn | 0742 | 0812 | past | :12 | | 2012 | 2042 |
| Swanpool Almond Avenue | 0745 | 0815 | each | :15 | | 2015 | 2045 |
| The Junction | 0750 | 0820 | hour | :20 | | 2020 | 2050 |
| LINCOLN City Bus Station | 0800 | 0830 | | :30 | | 2030 | 2100 |
| NOTES | | | | | | | | |
| S – Saturday only | | | | | | | | |
| NS – Not Saturday | | | | | | | | |

The first bus sets off from Lincoln Bus Station at 0715, but the **S** at the top means that this bus only runs on Saturdays. If you want the first bus on a weekday, you need the **NS** column.

The buses run every hour. There is not a column for every bus. Instead you can see how many minutes past each hour the buses stop at different places. So buses will leave Lincoln at 0845, 0945, 1045, etc.

Suppose you catch the bus at the Neighbourhood Centre. You want to be in Lincoln at 11 o'clock. The buses arrive in Lincoln at half past each hour, so you would need to catch the bus that arrives at 1030. This leaves the Neighbourhood Centre at 1010.

# Try It Out

Answer these questions using the bus timetable above.

1  What time does the first bus on a Monday stop at the Wildlife Inn?

2  How long does it take to travel from the Neighbourhood Centre to the Junction?

3  Jessica is shopping in Lincoln on Saturday. She wants to be back at the Neighbourhood Centre by six o'clock. Which bus should she catch from the Bus Station?

4  Pete arrives at Almond Avenue bus stop at 8.55am. How long does he have to wait for the Lincoln bus?

5  Ryan is meeting someone at the Wildlife Inn at 6.15pm on Saturday. He gets to the Bus Station at 5.50. How late will he be?

# Practice

**F** Below are parts of a train timetable. Use them to answer the questions that follow.

## North East England and Scotland to London

### Mondays to Fridays

| | ✕ | | ✕ | ✕ | ✕ | | ✕ | ✕ | ✕ |
|---|---|---|---|---|---|---|---|---|---|
| Aberdeen | | | | 0508e | | 0650e | 0755 | | |
| Dundee | | | 0616e | 0639e | 0720e | 0805e | 0906 | | |
| Edinburgh | 0700 | | 0800 | 0900 | 0930 | 1000 | 1031 | 1100 | 1130 |
| Berwick-on-Tweed | 0739 | | | 0945 | 1010 | 1039 | | 1141 | |
| Newcastle | 0828 | 0900 | 0928 | 1032 | 1056 | 1126 | 1157 | 1231 | 1255 |
| Darlington | 0902 | 0930 | 0955 | 1103 | 1123 | 1157 | | 1305 | |
| York | 0932 | 1001 | 1026 | 1131 | 1151 | 1229 | 1248 | 1333 | 1346 |
| Doncaster | 0958 | 1026 | 1053 | 1158 | | 1254 | | 1400 | |
| Peterborough | 1050 | 1112 | 1230o | | 1256 | 1344 | 1401 | 1446 | 1456 |
| London King's Cross | 1145 | 1211 | 1235 | 1336 | 1350 | 1443 | 1458 | 1543 | 1554 |

NOTES:  e change at Edinburgh   ✕ restaurant service
o change at Doncaster

## London to North East England and Scotland

### Mondays to Fridays

| | ✕ | ✕ | ✕ | ✕ FX | ✕ FO | ✕ | ✕ | | |
|---|---|---|---|---|---|---|---|---|---|
| London King's Cross | 1700 | 1730 | 1800 | 1820 | 1820 | 1830 | 1900 | 2000 | 2200 |
| Peterborough | | 1814 | | 1906 | 1906 | 1919 | 1944 | 2044 | 2259 |
| Doncaster | | | 1930 | | | 2017 | 2032 | 2132 | 2355 |
| York | 1847 | 1926 | 1956 | 2017 | 2017 | 2042 | 2057 | 2157 | 0020 |
| Darlington | 1914 | 1954 | 2024 | 2049 | 2049 | 2110 | 2125 | 2230 | 0048 |
| Newcastle | 1946 | 2029 | 2055 | 2126 | 2126 | 2147 | 2200 | 2310 | 0139 |
| Berwick-on-Tweed | | 2124 | 2140 | | 2212 | | 2251 | | |
| Edinburgh | 2114 | 2214 | 2223 | | 2300 | | 2337 | | |
| Dundee | 2254e | 0004e | | | 0038e | | | | |
| Aberdeen | 0018e | | | | | | | | |

NOTES:   e change at Edinburgh   ✕ restaurant service   FX not Fridays
FO Fridays only

**1** What time does the 0900 from Newcastle arrive in London?

**2** Adam is travelling from Newcastle. He wants to be in Peterborough by 11.30am. He wants to have his breakfast on the train. Which train should he catch?

**3** How long does the 1800 from King's Cross take to reach Darlington?

**4** Scott lives in Dundee. He needs to be in London by 2pm. Which train should he catch?

**5** How many stations does the 1100 from Edinburgh stop at before it reaches King's Cross?

**6** Duncan needs to get home to Aberdeen from London. What is the latest train he can catch?

**7** What is different about the 1820 train from King's Cross on Fridays?

**8** Siobhan needs to get home to Dundee from York on a Tuesday. What is the latest train she can catch?

**Finished Early?**
➡ Go to page 410

# Further Practice

Here is part of a train timetable. Use it to answer the questions that follow.

**North-West England to The Midlands and East Anglia**

**Saturdays**

| | ✗ | ✗ | | ✗ | ✗ | ✗ | | | |
|---|---|---|---|---|---|---|---|---|---|
| Liverpool Lime Street | 1352 | 1452 | 1552 | 1652 | 1752 | 1852 | 1952 | 2052 | |
| Warrington Central | 1418 | 1518 | 1618 | 1718 | 1818 | 1918 | 2018 | 2118 | |
| Manchester Piccadilly | 1443 | 1543 | 1643 | 1743 | 1843 | 1943 | 2043 | 2145 | 2228 |
| Stockport | 1453 | 1553 | 1653 | 1753 | 1853 | 1953 | 2053 | 2155 | 2238 |
| Sheffield | 1540 | 1638 | 1747 | 1840 | 1940 | 2038 | 2140 | 2238 | 2340 |
| Chesterfield | 1554 | 1654 | 1801 | 1854 | 1954 | 2053 | 2154 | 2302 | 0002 |
| Nottingham | 1625 | 1733 | 1840 | 1926 | 2041 | 2130 | 2229 | 2344 | 0042 |
| Grantham | — | 1813 | — | — | 2112 | — | — | — | — |
| Peterborough | — | 1852 | 2001 | — | 2143 | — | — | — | — |
| Ely | — | 1925 | 2033 | — | 2231 | — | — | — | — |
| Thetford | — | 1952 | 2100 | — | 2251 | — | — | — | — |
| Norwich | — | 2026 | 2129 | — | 2326 | — | — | — | — |

NOTES: ✗ food trolley service

**1 (a)** What time does the 1352 from Liverpool arrive at Chesterfield?
**(b)** How long does that journey take?

**2** Vandra is in Stockport. She wants to be home in Ely before 10pm. Which train should she catch?

**3** Mel is in Grantham. She needs to arrive in Norwich before 10pm. Which train should she catch?

**4** John just misses the 2145 at Manchester. How long does he have to wait for the next train?

**5** Sanjay gets on the 1840 train at Sheffield. He is travelling to Peterborough.
**(a)** What mistake has he made?
**(b)** How long must he wait for the next train?
**(c)** How long does his journey take altogether?

**6** Alyssa travels on the 1418 from Warrington to Nottingham. While in Nottingham she loses her timetable. She remembers that the train home leaves at 2035. It takes the same time as her first journey. What time will she get back to Warrington?

**7** The train company decides that the last train will start at Liverpool instead of Manchester. Work out the times that will go in the two blank spaces on the timetable.

**Finished Early?**
Go to page 410

# T ③ Speed

## Learn About It

When things move, they have **speed**.

Speed is measured in units such as **kilometres per hour** (km/h) or **metres per second** (m/s).

To work out the speed of something, you need to know the **distance** travelled and the **time** taken.

You can only work out the **average** speed. Things rarely travel at the same speed all the time.

| | |
|---|---|
| **Example** | A car travels 20 km in 30 minutes. What is its average speed in kilometres per hour? |
| **Working** | Distance = 20 km, time = 30 minutes or $\frac{1}{2}$ hour. So the car would travel twice as far in 1 hour: 40 km. |
| **Answer** | 40 km/h |

Sometimes you need to change units to get the answer.

### Word Check

speed  how fast something moves

## Try It Out

**H** Work out the average speeds, in km/h for these journeys.

**1** 50 km in 1 hour

**2** 80 km in 2 hours

**3** 12 km in $\frac{1}{2}$ hour

**4** 900 km in 10 hours

**5** 60 km in $1\frac{1}{2}$ hours

**6** 5000 km in 8 hours

**7** 990 000 km in 24 hours

**8** 1 km in $\frac{1}{4}$ hour

**I** These journey times are measured in mixed units. Work out the average speeds in km/h.

**1** 1 km in 1 minute

**2** 50 km in 20 minutes

**3** 20 m in 1 second

**4** 2 km in 1 second

**5** 400 m in 5 seconds

**6** 0.8 km in 2 minutes

**7** 15 cm in $\frac{1}{10}$ second

**8** 1 m in 12 seconds

## Learn More About It

Distance, time and speed are all connected. If you know two of them, you can always work out the other one.

Using $d$ for distance, $s$ for speed and $t$ for time, you can write these using algebra:

$$s = \frac{d}{t}, \quad t = \frac{d}{s}, \quad d = st$$

**Key Fact**

Speed = distance ÷ time.

Time = distance ÷ speed.

Distance = speed × time.

You can remember this using the **distance–speed–time** triangle.

To use it, cover up the letter you want to work out. The other two will give the right formula.

This example shows $t = \frac{d}{s}$ .

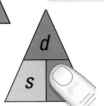

You have to make sure the units match. It is no good dividing kilometres by metres per second. Change units before you work out the answer.

| | |
|---|---|
| **Example** | A car travels at 45 km/h for 12 minutes. How far does it travel? |
| **Working** | 12 minutes is $\frac{12}{60}$ hour $= \frac{1}{5}$ hour. |
| | $d = st$ |
| | $= 45 \times \frac{1}{5} = 45 \div 5 = 9$ km |
| **Answer** | 9 km |

## Try It Out

Work out the distance covered if you travel at:

**1** 20 km/h for 4 hours

**2** 15 m/s for 30 seconds

**3** 180 km/h for $1\frac{1}{2}$ hours

**4** 30 km/s for 2 minutes

**5** 12 m/s for 1 hour

**6** 90 km/h for 1 minute

**7** 100 m/s for 18 minutes

**8** 36 000 km/h for 20 seconds.

Work out the time taken to travel:

**1** 100 km at 25 km/h

**2** 300 km at 60 km/h

**3** 250 m at 12.5 m/s

**4** 180 m at 36 m/s

**5** 12 km at 30 km/h

**6** 3 km at 20 m/s

**7** 50 m at 18 km/h

**8** 120 m at 30 km/h.

# Practice

**1** This diagram shows a train journey.

Allerton ——— 100 km/h ——— Benston ——— 80 km/h ——— Clipham ——— 120 km/h ——— Dransfield
75 km          stop: 5 min    30 min     stop: 10 min    80 km

(a) How long did it take to travel from Allerton to Benston?
(b) How far is it from Benston to Clipham?
(c) How long did it take to travel from Clipham to Dransfield?
(d) How far is it from Allerton to Dransfield?
(e) How long did the whole journey take?
(f) The train left Allerton at 1432. What time did it arrive in Dransfield?
(g) What was the average speed for the whole journey?

**2** Molly's journey to work is shown in this table.

| Stage of journey | Distance (km) | Time taken (minutes) | Average speed (km/h) |
|---|---|---|---|
| Drive children to school | 5 | 10 | |
| Park and drop off children | 0 | 5 | |
| School to motorway | 4 | 6 | |
| Motorway to office | 15 | 10 | |
| Whole journey | | | |

Copy and complete the table.

**3** Work out the time spent in the air by each of the following objects.

Arrow
Speed: 40 m/s
Distance: 60 m

Tennis ball
Speed: 180 km/h
Distance: 20 m

Javelin throw
Speed: 12.5 m/s
Distance: 80 m

Bullet
Speed: 250 m/s
Distance: 2 km

Missile
Speed: 3000 km/h
Distance: 600 km

**Finished Early?**
➡ Go to page 410

NUMBER SKILLS Calculate with numbers of any size,
convert length and time units

# Further Practice

This is part of the Central Line on the London Underground.

The numbers show the distances between the stations, in metres.

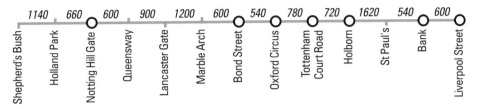

The average speed of a tube train between stations is 10 m/s.

**1** Work out how long it takes to travel between each station and the next.

| | |
|---|---|
| **Example** | Liverpool Street to Bank. |
| **Working** | Distance = 600 m. Average speed = 10 m/s. |
| | Time = distance ÷ speed |
| | = 600 ÷ 10 |
| | = 60 s. |
| **Answer** | 1 minute |

**2** Suppose the trains wait in each station for exactly one minute. At any station, the departure time is always 1 minute after the arrival time.

A train leaves Liverpool Street at exactly 0846. Copy and complete the timetable for this train.

| Station | Arrive | Depart | Travel time |
|---|---|---|---|
| Liverpool Street | | 0846 | 1 min |
| Bank | 0847 | 0848 | |
| St Paul's | | | |
| | | | |
| Shepherd's Bush | | | |

**3** How far is it from Liverpool Street to Shepherd's Bush?

**4** How long does it take to travel from Liverpool Street to Shepherd's Bush?

**5** What is the average speed for the whole journey including the stops?

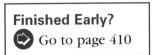

**Finished Early?**
➡ Go to page 410

# Unit 10 *Measures*

## Summary of Chapters 19 and 20

### Length, Mass and Capacity

- 100 **centimetres** (cm) = 1 m    1000 **millimetres** (mm) = 1 m
  10 mm = 1 cm    1 **kilometre** (km) = 1000 m
- **Weight** is measured in units of **mass**.
  1 **kilogram** (kg) = 1000 g    1000 kg = 1 **tonne** (t)
- Volume of liquid is called **capacity**.
  100 cl = 1 *l*    1000 ml = 1 *l*    10 ml = 1 cl
- To change from one unit to another:
  **1** Work out how many of the smaller units make the bigger unit.
  **2** If you are changing to **smaller** units, **multiply**.
    If you are changing to **bigger** units, **divide**.
- The **accuracy** of a measurement tells you the range of values it could have.
  If $x$ = 5 cm to the nearest centimetre, then 4.5 cm $\leqslant x <$ 5.5 cm. 4.5 cm is
  the **lower bound** and 5.5 cm is the **upper bound**.
  If $x$ = 5 cm to 1 d.p., then 4.95 cm $\leqslant x <$ 5.05 cm.
  These ranges of values affect the results of calculations.

### Time

- Times are written using a 12-hour or 24-hour clock.

| 12-hour | 2am | 8.30am | 12 noon | 4pm | 7.30pm | 10pm | 12 midnight |
|---------|-----|--------|---------|-----|--------|------|-------------|
| 24-hour | 02:00 | 08:30 | 12:00 | 16:00 | 19:30 | 22:00 | 00:00 |

- To add and subtract times, work in separate units or change all the units to the same type.
- You can organise information about time in a **timetable**.
- Speed is measured in units such as **kilometres per hour** (km/h) or **metres per second** (m/s).
- You can remember the rules for speed calculations using the **distance–speed–time triangle**.
  Speed = distance ÷ time
  Time = distance ÷ speed
  Distance = speed × time

# Brush Up Your Number 11

## ● Equivalent Fractions

### Learn About It

These are **equivalent fractions**.

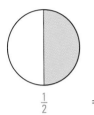 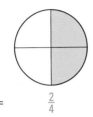 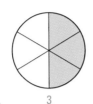 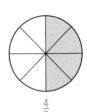 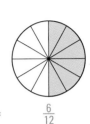

$$\frac{1}{2} \quad = \quad \frac{2}{4} \quad = \quad \frac{3}{6} \quad = \quad \frac{4}{8} \quad = \quad \frac{6}{12}$$

You can make an equivalent fraction for any fraction. Multiply its numerator and denominator by the same number.

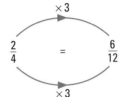

$$\times 3$$
$$\frac{2}{4} = \frac{6}{12}$$
$$\times 3$$

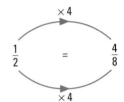

$$\times 4$$
$$\frac{1}{2} = \frac{4}{8}$$
$$\times 4$$

You can make equivalent fractions by dividing too. This is called **cancelling**.

When you cannot divide any further, the fraction is in its **lowest terms**.

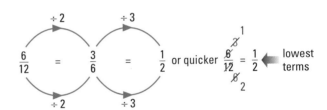

$$\div 2 \qquad \div 3$$
$$\frac{6}{12} = \frac{3}{6} = \frac{1}{2} \quad \text{or quicker} \quad \frac{\cancel{6}^{1}}{\cancel{12}_{2}} = \frac{1}{2} \quad \Leftarrow \quad \text{lowest terms}$$
$$\div 2 \qquad \div 3$$

### Try It Out

**1** Write down three fractions equivalent to each of these.

(a) $\frac{3}{4}$     (b) $\frac{2}{5}$     (c) $\frac{4}{7}$     (d) $\frac{1}{6}$     (e) $\frac{3}{8}$

**2** Fill in the missing numbers.

(a) $\frac{2}{3} = \frac{?}{6}$   $\frac{2}{3} = \frac{8}{?}$   $\frac{2}{3} = \frac{?}{15}$   $\frac{2}{3} = \frac{20}{?}$

(b) $\frac{3}{5} = \frac{?}{10}$   $\frac{3}{5} = \frac{15}{?}$   $\frac{3}{5} = \frac{?}{35}$

(c) $\frac{1}{6} = \frac{?}{12} = \frac{4}{?} = \frac{?}{30} = \frac{8}{?} = \frac{?}{60} = \frac{100}{?}$

**3** Cancel these fractions to their lowest terms, by dividing the numerator and denominator by the same number.

(a) $\frac{6}{8}$     (b) $\frac{8}{24}$     (c) $\frac{50}{80}$     (d) $\frac{20}{36}$     (e) $\frac{16}{22}$

(f) $\frac{36}{50}$     (g) $\frac{42}{60}$     (h) $\frac{36}{96}$     (i) $\frac{84}{100}$     (j) $\frac{350}{1000}$

# Learn More About It

2 wholes and 3 quarters

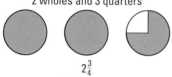

$2\frac{3}{4}$
mixed number

$=$

11 quarters

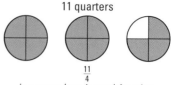

$=$

$\frac{11}{4}$
improper (top-heavy) fraction

| **Example** | Change $2\frac{3}{4}$ to an improper fraction. |
| --- | --- |
| **Working** | 2 wholes = 2 × 4 = 8 quarters 8 + 3 = 11 quarters altogether |
| **Answer** | $\frac{11}{4}$ |

| **Example** | Change $\frac{11}{4}$ to a mixed number. |
| --- | --- |
| **Working** | 4 quarters make one whole. 11 ÷ 4 = 2 remainder 3 |
| **Answer** | $2\frac{3}{4}$ |

## Try It Out

**B** **1** Convert these mixed numbers to improper fractions.

(a) $2\frac{1}{5}$      (b) $1\frac{5}{6}$      (c) $7\frac{1}{4}$      (d) $4\frac{2}{3}$

**2** Convert these improper fractions to mixed numbers.

(a) $\frac{11}{2}$      (b) $\frac{27}{4}$      (c) $\frac{19}{6}$      (d) $\frac{40}{9}$

## Practice

**C** **1** Fill in the missing numbers.

(a) $\frac{7}{10} = \frac{?}{30} = \frac{14}{?} = \frac{?}{70} = \frac{70}{?} = \frac{?}{200}$      (b) $\frac{4}{6} = \frac{?}{18} = \frac{12}{?} = \frac{?}{30} = \frac{60}{?} = \frac{?}{6000}$

(c) $\frac{5}{8} = \frac{?}{16} = \frac{30}{?} = \frac{?}{40} = \frac{40}{?} = \frac{?}{200}$      (d) $\frac{3}{20} = \frac{6}{?} = \frac{?}{100} = \frac{30}{?} = \frac{?}{240} = \frac{240}{?}$

(e) $\frac{11}{12} = \frac{?}{36} = \frac{55}{?} = \frac{?}{120} = \frac{99}{?} = \frac{?}{96}$      (f) $3 = \frac{3}{?} = \frac{?}{2} = \frac{15}{?} = \frac{?}{20} = \frac{300}{?}$

**2** Cancel these improper fractions to their lowest terms. Then convert them to mixed numbers.

(a) $\frac{18}{4}$    (b) $\frac{15}{9}$    (c) $\frac{26}{6}$    (d) $\frac{45}{20}$    (e) $\frac{48}{10}$

(f) $\frac{32}{24}$    (g) $\frac{100}{45}$    (h) $\frac{420}{200}$    (i) $\frac{24}{6}$    (j) $\frac{70}{25}$

**3** Convert these mixed numbers to improper fractions.

(a) $1\frac{2}{5}$    (b) $2\frac{3}{4}$    (c) $5\frac{1}{3}$    (d) $8\frac{1}{2}$    (e) $2\frac{4}{7}$

(f) $5\frac{3}{5}$    (g) $3\frac{9}{10}$    (h) $2\frac{7}{15}$    (i) $7\frac{51}{100}$    (j) $3\frac{333}{1000}$

> **Finished Early?**
> ⇨ Go to page 411

# 21 Ratio and Proportion

In this chapter you will learn about …
1. ratios
2. using ratios
3. proportional quantities

## Ratios

### Remember?

Convert units using this list of measurements.

| | | |
|---|---|---|
| 1 km = 1000 m | 1 t = 1000 kg | 1 hour = 60 minutes |
| 1 m = 100 cm | 1 kg = 1000 g | 1 minute = 60 seconds |
| 1 cm = 10 mm | | |

## Try It Out

Convert these units.

**1** 3 m to cm
**2** 2 kg to g
**3** 7 km to m
**4** 9 t to kg
**5** 2 cm to mm
**6** 3 hours to minutes
**7** $3\frac{1}{2}$ kg to g
**8** $2\frac{1}{4}$ m to cm
**9** 5.2 km to m
**10** 7.5 cm to mm
**11** 0.3 t to kg
**12** $5\frac{1}{2}$ minutes to seconds

# Learn About It

Anthea and Marcus divided this liquorice rope into four equal parts.

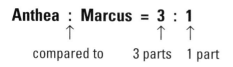

Anthea
has 3 parts

Marcus
has 1 part

Anthea had 3 parts and Marcus had 1 part. In maths, you compare two
**quantities** using a **ratio**. This is like a fraction but instead of writing one
number above the other you use a colon (:) like this:

**Anthea : Marcus = 3 : 1**

compared to    3 parts   1 part

Anthea divided an identical liquorice
rope into eight equal parts.

### Word Check

**quantity** amount

**ratio** a comparison of two or
more quantities

**equivalent ratios** ratios that
mean the same thing

Anthea
has 6 parts

Marcus
has 2 parts

This time, their ratio is:

**Anthea : Marcus = 6 : 2**

Marcus said, 'We've got the same lengths as before!'

The ratios 3:1 and 6:2 mean the same thing. They are **equivalent ratios**.
3:1 = 6:2

If you multiply both numbers in a ratio
by another number, you get an equivalent
ratio, just like equivalent fractions.

You can **cancel** ratios just like fractions too.

$\cancel{12}^{3} : \cancel{4}^{1} = 3 : 1$

$\times 2$

$3{:}1 = 6{:}2$   $3{:}1 = 9{:}3$   $3{:}1 = 12{:}4$

$\div 2$

$6{:}2 = 3{:}1$   $9{:}3 = 3{:}1$   $12{:}4 = 3{:}1$

Anthea, Marcus and Sohal are sharing 20 cm of liquorice rope.

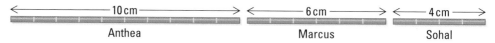

|←————— 10 cm —————→|←——— 6 cm ———→|←— 4 cm —→|

Anthea        Marcus        Sohal

The ratio of their pieces is:

|   | **Anthea** | : | **Marcus** | : | **Sohal** |
|---|---|---|---|---|---|
| = | 10 cm | : | 6 cm | : | 4 cm |
| = | 10 | : | 6 | : | 4 |
| = | 5 | : | 3 | : | 2 |

Because the units are all
the same, you can leave
them out.

Cancel to lowest terms.

## Try It Out

**1** Fill in the missing numbers.

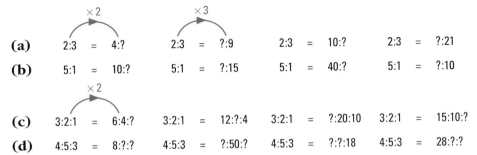

**(a)** 2:3 = 4:?     2:3 = ?:9     2:3 = 10:?     2:3 = ?:21

**(b)** 5:1 = 10:?     5:1 = ?:15     5:1 = 40:?     5:1 = ?:10

**(c)** 3:2:1 = 6:4:?     3:2:1 = 12:?:4     3:2:1 = ?:20:10     3:2:1 = 15:10:?

**(d)** 4:5:3 = 8:?:?     4:5:3 = ?:50:?     4:5:3 = ?:?:18     4:5:3 = 28:?:?

**2** Cancel these ratios to their lowest terms.

(a) 8 g:6 g        (b) 12 cm:9 cm
(c) 30 m:12 m      (d) 6 kg:16 kg
(e) 24 mm:20 mm   (f) 21 minutes:35 minutes
(g) 12 m:8 m:2 m    (h) 15 g:6 g:21 g
(i) 20 t:35 t:50 t      (j) 200 mm:150 mm:60 mm

### Word Check

**cancel** divide the numbers of a ratio or fraction by the same number to
    make them smaller

**lowest terms** having no common factor (other than 1) that could be used
    to cancel

## Learn More About It

The ratio 3:1 shows that Anthea's
liquorice is 3 times Marcus's liquorice.
The length of Anthea's liquorice
= 3 × the length of Marcus's liquorice.

Anthea has 3 parts     Marcus has 1 part

So ratios in the form $n$:1 (where $n$ is any number) are very useful.
You can change any ratio number
to 1 by dividing.

— 9 cm —    — 4 cm —
Darren     Wendy

Darren: Wendy = 9 cm:4 cm
Wendy has the smaller piece.

$$= 9:4$$
$$= \frac{9}{4}:\frac{4}{4}$$      Divide both numbers by 4 to change Wendy's
$$= 2\frac{1}{4}:1$$      number to 1.

Darren's liquorice is $2\frac{1}{4}$ times the length of Wendy's.

## Try It Out

**1** Change the red number in each ratio to 1 by dividing each side, then write each ratio using fractions.

(a) 20:5          (b) 3:15          (c) 6:9
(d) 10:4          (e) 20:15         (f) 4:11
(g) 8:5           (h) 25:120        (i) 1000:20
(j) 20:10:5       (k) 36:20:16

**2** Write your answers to question 1 using decimals.

**3** (a) Write down the ratio Jeremy:Ming.
(b) By dividing both sides, change the ratio number for Ming to 1.
(c) What does your ratio tell you?

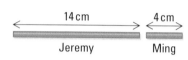

14 cm          4 cm
Jeremy         Ming

## Practice

In each ratio below, change the quantities to the same units. Cancel the ratios to their lowest terms.

> ### Key Fact
> Convert quantities to the same units before working with ratios.

| **Example** | 2.6 kg:400 g | |
|---|---|---|
| **Working** | 2.6 kg = 2.6 × 1000 g = 2600 g | |
| | So 2.6 kg:400 g = 2600 g:400 g | *(Make the units the same.)* |
| | = 2600:400 | *(Now you can drop the units.)* |
| | = 13:2 | *(Cancel to lowest terms.)* |
| **Answer** | 13:2 | |

**1** 2 m:40 cm

**2** 15 mm:5 cm

**3** 4 minutes:50 seconds

**4** 7 t:450 kg

**5** 275 m:5 km

**6** 1.6 km:500 m

**7** 350 g:1.4 kg

**8** 0.6 m:25 cm

**9** $1\frac{3}{4}$ hours:24 minutes

**10** 25 cm:0.8 m:50 cm

**11** 0.05 kg:300 g:0.15 kg

**12** 10 cm:40 mm:2 m

**13** 1.8 m:120 mm:48 cm

**14** 250 ml:70 cl:1.5 *l*

Compare the family size pack of each product to the standard size using ratios.

| Example | Family size |
|---|---|
| | Corn flakes 300g |
| | Standard size |
| | Corn flakes 125g |
| **Working** | Family: Standard |
| | = 300 g:125 g |
| | = 300:125 |
| | = $\frac{305}{125}:\frac{125}{125}$ |
| | = 2.4:1 |
| **Answer** | 2.4:1 |

| | | Family size | Standard size |
|---|---|---|---|
| 1 | TISSUES | 225 | 125 |
| 2 | | 600 g | 400 g |
| 3 | ORANGE | 150 cl | 60 cl |
| 4 | BUTTER | 800 g | 250 g |
| 5 | SUGAR | 0.2 kg | 500 g |
| 6 | | 2.5 m | 80 cm |

**Finished Early?**
➡ Go to page 411

## Further Practice

Change the following ratios to equivalent ratios with whole numbers.

| Example | 0.5: 0.4 |
|---|---|
| **Working** | 0.5 × 10: 0.4 × 10 |
| | = 5: 4 |
| **Answer** | 5:4 |

| Example | $\frac{3}{4}:\frac{1}{5}$ |
|---|---|
| **Working** | Lowest common denominator is 20. |
| | $\frac{3}{4} \times 20 : \frac{1}{5} \times 20$ |
| | = 15:4 |
| **Answer** | 15: 4 |

**1** 0.8:0 .6    **2** 2.5:2    **3** 0.2:1    **4** 3.2:1.2    **5** 0.3:2:0.7

**6** $\frac{1}{4}:3$    **7** $\frac{2}{5}:\frac{3}{5}$    **8** $\frac{3}{10}:\frac{7}{20}$    **9** $2\frac{1}{3}:5$    **10** $1\frac{1}{2}:2\frac{1}{2}:3$

Compare the sale price of each of these products to the usual price using ratios.

| Example | Usual price £8 Sale price £12 |
|---|---|
| **Working** | Sale price: Usual price |
| | = £8:£12 |
| | = 8:12 |
| | = $\frac{8}{12}:\frac{12}{12}$ |
| | = $\frac{2}{3}:1$ |
| **Answer** | $\frac{2}{3}:1$ |

| | | Sale price | Usual price |
|---|---|---|---|
| 1 | | £9 | £15 |
| 2 | | 24p | 30p |
| 3 | | £35 | £40 |
| 4 | | £4.80 | £6 |
| 5 | | 75p | £1.25 |
| 6 | | £240 | £280 |

**Finished Early?**
➡ Go to page 411

# T ❷ Using Ratios

## Learn About It

Emily is a cook. She writes all her recipes using ratios.

Chocolate Cream is made of 2 parts sugar, 5 parts cream and 3 parts cocoa.

That's 2 + 5 + 3 = 10 parts altogether.

Emily is making 400 g of Chocolate Cream. She needs to work out how much sugar, cream and cocoa to use.

First she finds how much 1 part is:
10 parts = 400 g
1 part = 400 g ÷ 10 = 40 g

Now she can find the amounts to use:
Sugar = 2 parts = 2 × 40 g = 80 g
Cream = 5 parts = 5 × 40 g = 200 g
Cocoa = 3 parts = 3 × 40 g = 120 g

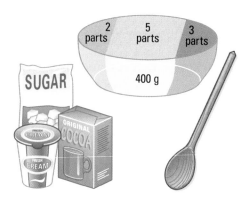

Chocolate cream
sugar : cream : cocoa
2 : 5 : 3

2 parts  5 parts  3 parts
400 g

SUGAR

Emily has 45 g of cocoa left in the packet to make more Chocolate Cream. She has lots of sugar and cream left. Cocoa is 3 parts of the recipe.

3 parts = 45 g
1 part = 15 g

Now she can work out how much sugar and cream to use.
Sugar = 2 parts = 2 × 15 g = 30 g
Cream = 5 parts = 5 × 15 g = 75 g

She has enough ingredients to make 45 g + 30 g + 75 g = 150 g more Chocolate Cream.

## Try It Out

**H** **1** Find the quantity of each ingredient needed for each recipe.

(a) 400 g of Fish Cakes
(b) 750 g of Bean Burgers
(c) 96 g of Nut Crunch

**2** The following quantities are left over. Find how much of each recipe can be made if there is plenty of the other ingredients left.

(a) 90 g of fish      (b) 100 g of onion      (c) 54 g of butter

Fish Cakes
fish : potato : flour
3 : 4 : 1

Nut Crunch
nuts : oats : butter
5 : 4 : 3

Bean Burgers
beans : onion : breadcrumbs
8 : 2 : 5

# Practice

**1** Danielle mixes together aromatherapy oils to make perfume. She writes the recipe on the bottle. Calculate the amount of each type of oil in each bottle.

**2** How much perfume would each of these bottles contain?

(a) A bottle of Sunrise that contains 15 ml of grapefruit oil.

(b) A bottle of Heaven that contains 27 ml of eucalyptus oil.

(c) A bottle of Champagne that contains 45 ml of orange oil.

(d) A bottle of Blue Stone that contains 10 ml of rosemary oil.

**3** (a) How much fennel oil does a bottle of Pandora have if it contains 5 ml of rosemary?

(b) How much geranium oil does a bottle of Attraction have if it contains 30 ml of lemon?

| **Finished Early?** |
| --- |
| ➡ Go to page 412 |

Go to page 412

# Further Practice

**1** Calculate the amounts these children pay if the cost is divided **in proportion** to their ages.

| **Example** | Fatima (7), Malcolm (8) and Calvin (10) buy a £12 computer game. |
| --- | --- |
| **Working** | Divide £12 in the ratio of their ages 7:8:10. <br> 7 + 8 + 10 = 25 parts <br> So 25 parts = £12 <br> So 1 part = £12 ÷ 25 = £0.48 |
| **Answer** | Fatima pays 7 parts = 7 × £0.48 = £3.36 <br> Malcolm pays 8 parts = 8 × £0.48 = £3.84 <br> Calvin pays 10 parts = 10 × £0.48 = £4.80 |

(a) Paul (9) and Sarah (11) buy a £30 personal stereo.

(b) Angus (7) and Marion (8) buy a magician's set for £12.

(c) Roy (10) and Alam (15) buy table tennis bats for £10.

(d) Umar (8) and Elma (10) buy a quiz book for £5.40.

(e) Sharon (11), Jes (12) and Steve (9) buy a giant bar of chocolate for £4.80.

**2** The same children as in question 1 buy some more items, dividing the cost in proportion to their ages. Answer these questions.

**(a)** Paul (9) pays 27p towards a blank cassette tape. How much does Sarah (11) pay?

**(b)** Marion (8) pays £1.20 towards a magician's hat. How much does Angus (7) pay?

**(c)** Roy (10) pays 80p towards table tennis balls. How much does Alam (15) pay?

**(d)** Elma (10) pays 30p towards a pen. How much does Umar (8) pay?

**(e)** Jes (12) pays 60p towards a bag of balloons. How much do Sharon (11) and Steve (9) pay?

> **Finished Early?**
> ➦ Go to page 412

# P ❸ Proportional Quantities

## Learn About It

£5 per metre

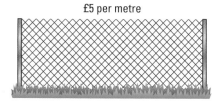

1 m of wire fencing costs £5,
so 2 m cost £5 × 2 = £10
and 3 m cost £5 × 3 = £15.

**1** How much do 4 m cost?

You find the cost of wire fencing by multiplying £5 by the length:

cost = £5 × length or, using algebra, $C = 5L$

So cost is **proportional** to length.

> **Word Check**
> Two quantities are **proportional** if one is a multiple of the other.

**2** Copy and complete this table.

| Length of wire fencing (m) | 0 | 1 | 2 | 3 | 4 | 5 | 6 | 7 |
|---|---|---|---|---|---|---|---|---|
| Cost (£) | | 5 | 10 | 15 | | | | |

3 m of wooden fencing cost £24. Hamid wants to buy 20 m of fencing.

**Special offer**
3 m for £24

If Hamid finds how much 1 m of fencing costs, he can calculate the cost of 20 m.
3 m cost £24 so 1 metre costs £24 ÷ 3 = £8
and 20 metres cost £8 × 20 = £160.

**3** Cost (£$C$) is proportional to length ($L$ metres). Write a formula connecting $C$ and $L$.

**4** Copy and complete this table.

| Length of wooden fencing (m) | 0 | 5 | 10 | 15 | 20 | 25 | 30 | 35 |
|---|---|---|---|---|---|---|---|---|
| Cost (£) | | | | | 160 | | | |

# Try It Out

4 m of hose pipe cost £12.

**1** How much does 1 metre cost?

**2** Write down a formula to find the cost (£C) of a length (L metres) of hose pipe. Write your formula in words first, then algebra.

**3** Copy and complete the table.

| Length of hose pipe (m) | 0 | 2 | 4 | 6 | 8 | 10 | 12 | 14 |
|---|---|---|---|---|---|---|---|---|
| Cost (£) | | | 12 | | | | | |

# Learn More About It

Graph paper

Here is the table for the cost of wire fencing.

**1** Copy the axes below.

Use these scales: *Length axis* 2 cm = 1 m
*Cost axis* 2 cm = £5

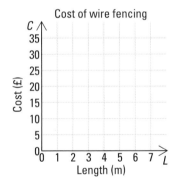

Cost of wire fencing

| Length of wire fencing (m) | Cost (£) |
|---|---|
| 0 | 0 |
| 1 | 5 |
| 2 | 10 |
| 3 | 15 |
| 4 | 20 |
| 5 | 25 |
| 6 | 30 |
| 7 | 35 |

**2** Plot the points in the table and join them up. What do you notice about your graph?

## Key Fact

The graph of proportional quantities is a straight line that passes through the origin.

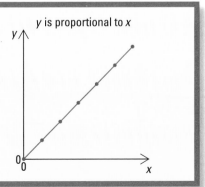

y is proportional to x

## Try It Out

Graph paper

  The tables show the prices and weights of two brands of tinned beans.

| Bargain Beans | | |
| --- | --- | --- |
| | Weight (g) | Cost (p) |
| Small | 200 | 30 |
| Medium | 400 | 60 |
| Large | 600 | 90 |

| Beanz | | |
| --- | --- | --- |
| | Weight (g) | Cost (p) |
| Small | 200 | 40 |
| Medium | 400 | 60 |
| Large | 600 | 80 |

**1** Draw a graph for each brand. Use these scales:

*Weight axis*:  2 cm to 100 g
*Cost axis*:     1 cm to 10p.

**2** For which brand is the cost proportional to the weight? Explain your answer.

## Practice

  **1** Are the following quantities proportional to each other? If so, write a formula.

| | |
| --- | --- |
| **Example** | 2 days' car hire costs £40. 3 days' costs £55. |
| **Working** | 2 days' car hire costs £40. |
| | So 1 day costs £40 ÷ 2 = £20. |
| | If cost and number of days are proportional, 3 days should cost |
| | 3 × £20 = £60. But 3 days costs £55. |
| **Answer** | Cost and number of days are not proportional. |

(a) A 40 cm TV set weighs 25 kg. A 50 cm TV set weighs 30 kg.
(b) A 20 link chain is 50 cm long. A 36 link chain is 90 cm long.
(c) 20 °C is 68 °F. 30 °C is 86 °F.
(d) 2 kg of potatoes cost 80p. 5 kg of potatoes cost £2.
(e) A plant is 75 cm tall after 3 years. It is 105 cm tall after 5 years.

Graph paper

**2** The tables show insurance costs for two companies.

| Safe Travel | |
| --- | --- |
| Number of days | Cost (£) |
| 3 | 21 |
| 7 | 49 |
| 10 | 70 |

| Group 5 Insurance | |
| --- | --- |
| Number of days | Cost (£) |
| 3 | 30 |
| 7 | 50 |
| 10 | 65 |

(a) Draw a graph and plot the data on it for each company. Use these scales:

*Number of days axis*:  1 cm = 1 day

*Cost axis*:               1 cm = £5.

(b) For which insurance company is the cost proportional to the number of days? Explain your answer.

(c) Find the cost of 1 day's insurance through this company.

(d) Write a formula for the cost (£$C$) of insurance for a number ($n$) of days.

**Finished Early?**

➡ Go to page 412

## Further Practice

**1** Which of these graphs are for proportional quantities? Explain your answer.

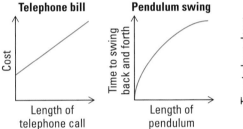

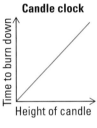

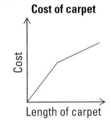

**2** Use the graph to answer the following questions.

(a) How much do 4 lemons weigh?

(b) How much does 1 lemon weigh?

(c) Write a formula for the weight ($W$ g) of a number ($n$) of lemons.

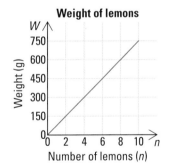

**Finished Early?**

➡ Go to page 412

# Unit 11 *Ratio and Proportion*

## Summary of Chapter 21

- A **ratio** compares two or more quantities.

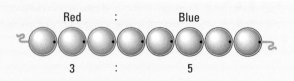

Red : Blue

3 : 5

- If you multiply/divide all the numbers of a ratio by the same number, you get an equivalent ratio.

× 2
3:5 = 6:10

÷ 2
6:10 = 3:5

- Convert quantities to the same units before cancelling.

3 cm:15 mm = 30 mm:15 mm = 30:15 = 2:1

- The ratio $n$:1 means the first quantity is $n$ times the second. For example, if Jack and Jill's ages are in the ratio 2:1, then Jack is twice the age of Jill.

- A ratio can show the parts that make a whole.

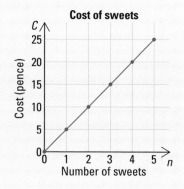

breadcrumbs / onion
nuts
NUT LOAF 270g

Nuts: Breadcrumbs: Onions
= 3 : 4 : 2
There are 3 + 4 + 2 = 9 parts altogether.
9 parts weigh 270 g so 1 part weighs 270 g ÷ 9 = 30 g.
Nuts are 3 parts = 3 × 30 g = 90 g.
Breadcrumbs are 4 parts = 4 × 30 g =120 g.
Onions are 2 parts = 2 × 30 g = 60 g.

- Two quantities are **proportional** if one is a multiple of the other.

Cost of sweets = 5 × number of sweets

$C = 5n$

The graph of proportional quantities is a straight line that passes through the origin.

# Brush Up Your Number 12

## Decimal Calculations

### Learn About It

To multiply one decimal by another:
- ignore the decimal points
- multiply the numbers together
- put the decimal point back into the answer.

---

**Example**     $3.25 \times 1.6$

**Working**     $325 \times 16$     *(Ignore the decimal points.)*

$$
\begin{array}{r}
3\ 2\ 5 \\
\times\quad 1\ 6 \\
\hline
1\ 9\ 5\ 0 \\
3\ 2\ 5\ 0 \\
\hline
5\ 2\ 0\ 0 \\
\end{array}
$$

3.25 has 2 digits after the decimal point.

1.6 has 1 digit after the decimal point.

So the answer must have 3 digits after the decimal point.

The zeros at the end are not needed once the decimal point has been positioned.

5200     5200     5.200
            3 digits

**Answer**     5.2

---

Multiplying by a number smaller than 1 makes the answer **smaller**.

---

**Example**     $6.2 \times 0.33$

**Working**     $62 \times 33 = 2046$

There are 1 + 2 decimal places in the question. So there are 3 decimal places in the answer.

**Answer**     2.046

---

### Try It Out

Work out the answers.

**1 (a)** $32 \times 7$      **(b)** $3.2 \times 7$      **(c)** $32 \times 0.7$
   **(d)** $3.2 \times 0.7$     **(e)** $3.2 \times 0.07$

**2 (a)** $24 \times 13$      **(b)** $24 \times 1.3$      **(c)** $24 \times 0.13$
   **(d)** $2.4 \times 13$     **(e)** $2.4 \times 0.13$

### Learn More About It

To divide one decimal by another:
- ignore the decimal points and treat as whole numbers
- divide the whole numbers
- move the digits in steps of $\times 10$ or $\div 10$ until the calculation is correct.

> **Example**  $6.86 \div 1.4$
> **Working**  $686 \div 14 = 49$    *(Start with whole numbers.)*
> $68.6 \div 14 = 4.9$    *(First number ÷ 10, answer ÷ 10.)*
> $6.86 \div 14 = 0.49$    *(First number ÷ 10, answer ÷ 10.)*
> $6.86 \div 1.4 = 4.9$    *(Second number ÷ 10, answer × 10.)*
> **Answer**  $4.9$

Dividing by a number smaller than 1 makes the answer **bigger**.

> **Example**  $13.2 \div 0.055$
> **Working**  $132 \div 55 = 2.4$    *(Start with whole numbers.)*
> $13.2 \div 55 = 0.24$    *(First number ÷ 10, answer ÷ 10.)*
> $13.2 \div 5.5 = 2.4$    *(Second number ÷ 10, answer × 10.)*
> $13.2 \div 0.55 = 24$    *(Second number ÷ 10, answer × 10.)*
> $13.2 \div 0.055 = 240$    *(Second number ÷ 10, answer × 10.)*
> **Answer**  $240$

## Try It Out

**B** Work out the answers.

**1 (a)** $56 \div 4$  **(b)** $5.6 \div 4$  **(c)** $0.56 \div 4$
  **(d)** $5.6 \div 0.4$  **(e)** $5.6 \div 0.04$  **(f)** $56 \div 0.04$

**2 (a)** $432 \div 12$  **(b)** $43.2 \div 12$  **(c)** $4.32 \div 12$
  **(d)** $43.2 \div 1.2$  **(e)** $43.2 \div 0.12$  **(f)** $432 \div 0.12$

**3 (a)** $1125 \div 25$  **(b)** $1125 \div 2.5$  **(c)** $1125 \div 0.25$
  **(d)** $112.5 \div 0.25$  **(e)** $11.25 \div 0.25$  **(f)** $0.1125 \div 0.25$

## Practice

**C** Copy and complete this decimal crossnumber.

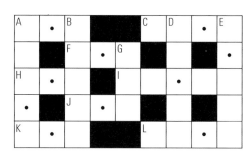

*Across*
**A** $2.4 \times 1.5$
**C** $7.8 \times 8.5$
**F** $2.75 \times 1.6$
**H** $1.875 \times 0.8$
**I** $9.9^2$
**J** $0.28 \times 2.5$
**K** $1.25 \times 0.8$
**L** $7.5 \times 3.4$

*Down*
**A** $68.22 \div 0.2$
**B** $10\,320 \div 0.16$
**D** $401.6 \div 6.4$
**E** $2.75 \div 0.88$
**G** $34.79 \div 0.07$

> **Finished Early?**
> ⇨ Go to page 413

# 22 Area and Perimeter

In this chapter you will learn about …
1. parallelograms and triangles
2. compound shapes
3. Pythagoras' theorem

## Parallelograms and Triangles

### Remember?

**Area** is the amount of surface something takes up.

You measure area in units such as square centimetres ($cm^2$).

There are $10 \times 10 = 100$ $mm^2$ in 1 $cm^2$.

There are $100 \times 100 = 10\,000$ $cm^2$ in 1 $m^2$.

To work out the area ($A$) of a rectangle,
multiply length ($l$) by width ($w$).

The formula is $A = lw$.

length (*l*)

width (*w*)

 Sometimes the length and width of a rectangle are given in different units. You cannot multiply them straight away. You have to change one so they match.

| Example | |
|---|---|

12 cm

6 mm

**Working (1)**   Change 12 cm to 120 mm.
Area = length × width = $120 \times 6 = 720$ $mm^2$.

**Working (2)**   Change 6 mm to 0.6 cm.
Area = length × width = $12 \times 0.6 = 7.2$ $cm^2$.

**Answer**   720 $mm^2$ or 7.2 $cm^2$
*(These are the same because 100 $mm^2$ = 1 $cm^2$.)*

If you know the area of a rectangle and the length of one side, you can work out the length of the other side.

You work out area by multiplying, so **divide** instead.

| | |
|---|---|
| **Example** | The area of a metal plate is $400$ cm$^2$. It is $16$ cm wide. How long is it? |
| **Working** | $400 \div 16 = 25$ cm |
| **Answer** | $25$ cm |

400 cm²  16 cm

Once you know the length and width, you can work out the perimeter.

 Sometimes the area and sides of a rectangle are given in different units. You cannot divide them straight away. You have to change one so they match.

Squares are slightly different. To find the length of the sides of a square, find the **square root** of the area.

| | |
|---|---|
| **Example** | A square tarpaulin covers $9$ m$^2$. How big is it? |
| **Working** | $\sqrt{A} = 3$ (because $3 \times 3 = 9$). |
| **Answer** | $3$ m $\times$ $3$ m |

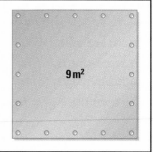

9 m²

# Try It Out

 **1** Find the areas of these rectangles.
  (a) $2$ cm $\times$ $5$ cm    (b) $7$ m $\times$ $4$ m    (c) $20$ mm $\times$ $10$ mm

**2** Find the areas of these squares.
  (a) $4$ cm sides    (b) $10$ km sides    (c) $2$ m sides

**3** Work out the area of each shape.
  Remember to show each step in your working.
  (a)

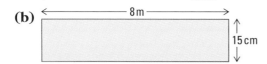

6 mm
20 cm

  (b)  8 m

15 cm

**4** For each rectangle, find **(i)** the missing length **(ii)** the perimeter.

**(a)**

10 cm

60 cm²

**(b)**

50 mm

75 mm²

## Learn About It

Squared paper

**1** Draw three identical parallelograms with base 4 cm and height 3 cm.

**2** Stick parallelogram 1 into your book.

**3** Cut parallelogram 2 along the dotted line as shown. Stick the two parts in your book, like this.

**4** Cut parallelogram 3 along the dotted line. Stick the two parts in your book, like this.

The area of the parallelogram must be the same as that of the rectangle you have made.

The area is $4 \times 3 = 12$ cm².

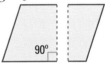

The **height** of the rectangle is 3 cm. It's the same as the dotted line you cut. The **base** is 4 cm long. The height is always **perpendicular** (at right angles) to the base.

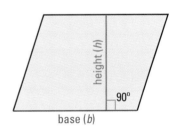

base (*b*)

height (*h*)

90°

### Key Fact

Area of a parallelogram = base × height.
The formula is $A = bh$.

The formulae for base (*b*) and height (*h*)
of a parallelogram with area $A$ are

$b = \dfrac{A}{h}$ and $h = \dfrac{A}{b}$.

### Word Check

**parallelogram** a quadrilateral with two pairs of parallel sides

**base** the 'bottom' of a shape; called its length

**perpendicular** making a right angle

# Try It Out

**B** Find the areas of these parallelograms.

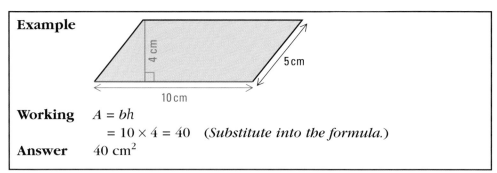

**Example**

**Working**   $A = bh$
                $= 10 \times 4 = 40$   (*Substitute into the formula.*)

**Answer**   $40 \text{ cm}^2$

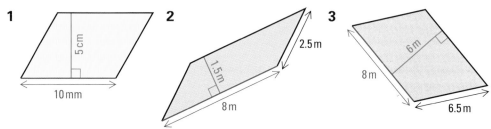

1

5 cm

10 mm

2

2.5 m

1.5 m

8 m

3

6 m

8 m

6.5 m

**C** Find the missing lengths.

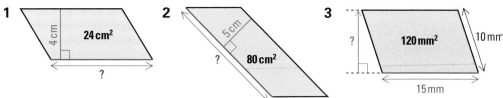

1

4 cm

24 cm²

?

2

5 cm

?   80 cm²

3

?   120 mm²   10 mm

15 mm

# Learn More About It

**1** Cut out three identical right-angled triangles.

**2** Stick triangle 1 into your book.

**3** Stick triangles 2 and 3 into your book like this.

The two triangles make a rectangle. So the area of
each triangle must be half the area of the rectangle.

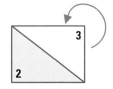

**4** Cut out three identical triangles.

**5** Stick triangle 1 into your book.

**6** Stick triangles 2 and 3 into your book like this.

The two triangles make a parallelogram. So the area
of each triangle must be half the area of the
parallelogram.

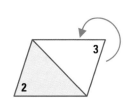

This means that, whatever shape of triangle you have, the area is base × height ÷ 2.

You can find missing measurements by dividing the area by the base or height, but then you have to **double** the answer. This undoes the 'half' in the area formula.

## Key Fact

Area of a triangle = base × height ÷ 2.

The formula can be written as $A = \dfrac{bh}{2}$ or $A = bh \div 2$ or $A = \frac{1}{2}bh$.

The formulae for the base ($b$) and height ($h$) of a triangle with area $A$ are $b = \dfrac{2A}{h}$ and $h = \dfrac{2A}{b}$.

---

**Example**   Find the area of this triangle.

**Working**   $A = bh \div 2$

$\quad\quad\quad\quad = 8 \times 6 \div 2$

$\quad\quad\quad\quad = 48 \div 2 = 24$

**Answer**   24 cm²

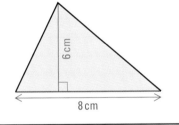

---

**Example**   Find the missing length marked $x$.

**Working**   Base = area ÷ height × 2

$\quad\quad\quad x = 50 \div 5 \times 2$

$\quad\quad\quad\quad = 10 \times 2$

$\quad\quad\quad\quad = 20$ cm

**Answer**   $x = 20$ cm

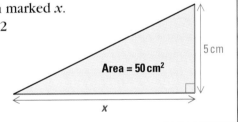

---

## Try It Out

Find the areas of these triangles.

**1**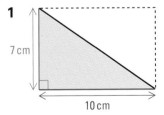

**2**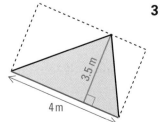

**3**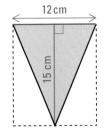

**E** Find the missing lengths marked $x$.

**1** **2**

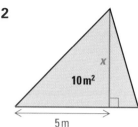

30 cm² 10 m²

10 cm 5 m

$x$ $x$

**3**

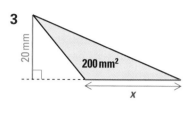

20 mm 200 mm²

$x$

## Practice

A4 squared paper or dotted paper (long side horizontal)

**F** Draw a set of axes. Label the $x$-axis from 0 to 20 and the $y$-axis from 0 to 15.

For each question below:

**(a)** plot the coordinates

**(b)** join the points, in order, with straight lines to make a shape

**(c)** measure and label the base and height of the shape

**(d)** work out the area.

**1** $(1, 1) \rightarrow (4, 1) \rightarrow (5, 3) \rightarrow (2, 3) \rightarrow (1, 1)$

**2** $(1, 10) \rightarrow (6, 10) \rightarrow (1, 3) \rightarrow (1, 10)$

**3** $(1, 15) \rightarrow (11, 11) \rightarrow (3, 11) \rightarrow (1, 15)$

**4** $(7, 10) \rightarrow (17, 8) \rightarrow (7, 8) \rightarrow (7, 10)$

**5** $(16, 6) \rightarrow (20, 7) \rightarrow (20, 1) \rightarrow (16, 0) \rightarrow (16, 6)$

**6** $(15, 13) \rightarrow (20, 15) \rightarrow (20, 11) \rightarrow (15, 13)$

**G** For each shape below, use the information given to:

**(a)** calculate the area of the shape

**(b)** work out the missing length marked with a letter.

**1** **2** **3**

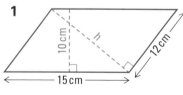

10 cm $h$ 12 cm

15 cm

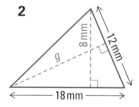

8 mm 12 mm $g$

18 mm

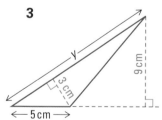

$y$ 3 cm 9 cm

5 cm

---

**Finished Early?**

➡ Go to page 414

# Further Practice

Protractor

For each question below:
- **(a)** draw the triangle using the information given in the table
- **(b)** draw the perpendicular height and measure it to the nearest 0.1 cm
- **(c)** work out the area of the triangle.

the other corner is where the lines cross

height (draw this last)

angle P (draw this second)     base (draw this first)     angle Q (draw this third)

| | Base | Angle P | Angle Q |
|---|---|---|---|
| **1** | 10 cm | 40° | 40° |
| **2** | 6 cm | 30° | 80° |
| **3** | 12 cm | 60° | 20° |
| **4** | 8 cm | 70° | 70° |
| **5** | 5 cm | 30° | 120° |

Find the missing base lengths. The two long straight lines are parallel.

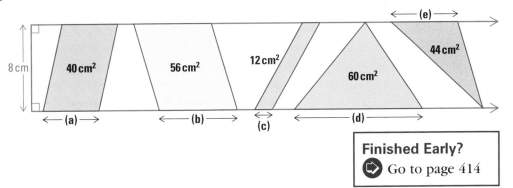

8 cm

40 cm²     56 cm²     12 cm²     60 cm²     44 cm²

←(e)→

←(a)→    ←(b)→   (c)   ←(d)→

**Finished Early?**
➡ Go to page 414

# Compound Shapes

## Learn About It

**Compound shapes** are made from simple shapes. This trapezium is made from two triangles and a rectangle.

So to find the area, split it up into these shapes.

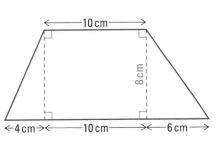

*First triangle*: base = 4 cm, height = 8 cm.
Area = 4 × 8 ÷ 2 = 16 cm².

*Rectangle*: length = 10 cm, width = 8 cm. Area = 10 × 8 = 80 cm².

*Second triangle*: base = 6 cm, height = 8 cm. Area = 6 × 8 ÷ 2 = 24 cm².

So the total area = 16 + 80 + 24 = 120 cm².

Compound shapes can also be made by cutting one shape out of another.

This metal plate is made by cutting one parallelogram out from another.

So to find the area of the plate, take the area of the small parallelogram away from that of the large one.

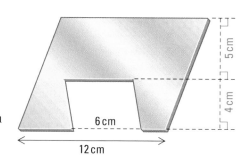

*Large parallelogram*: base = 12 cm, height = 9 cm. Area = 12 × 9 = 108 cm².

*Small parallelogram*: base = 6 cm, height = 4 cm. Area = 6 × 4 = 24 cm².

Area of plate = 108 − 24 = 84 cm².

## Word Check

**compound shape** any shape made from other shapes; you can add the shapes together or take them away.

## Try It Out

**J** Find the area of each shape.
Hints are given in brackets.

**1**

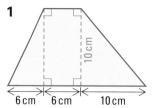

*(triangle + rectangle + triangle)*

**2**

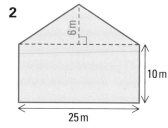

*(triangle + rectangle)*

**3**

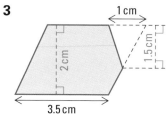

*(parallelogram − triangle)*

**4**

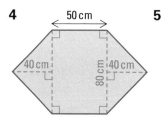

*(triangle + rectangle + triangle)*

**5**

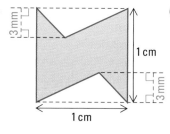

*(parallelogram − two triangles)*

**6**

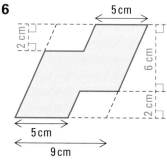

*(big parallelogram − two small parallelograms)*

# Practice

A4 squared paper or dotted paper, long side horizontal.

Draw a set of axes on your paper. Label the *x*-axis from 0 to 20 and the *y*-axis from 0 to 15.

For each part:
**(i)** plot the coordinates
**(ii)** join the points, in order, to draw the shape
**(iii)** draw extra lines to help you split up the shape
**(iv)** work out the area.

**1** These all need to be split up.
    **(a)** $(1, 12) \to (3, 15) \to (9, 12) \to (3, 9) \to (1, 12)$
    **(b)** $(9, 15) \to (20, 15) \to (16, 11) \to (20, 8) \to (5, 8) \to (11, 11) \to (9, 15)$
    **(c)** $(4, 7) \to (14, 7) \to (20, 6) \to (20, 3) \to (14, 1) \to (4, 1) \to (1, 5) \to (4, 7)$

**2** Draw new axes for these. You need to take shapes away from other shapes.
    **(a)** $(5, 9) \to (12, 1) \to (7, 4) \to (1, 1) \to (5, 9)$
    **(b)** $(13, 8) \to (16, 3) \to (20, 8) \to (20, 1) \to (13, 1) \to (13, 8)$
    **(c)** $(1, 15) \to (2, 15) \to (6, 11) \to (7, 15) \to (14, 15) \to (19, 11) \to (17, 15)$
        $\to (20, 15) \to (20, 10) \to (14, 10) \to (12, 14)$
        $\to (9, 14) \to (7, 10) \to (1, 10) \to (1, 15)$

> **Finished Early?**
> ⇨ Go to page 414

# Further Practice

Work out the area of each shape.

**1**

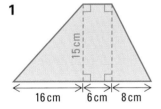

15 cm    16 cm   6 cm   8 cm

*(triangle + rectangle + triangle)*

**2**

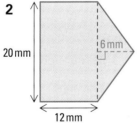

20 mm    6 mm    12 mm

*(rectangle + triangle)*

**3**

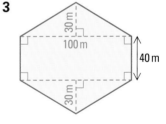

30 m   100 m   40 m   30 m

*(rectangle + two triangles)*

**4**

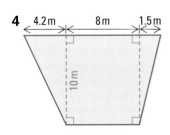

4.2 m   8 m   1.5 m    10 m

*(rectangle + two triangles)*

**5**

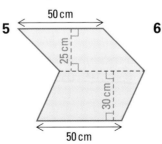

50 cm   25 cm   30 cm   50 cm

*(two parallelograms)*

**6**

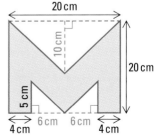

20 cm   10 cm   20 cm   5 cm   4 cm   6 cm   6 cm   4 cm

*(big rectangle – three triangles)*

> **Finished Early?**
> ⇨ Go to page 414

# P ③ Pythagoras' Theorem

## Learn About It

The longest side of any right-angled triangle is called the **hypotenuse**.

The hypotenuse is opposite the right angle. It is the side that does not form part of the right angle.

Here the hypotenuse is labelled $c$. The perpendicular sides in the triangle are labelled $a$ and $b$. It doesn't matter which side is $a$ and which is $b$.

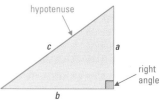

### Word Check

**hypotenuse** the longest side of a right-angled triangle; the side opposite the right angle

**perpendicular** making a right angle

Squared paper

**1** Draw ten different right-angled triangles. Start off with the three below, then draw seven more of your own. Vary the lengths of sides $a$ and $b$. Measure the length of the hypotenuse in each triangle (side $c$).

Triangle 1: $a = 6$ cm, $b = 8$ cm

Triangle 2: $a = 12$ cm, $b = 5$ cm

Triangle 3: $a = 3.5$ cm, $b = 12$ cm

**2** Copy and complete this table, with enough lines to record all your triangles.

| Triangle | $a$ | $b$ | $c$ | $a^2$ | $b^2$ | $c^2$ |
|----------|-----|-----|-----|-------|-------|-------|
| 1 | 6 | 8 | | 36 | 64 | |
| 2 | | | | | | |

**3** What do you notice about the numbers in the last three columns?

There is a connection between these numbers. This was discovered by the Greek mathematician Pythagoras. The rule is named after him and is called **Pythagoras' theorem**.

## Key Fact

**Pythagoras' theorem** connects the lengths of the sides of any right-angled triangle.

$c^2 = a^2 + b^2$.

To find the hypotenuse of a right-angled triangle:

- square the lengths of the perpendicular sides
- add together the squared lengths
- find the square root of the total to find the length of the hypotenuse.

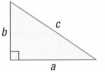

---

**Example**   Find the length of the hypotenuse.

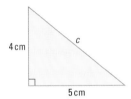

**Working**   Square the lengths of the perpendicular sides.

$a = 4$        $a^2 = 16$

$b = 5$        $b^2 = 25$

Add the squares of the two shortest sides.

$16 + 25 = 41$

$c^2 = 41$

$c = \sqrt{41} = 6.4$ (to 1 d.p.)

**Answer**   6.4 cm, to 1 d.p.

# Try It Out

**1** Look at these right-angled triangles. Which side is the hypotenuse in each?

(a)

(b)

(c)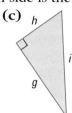

(d)

**2** Using Pythagoras' theorem, find the length of the hypotenuse in each of these right-angled triangles.

(a)

(b)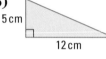

(c)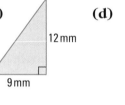

(d)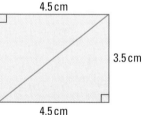

# Learn More About It

You can use Pythagoras' theorem to find the length of the diagonal of a rectangle.

| **Example** | Find the length of the diagonal of a 3.5 cm × 4.5 cm rectangle. |
|---|---|
| **Working** | The rectangle is made up of two right-angled triangles with perpendicular sides 3.5 cm and 4.5 cm. The diagonal is the hypotenuse of both triangles. |

Using Pythagoras' theorem, the length of the hypotenuse is

$$\sqrt{(3.5^2 + 4.5^2)}$$
$$= \sqrt{(12.25 + 20.25)}$$
$$= \sqrt{32.5}$$
$$= 5.7 \text{ cm (to 1 d.p.).}$$

**Answer**    5.7 cm (to 1 d.p.)

# Try It Out

Find the lengths of the diagonals of the following squares and rectangles. Give your answers correct to 1 d.p.

**1**
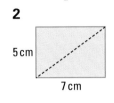
4 mm
6 mm

**2**
5 cm
7 cm

**3**

5 m
5 m

**4**
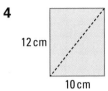
12 cm
10 cm

# Practice

**1** These kites are made from two pieces of wood joined together. Work out the lengths of their sides.

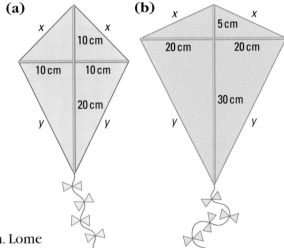

**(a)**
x   x
10 cm
10 cm   10 cm
20 cm
y   y

**(b)**
x   x
5 cm
20 cm   20 cm
30 cm
y   y

**2** Accra is due south of 'Agadou. Lome and Porto-Novo are due east of Accra. Abidjan is due west of Accra.

The distance between Accra and 'Agadou is 900 km.

The distance between Accra and Lome is 200 km.

The distance between Accra and Porto-Novo is 300 km.

The distance between Accra and Abidjan is 500 km.

Find the distance, to the nearest 50 km, between the other cities and 'Agadou 'as the crow flies'.

BURKINA FASO
'Agadou
CÔTE D'IVOIRE
BENIN
GHANA
TOGO
Abidjan   Accra   Lome   Porto-Novo

**3** A square has a perimeter of 40 cm. Calculate the length of its diagonal to the nearest centimetre.

**Finished Early?**
➡ Go to page 415

# Further Practice

**1** The roof of a farmer's barn is to be made of corrugated iron. Find the length of corrugated iron needed for *x* and *y*. Give your answers to 1 d.p.

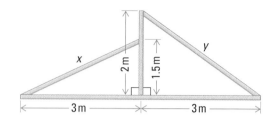

**2** Jack walks from one corner of this field to the corner diagonally opposite. How far does he walk, to the nearest metre?

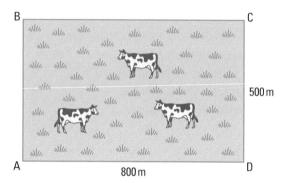

**3** Find the perimeter of the following triangles. Give your answers correct to 1 d.p. All measurements are in cm.

**(a)**

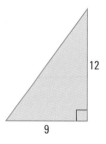

**(b)**

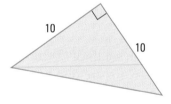

**(c)**

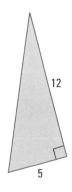

**(d)**

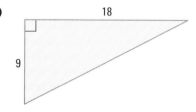

**Finished Early?**
 Go to page 415

# 23 Circles

In this chapter you will learn about ...
1. measuring circumferences
2. circumference calculations
3. areas of circles

## Measuring Circumferences

### Learn About It

**Key Fact**

Two **radii** make one diameter.

$2r = d$

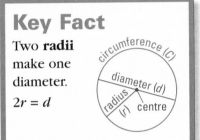

**Word Check**

**circumference** the perimeter of a circle

**radius** a line from the centre of a circle to its circumference

**diameter** a line from one side of a circle to the other, going through the centre; twice the length of the radius

### Try It Out

A length of string or thread with a knot at one end, some round objects

**1** Measure the diameter and circumference of several circular objects as accurately as you can. Copy and complete the table below. Leave the right-hand column blank for now.

| Object | Diameter ($d$) | Circumference ($C$) | $\frac{C}{d}$ (to 2 d.p.) |
|---|---|---|---|
|  |  |  |  |

**2** When you have completed your measurements, fill in the last column. Work out circumference ÷ diameter $\left(\frac{C}{d}\right)$ for each object you measured. Round the answers to 2 d.p.

**3** Now work out the average (mean) value of the numbers in the last column by adding up all the numbers in this column, then dividing by the number of objects you measured. Write this down.

## Learn More About It

The number you get by measuring very accurately and working out $\frac{C}{d}$ is about 3.14. This number is very important in mathematics and has been given a name, **pi**. You pronounce it 'pie', and it is written using a letter from the Greek alphabet, π.

The decimal for π starts like this:
3.141 592 653 589 793 238 462 643 383 297 502 ...
and goes on for ever without repeating!

If you have a scientific calculator, you should have a π button. Press it and see what you get in the display.

> ### Word Check
> π *pi* (pronounced 'pie'), the number of times the diameter of a circle fits into its circumference; roughly 3.14

## Try It Out

 **B** These calculations give answers very close to π. Work them out. For each one, write down how many of its decimal places match the value of π above. Which is the closest?

**1** 22 ÷ 7      **2** 79 ÷ 25      **3** 249 ÷ 79

**4** 8183 ÷ 2605      **5** 31 437 ÷ 10 007      **6** 1536 ÷ 489

**7** √10      **8** 148 ÷ 47      **9** 79 938 ÷ 25 445

**10** 355 ÷ 113      **11** 3820 ÷ 1216      **12** 801 ÷ 255

## Practice

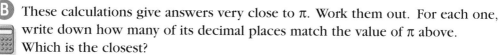 Squared paper (1 cm or 5 mm grid; 1 cm is best), compasses

**C** Here is another way to measure circumferences. Draw a table like this to record your results.

| Radius (*r*) | Diameter (*d*) | Circumference (*C*) | $\frac{C}{d}$ (to 2 d.p.) |
| --- | --- | --- | --- |
| | | | |

**1** Choose a whole number of centimetres to use as the radius of a circle. Put the point of your compasses where gridlines cross on your paper, then draw a circle. This example has a 4 cm radius.

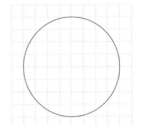

**2** Now 'measure' the circumference like this.

If the circle crosses a square like this ☐ count 1 cm. If it crosses like this ◹ count 1.4 cm. If it crosses like any of these ◹ ◿ ◺ count 1.2 cm. If it crosses like this ◿ count 0.7 cm.

You might want to keep a tally of the different types in a table like this:

| Length | Tally | Frequency | Total length |
|--------|-------|-----------|--------------|
| 0.7 cm | | | |
| 1 cm | | | |
| 1.2 cm | | | |
| 1.4 cm | | | |

**3** Repeat for at least six different sized circles.

**4** Work out your average value for $\dfrac{C}{d}$. How close to $\pi$ did you get?

> **Finished Early?**
> ⮞ Go to page 415

## Further Practice

You can measure the circumference of a small round object such as a coin by rolling.

You will need a table like this to record your results.

| Diameter ($d$) | Number of turns ($n$) | Circumference $(C = \dfrac{L}{n})$ | $\dfrac{C}{d}$ (to 2 d.p.) |
|----------------|----------------------|-----------------------------------|----------------------------|
| | | | |

**1** Measure the diameter of a coin and record it in your table.

**2** Put the coin flat against the 0 cm mark on a ruler. Roll it, without slipping, until you reach the last mark on the ruler (e.g. 30 cm).

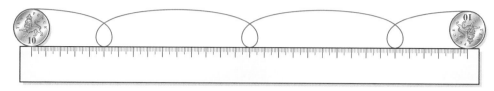

Note carefully how many times the coin turns, to the nearest quarter turn. Use decimals, so $5\frac{1}{4}$ turns would be 5.25. This is $n$ in the table.

**3** Divide the length of your ruler ($L$ in the table) by the number of turns. This is the circumference of the coin. Then work out $\frac{C}{d}$.

**4** Repeat this for at least six other **small** round objects.

**5** Work out your average value for $\frac{C}{d}$. How close to $\pi$ did you get?

> **Finished Early?**
> ➡ Go to page 415

# ❷ Circumference Calculations

## Learn About It

The number of times the diameter of a circle fits into the circumference is about 3.142. This is the special number $\pi$ (pi).

You can use $\pi$ to do calculations with circles.

If you want to work out the circumference of a circle, multiply its diameter by $\pi$. You can use the [π] key on your calculator. If you do not have one, use 3.142 instead.

---

### Key Fact

diameter ($d$) [ ×π ] ▷ circumference ($C$)

The formula for the circumference of a circle ($C$) with diameter $d$ is $C = d \times \pi$, i.e. $C = \pi d$.

---

**1** Do this example on your calculator.

| | |
|---|---|
| **Example** | The diameter of a paint-tin lid is 15 cm. What is the circumference of the lid? Give your answer to the nearest millimetre. |
| **Working** | $C = d \times \pi$ |
| | $= 15 \times \pi$ |
| | If you have a [π] key, press [1] [5] [×] [π] [=] |
| | The display will look something like this: `47.123890` |
| | If you *do not* have a [π] key, press |
| | [1] [5] [×] [3] [.] [1] [4] [2] [=] |
| | The display will look like this: `47.13` |
| | Both of these answers round to 47.1. |
| **Answer** | 47.1 cm |

**2** The diameter of a circle is 8 cm. What is its circumference? Give your answer to the nearest millimetre.

If you want to find the circumference of a circle and you know the radius, work out the diameter first. Do this because the circumference rule uses the diameter.

radius (*r*) [×2] ⟩ diameter (*d*) [×π] ⟩ circumference (*C*)

| | |
|---|---|
| **Example** | Wesley sets his compasses to 5.5 cm and draws a circle. What is its circumference? Give your answer to the nearest millimetre. |
| **Working** | $d = r \times 2$    (*Work out the diameter.*) |
| | $= 5.5 \times 2$ |
| | $= 11$ cm |
| | $C = d \times \pi$    (*Work out the circumference.*) |
| | $= 11 \times \pi$ |
| | $= 34.557\,519$ |
| | $= 34.6$ cm (*Rounded to the nearest millimetre.*) |
| **Answer** | 34.6 cm |

**3** The radius of a circle is 3.3 cm. What is its circumference? Give your answer to the nearest millimetre.

Every time a wheel turns round once, it moves forward. The distance it moves is the same as its circumference.

Turning round once is called a **revolution**.

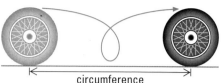

circumference

---

**Example** The wheels on Javed's bike are 61 cm across. He cycles to his grandmother's house. The wheels make 1500 revolutions on the journey. How far did Javed cycle? Give the answer in kilometres, to the nearest 10 m.

**Working** $C = d \times \pi$      (*Work out the circumference of the wheel.*)

$= 61 \times \pi$

$= 191.637\,15$ cm

$= 1.916\,371\,5$ m   (*One revolution.*)

Distance travelled $= C \times 1500$

     (*Multiply by number of times the wheel turns.*)

$= 1.916\,371\,5 \times 1500$

$= 2874.557\,25$ m

$= 2870$ m, to the nearest 10 metres

     (*Round the answer and change to the correct units.*)

**Answer** 2.87 km

---

### Word Check

**revolution** a whole turn

## Try It Out

**E** Work out the circumference of each circle below. Give the answer to 3 s.f.

Be careful to check whether you are given the diameter or the radius.

**1** 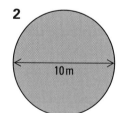 3 cm

**2** 10 m

**3**  18 mm

**4** 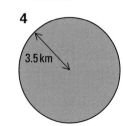 3.5 km

Work out how far each vehicle travels. Use sensible units for your answers and give them to 3 s.f.

**1** Go-kart: diameter of wheel = 40 cm; 1000 revolutions.

**2** Mountain bike: diameter of wheel = 75 cm; 50 revolutions.

**3** Radio-controlled car: radius of wheel = 2 cm; 300 revolutions.

**4** Tractor: radius of wheel = 0.825 m; 3000 revolutions.

## Learn More About It

If you know the circumference of a circle, you can work out its diameter. Just divide the circumference by π.

To work out the radius of a circle, just divide the diameter by 2.

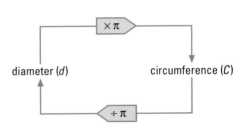

diameter (*d*)   ×π   circumference (*C*)   ÷π

| | |
|---|---|
| **Example** | A circular model railway track is 4.2 m long. How wide is the circle? |
| **Working** | $d = C \div \pi$ |
| | $= 4.2 \div \pi$ |
| | $= 1.336\,901\,5$ m |
| | $= 1.34$ m, to 2 d.p. (*Round sensibly.*) |
| **Answer** | 1.34 m |

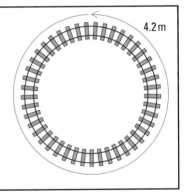

4.2 m

The radius of the railway track above is 1.34 ÷ 2 = 0.67 m.

There are more calculations you can do with rolling wheels.

| | |
|---|---|
| **Example** | A model car travels 100 m. Its wheels make 640 revolutions on the journey. How big are the wheels, to the nearest centimetre? |
| **Working** | Distance travelled = 100 m |
| | Distance for 1 revolution = 100 ÷ 640 |
| | $= 0.156\,25$ m |
| | This is the same as the circumference of a wheel. |
| | $d = C \div \pi$ |
| | $= 0.156\,25 \div \pi$ |
| | $= 0.049\,735\,919$ m |
| | $= 4.973\,5919$ cm |
| | $= 5$ (*Round to the nearest centimetre.*) |
| **Answer** | 5 cm |

## Try It Out

**G** Give all your answers to the following questions to the nearest millimetre.

**1** Find the diameter of the circle if the circumference is:

(a) 30 cm      (b) 40 cm      (c) 6.2 cm      (d) 15.5 cm.

**2** Find the radius of the circle if the circumference is:

(a) 65 cm      (b) 12 cm      (c) 3.5 cm      (d) 92 cm.

**3** Mel cycles 6 km. The wheels on her bike make 3000 revolutions on the journey. What is the radius of a wheel, to the nearest centimetre?

## Practice

**H 1** A label has to wrap exactly round a tin once.

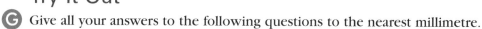

Work out how long each label should be, to the nearest millimetre.

(a) 9.5 cm      (b) 5.8 cm      (c) 6.5 cm

**2** These are the lengths of the labels for some other tins. Work out the diameter of each tin, to the nearest millimetre.

(a) 24 cm      (b) 14.2 cm      (c) 43.4 cm      (d) 35.2 cm

**3** The following designs are made from wire.

The large circles have a radius of 4 cm. The small ones have a radius of 2 cm.

Work out the length of wire needed to make each one.

(a)            (b)

(c)

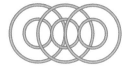

**4** The wheels on Sheila's truck are 90 cm across.

The readings below show how many revolutions the wheels made on some of her journeys. Work out how far she travelled each time. Give your answers in kilometres, to 1 d.p.

**(a)** $\boxed{0}\boxed{1}\boxed{5}\boxed{0}\boxed{0}\boxed{0}$  **(b)** $\boxed{0}\boxed{2}\boxed{5}\boxed{4}\boxed{0}\boxed{0}$  **(c)** $\boxed{0}\boxed{0}\boxed{9}\boxed{5}\boxed{6}\boxed{0}$  **(d)** $\boxed{0}\boxed{8}\boxed{0}\boxed{5}\boxed{7}\boxed{7}$

> **Finished Early?**
> ➡ Go to page 416

## Further Practice

**1** Copy and complete this table. Give your answers to 3 s.f.

| | Radius | Diameter | Circumference |
|---|---|---|---|
| **1** | | 12 cm | |
| **2** | | 3 cm | |
| **3** | 4 cm | | |
| **4** | 21 cm | | |
| **5** | | | 25 cm |
| **6** | | | 129 cm |
| **7** | | 1.5 mm | |
| **8** | 2.8 cm | | |
| **9** | | | 4 m |
| **10** | 12.5 m | | |

> **Finished Early?**
> ➡ Go to page 416

# ❸ Areas of Circles

## Learn About It

This circle has a radius of 10 cm. It has been drawn inside a square divided into four 10-cm squares.

Each small square has an area of $10 \times 10 = 100 \text{ cm}^2$.

About $\frac{3}{4}$ of each small square is taken up by the circle. The shaded area is about 75 cm² ($\frac{3}{4}$ of 100 = 75) so the whole circle must cover about $4 \times 75 = 300 \text{ cm}^2$.

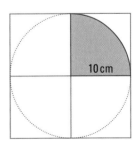

That is the same as three of the small squares ($3 \times 100 = 300 \text{ cm}^2$).

In fact, the circle covers slightly more area than 3 small squares.

The correct number is about 3.14 which is π!

In the circle on the right, you find the area of the small square by working out $r \times r$ or $r^2$.

If you multiply the answer by π, you get the area of the circle.

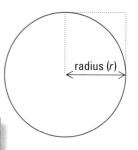

radius (r)

## Key Fact

The formula for the area ($A$) of a circle with radius $r$ is $A = r^2 \times \pi$, i.e. $A = \pi r^2$.

---

**Example**   What is the area of this circle?

**Working**   Area = $r^2 \times \pi$

$= 3^2 \times \pi$

$= 9 \times \pi$

$= 28.274\,33\ldots$ cm$^2$

(*The … means the decimal goes on further than this.*)

**Answer**   28.3 cm$^2$, to 1 d.p.

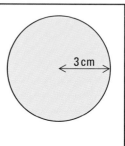

3 cm

---

If you know the diameter of the circle, halve it first to get the radius.

---

**Example**   What is the area of this circle?

**Working**   Radius = diameter ÷ 2

$= 10 \div 2 = 5$ m.

Area = $r^2 \times \pi$

$= 5^2 \times \pi$

$= 25 \times \pi$

$= 78.539\,81\ldots$ m$^2$

**Answer**   78.5 m$^2$, to 1 d.p.

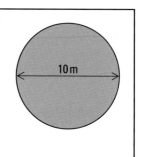

10 m

---

## Try It Out

**J** Work out the area of each circle below. If you don't have a 𝜋 key on your calculator, use 3.142 for π. Give the answers to 1 d.p. Be careful to check whether you are given the diameter or the radius.

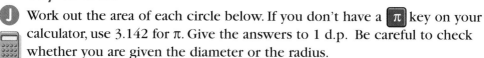

**1**

6 cm

**2**

25 mm

**3**

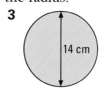

14 cm

**4**

0.7 mm

## Practice

**1** Kay is spraying a picture of a dinosaur
on her bedroom wall.

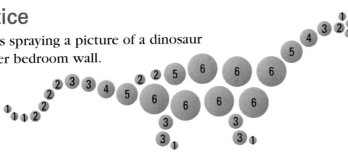

She uses these stencils. The measurement below each one gives the
diameter of the hole.

**1** 1.9 cm  **2** 2.6 cm  **3** 3.5 cm  **4** 4.2 cm  **5** 5.2 cm  **6** 7.1 cm

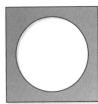

**(a)** For each stencil, work out the area that will be
covered with paint.
**(b)** Work out the area that will be covered with paint for the whole dinosaur.

**2** Handifone makes telephone tables to attach to the wall. Work out the area
of each one, to the nearest square centimetre.

**(a)** 42 cm  **(b)** 56 cm  **(c)** 18 cm  **(d)** 24 cm

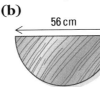

**Finished Early?**
➡ Go to page 417

## Further Practice

Copy and complete this table. Give your answers to 1 d.p.

| | radius | diameter | Area |
|---|---|---|---|
| 1 | 6.5 cm | | |
| 2 | 30 m | | |
| 3 | 12.4 mm | | |
| 4 | | 16 cm | |
| 5 | | 28 km | |
| 6 | | 17 mm | |
| 7 | 150 cm | | |
| 8 | | 25 mm | |
| 9 | 42 m | | |
| 10 | | 13 m | |

**Finished Early?**
➡ Go to page 417

# 24 Volume and Surface Area

In this chapter you will learn about …
1. volume of cuboids
2. volume of prisms
3. surface area

## P 1 Volume of Cuboids

### Remember?

**Volume** is the amount of space a 3D object occupies.

Volume is measured in **cubic** units, like these:

| 1 mm³ | 1 cm³ | 1 m³ | 1 km³ |
| cubic millimetre | cubic centimetre | cubic metre | cubic kilometre |

Finding the volume of something is just working out how many of these cubic units will fit into it.

## Try It Out

**A** Each cube is 1 cm³. What is the volume of each model?

1
2
3
4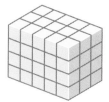

# Learn About It

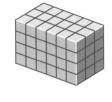

- This cuboid is made from 1-cm cubes. It is 6 cm long, 3 cm wide and 4 cm high.

  There are 4 layers. Each layer has 3 × 6 = 18 cubes.
  So the whole cuboid has 4 × 18 = 72 cubes.
  The volume is 72 cm³.

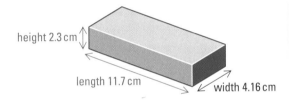

- You do not need to count the layers of cubes. You just use the measurements of the cuboid.

  6 × 3 × 4 = 72 cm³.
  The volume of the cuboid is
  length × width × height.

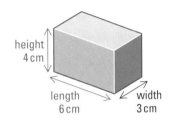

height 4 cm   length 6 cm   width 3 cm

**1** Work out the volume of this cuboid.

height 2.3 cm   length 11.7 cm   width 4.16 cm

> ## Key Fact
> Volume of a cuboid =
> length × width × height.
> The formula is $V = lwh$.
> In a cube, all the edges ($e$)
> are the same length.
> So $V = e \times e \times e = e^3$.

You need to be careful with cuboids like these. You must have all the measurements in the same unit.

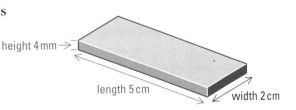

height 4 mm   length 5 cm   width 2 cm

*Work in centimetres*:
Change 4 mm to 0.4 cm.
Volume = length × width × height
$$= 5 \times 2 \times 0.4$$
$$= 4 \text{ cm}^3.$$

*Work in millimetres*:
Change 5 cm to 50 mm. Change 2 cm to 20 mm.
Volume = length × width × height
$$= 50 \times 20 \times 4$$
$$= 4000 \text{ mm}^3.$$

Convert to a more suitable unit:
$4000 \text{ mm}^3 = 4 \text{ cm}^3$

This diagram shows that there are $10 \times 10 \times 10 = 1000 \text{ m}^3$ in $1 \text{ cm}^3$.

There are $100 \text{ cm}$ in $1 \text{ m}$. So there are $100 \times 100 \times 100 \text{ cm}^3$ in $1 \text{ m}^3$.
That's $1\,000\,000 \text{ cm}^3$!

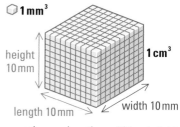

The volume of liquid (capacity) is measured in ml. $1 \text{ ml} = 1 \text{ cm}^3$.

volume = length × width × height
    = 10 × 10 × 10
    = 1000 mm³

## Key Facts

$$1000 \text{ mm}^3 = 1 \text{ cm}^3$$
$$1\,000\,000 \text{ cm}^3 = 1 \text{ m}^3$$
$$1\,000\,000\,000 \text{ mm}^3 = 1 \text{ m}^3$$
$$1 \text{ cm}^3 = 1 \text{ ml}$$
$$1000 \text{ cm}^3 = 1 \text{ litre}$$
$$1000 \text{ litres} = 1 \text{ m}^3, \text{ because } 1\,000\,000 \text{ cm}^3 = 1 \text{ m}^3$$

Many everyday containers are shaped like cuboids. You can work out the volumes of these in cubic units. You can then change to capacity units to find out how much liquid they can hold.

| | |
|---|---|
| **Example** | A juice carton is 6 cm long, 4 cm wide and 8 cm high. How much juice does it hold? |
| **Working** | Volume of a cuboid = length × width × height |
| | $= 6 \times 4 \times 8$ |
| | $= 24 \times 8$ |
| | $= 192 \text{ cm}^3.$ |
| | $1 \text{ cm}^3 = 1 \text{ ml}$ |
| **Answer** | 192 ml |

# Try It Out

**B** Work out the volume of each of the following cuboids.

**1**

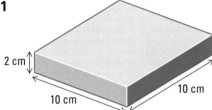

2 cm
10 cm
10 cm

**2**

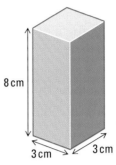

8 cm
3 cm   3 cm

**3**

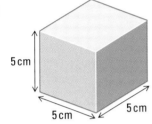

5 cm
5 cm   5 cm

**4** length = 4.2 m, width = 2.5 m, height = 1.3 m

**5** length = 1.5 cm, width = 4.8 mm, height = 8.5 mm

**6** height = 24 cm, width = 13 cm, length = 2.6 m

**7** 12 m × 14 m × 2.5 cm

**8** 2 mm × 3 mm × 20 m

**C** Work out the capacity of each container, in millilitres or litres.

**1**

15 cm
10 cm   3 cm

**2**

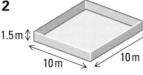

1.5 m
10 m   10 m

**3**

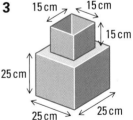

15 cm   15 cm
15 cm
25 cm
25 cm   25 cm

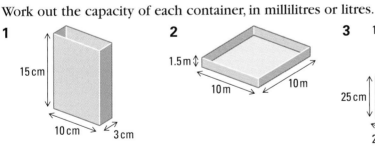

## Learn More About It

Just as with flat shapes, you can make **compound** solid shapes.

You can make them by adding cuboids together, like these.

You can make them by taking one cuboid away from another, like these.

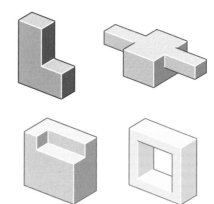

To work out the volume of a compound solid shape:
- decide whether you are adding cuboids together, or taking away
- make a sketch of the shape and mark all the measurements
- put on any extra lines to show where the shape is being split up
- calculate the volume of each cuboid
- add or subtract to get the final answer.

**Example**   Work out the volume of this compound shape.

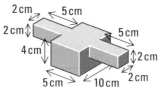

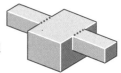

**Working**   The shape is made of three cuboids added together.
The two small cuboids have the same measurements.

*Large cuboid*: $V = lwh$
$$= 5 \times 10 \times 4$$
$$= 200 \text{ cm}^3$$

*Small cuboid*: $V = lwh$
$$= 5 \times 2 \times 2$$
$$= 20 \text{ cm}^3$$

*Total volume*   $= 200 + 20 + 20 = 240 \text{ cm}^3$.

**Answer**   $240 \text{ cm}^3$

**Example**    Work out the volume of this compound shape.

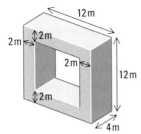

**Working**    This is one cuboid with another smaller cuboid taken from inside.

*Large cuboid*:  $V = lwh$
$$= 12 \times 4 \times 12$$
$$= 576 \, m^3$$

*Small cuboid*: The measurements are:

$$\text{length} = 12 - 2 - 2$$
$$= 8 \, m$$
$$\text{width} = 4 \, m$$
$$\text{height} = 12 - 2 - 2$$
$$= 8 \, m$$
$$V = lwh$$
$$= 8 \times 4 \times 8$$
$$= 256 \, m^3$$

*Total volume*:  $V = 576 - 256 = 320 \, m^3$

**Answer**    $320 \, m^3$

## Word Check

volume  the amount of 3D space an object takes up

capacity  the volume of a liquid, or a container for liquid

# Try It Out

**D** Find the volume of each of these compound shapes.

**1** These are made from cuboids added together.

**(a)**

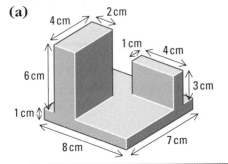

**(b)**

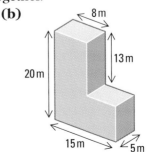

**2** These are made by taking cuboids away.

**(a)**

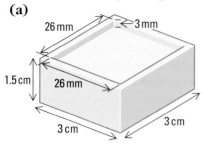

**(b)**

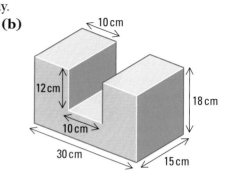

## Learn More About It

You can find a missing side in a cuboid if you know the volume and the other two sides.

| | |
|---|---|
| **Example** | The volume of a box is $200 \text{ cm}^3$. Its base is $10 \text{ cm} \times 5 \text{ cm}$. How tall is it? |

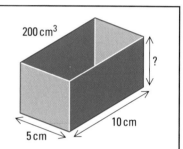

**Working**
$$V = lwh$$
$$200 = 10 \times 5 \times h$$
$$200 = 50h$$
$$50h = 200$$
$$h = \frac{200}{50}$$
$$h = 4$$

**Answer** 4 cm

## Try It Out

**E** Work out the missing side in each cuboid.

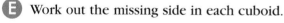

**1**

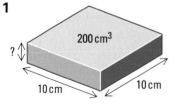

**2**

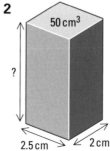

**3**

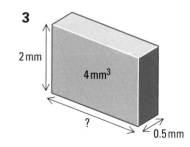

**4**

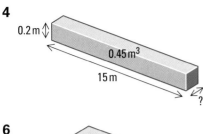

0.2 m
0.45 m³
15 m
?

**5**

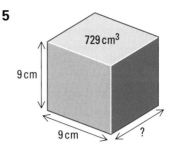

729 cm³
9 cm
9 cm
?

**6**

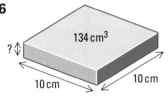

134 cm³
?
10 cm
10 cm

# Practice

**F** **1** Tins of Dino Beans come in three sizes.

**Small** 6.5 cm
5 cm
DINO BEANS
Volume = 166 cm³

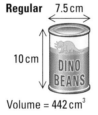

**Regular** 7.5 cm
10 cm
DINO BEANS
Volume = 442 cm³

**Jumbo** 12 cm
12 cm
DINO BEANS
Volume = 1357 cm³

The tins are packed into boxes like this.

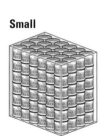

**Small**

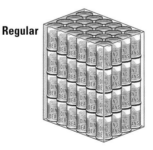

**Regular**

**Jumbo**

(a) (i) How many Small size tins fit into a box?
(ii) Work out the minimum length, width and height of the box.
(iii) Work out the volume of the box.
(iv) What volume inside the box is taken up by the tins?
(v) What volume of **air** is inside the box?
(vi) What percentage of the volume of the box is this?
(b) Repeat part (a) for the Regular size tins.
(c) Repeat part (a) for the Jumbo size tins.
(d) Which box wastes the smallest percentage of its space?

**2** This diagram shows the design for a space station.

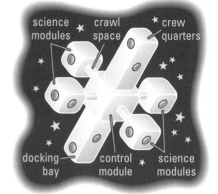

The control module is a 10-metre cube.
The science modules are 8-metre cubes.
The crew quarters and docking bay are the same shape and size. They are cuboids 17 m × 6 m × 6 m.
The crawl spaces are cuboids 8 m × 1.5 m × 1.5 m.

(a) Work out the volume of each part of the space station.

(b) What is the total volume of the station?

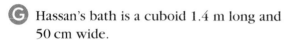 Hassan's bath is a cuboid 1.4 m long and 50 cm wide.

This graph shows the depth of the water as he fills the bath.

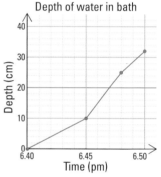

(a) What volume of water is in the bath at:

(i) 6.45 pm?

(ii) 6.48 pm?

(iii) 6.50 pm?

(b) When Hassan gets into the bath, the water rises by another 12 cm. How many litres does his body occupy?

(c) Hassan gets out of the bath, then lets out the water. When he empties the bath, 70 cl flows out every second. How long does it take the bath to empty?

(d) The cold water tank in Hassan's loft is a cuboid 1.25 m long and 70 cm wide. When he fills the bath, the level in the tank drops by 12 cm.

(i) How much cold water does he use?

(ii) How much hot water does he use?

(iii) What fraction of his bath is hot water?

(e) When Hassan's cold water tank is full, it contains 420 litres. How deep is the water in the tank then?

**Finished Early?**
➡ Go to page 417

# Further Practice

**1** This table contains the dimensions of various cuboids. Calculate their volumes.

|        | Length  | Width  | Height  | Volume |
|--------|---------|--------|---------|--------|
| **(a)** | 5 cm   | 3 cm   | 8 cm    |        |
| **(b)** | 10 m   | 2 m    | 2 m     |        |
| **(c)** | 6 cm   | 4 cm   | 14 cm   |        |
| **(d)** | 5 mm   | 5 mm   | 30 mm   |        |
| **(e)** | 3 m    | 50 cm  | 1 m     |        |
| **(f)** | 12 cm  | 12 cm  | 2 mm    |        |
| **(g)** | 8 m    | 2.5 m  | 2.5 m   |        |
| **(h)** | 4.4 km | 3 km   | 2.1 km  |        |

**2** Find the volume of each of these solid letters.

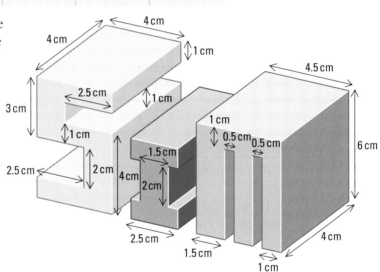

**3** Pisces Tanks make fish tanks. There are four sizes.

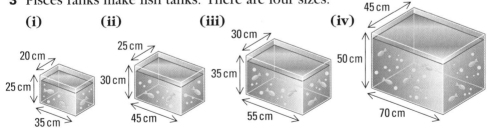

(i)   (ii)   (iii)   (iv)

**(a)** Work out the capacity of each size.

**(b)** Pisces recommend you leave a 5-cm air space at the top of the tank when you fill it. Work out how much water is actually needed to fill each tank.

**(c)** What percentage of each tank is full?

**Finished Early?**
➡ Go to page 417

# T ② Volume of Prisms

## Learn About It

A prism is a three-dimensional shape that has the same cross-section throughout its length.

irregular prism

hexagonal prism

triangular prism

trapezoidal prism

The volume of a prism is the area of its end multiplied by its length or height.

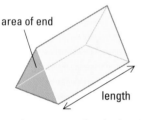

area of end

length

volume = area of end × length

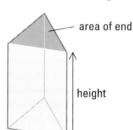

area of end

height

volume = area of end × height

---

| | |
|---|---|
| **Example** | Find the volume of this triangular prism. |
| **Working** | Volume = area of the end × length |
| | Area of the end = $\frac{1}{2} \times 4 \times 3 = 6\ \text{cm}^2$ |
| | Volume = $6 \times 10 = 60\ \text{cm}^3$ |
| **Answer** | $60\ \text{cm}^3$ |

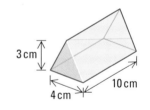

3 cm
10 cm
4 cm

---

## Word Check

**prism** a three-dimensional shape with a constant cross-section

## Key Fact

Volume of a prism =
area of end × length (height)

If you know the volume and length of a prism, you can work out the area of its end.

**Example** A cuboid has a length of 6 cm and a volume of 48 cm³. Find the area of its end.

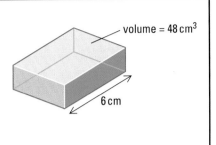
volume = 48 cm³

6 cm

**Working** Volume = length × area of end

so area of end = $\dfrac{\text{volume}}{\text{length}}$

Area of end $= \dfrac{48}{6} = 8 \text{ cm}^2$.

**Answer** 8 cm².

## Try It Out

**1** Find the volumes of the following prisms.

**(a)**

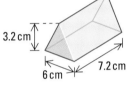
3.2 cm
6 cm
7.2 cm

**(b)**

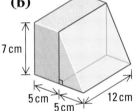
7 cm
5 cm
5 cm
12 cm

**(c)**

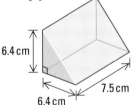
6.4 cm
6.4 cm
7.5 cm

**2** Find the area of the end of each cuboid cereal packet.

**(a)**

30.5 cm
volume = 65 880 cm³

**(b)**

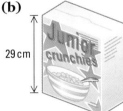
29 cm
volume = 3857 cm³

**(c)**

21 cm
volume = 1701 cm³

## Learn More About It

A circular prism is called a **cylinder**.

The volume of a cylinder
= Area of the end ($\pi r^2$) × length ($l$).

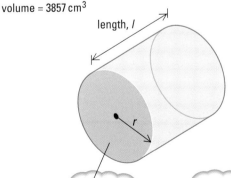
length, $l$

$r$

Area of end
= $\pi r^2$

so

Volume
= $\pi r^2 \times l$

### Word Check

cylinder a circular prism

**Example** Find the volume of this cylinder.
**Working**
Volume = area of end × height
Area of end = $\pi r^2 = \pi \times 2^2$
= 12.5663 cm$^2$
Volume = 12.5663 × 6
= 75.3982 cm$^3$
**Answer** 75.40 cm$^3$, to 2 d.p.

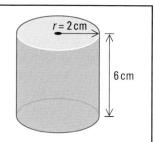

r = 2 cm

6 cm

## Try It Out

**J** Find the volumes of these cans of food.

**1**

r = 3.5 cm
BAKED BEANS
11 cm

**2**

r = 4.5 cm
TUNA
4 cm

**3** diameter = 6.5 cm

MUSHY PEAS
10 cm

**4** r = 4 cm

SWEETCORN
8.5 cm

## Practice

**K** **1** Find the volumes of the following prisms.

**(a)**
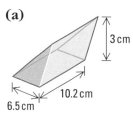
3 cm
10.2 cm
6.5 cm

**(b)**
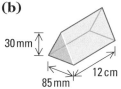
30 mm
12 cm
85 mm

**(c)**
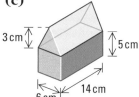
3 cm
5 cm
6 cm
14 cm

**(d)**

8.4 m
12.3 m

**(e)**
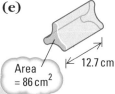
12.7 cm
Area = 86 cm$^2$

**(f)**
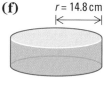
r = 14.8 cm
h = 9.2 cm

**2** This cuboid has a hole drilled through it.

    **(a)** Find the original volume of the cuboid.

    **(b)** Calculate the volume of material drilled out.

    **(c)** Calculate the volume of the remaining shape.

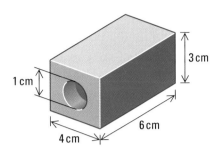

**3** The diagram shows the dimensions of a length of pipe.

Work out:

    **(a)** the volume of air in the centre

    **(b)** the volume of the whole pipe

    **(c)** the volume of the pipe wall.

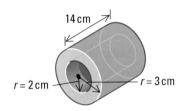

Finished Early?
Go to page 418

# Further Practice

**1** Find the volumes of the following prisms.

    **(a)**

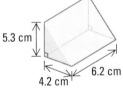

    **(b)**

    **(c)**

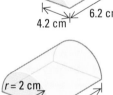

    **(d)**

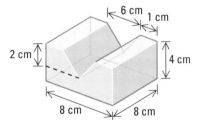

**2** The diagram shows the size and shape of a barn. Find its total volume.

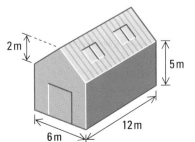

NUMBER SKILLS Multiply/divide HTU and decimals

3 The diagram show the dimensions
   of a swimming pool.
   (a) Find its total capacity.
   (b) The pool is drained so that
       water at the deep end is only
       1.5 m deep. Find the volume
       of the remaining water.

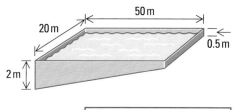

**Finished Early?**
➡ Go to page 418

# T ❸ Surface Area

## Learn About It

All 3D shapes have a **surface area**.

The surface area of a shape is the sum of the area of all the faces.

**Example** Find the surface area of this cuboid.

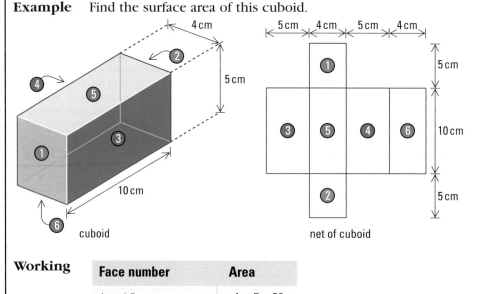

cuboid                                net of cuboid

**Working**

| Face number | Area |
|---|---|
| 1 and 2 | 4 × 5 = 20 |
| 3 and 4 | 5 × 10 = 50 |
| 5 and 6 | 4 × 10 = 40 |
| Total of the 3 pairs of faces | 110 |
| × 2 (for all faces) | 220 |

**Answer** 220 cm²

# Try It Out

Find the surface areas of the following cuboids.

**1** a block of wood 6 cm × 5 cm × 11 cm

**2** a cube with sides 3.5 cm

**3** a computer disc box 95 mm × 100 mm × 50 mm

**4** a bedroom 2.5 m × 2.5 m × 3.5 m

# Learn More About It

To find the surface area of a prism:

- calculate the area of both ends
- calculate the perimeter of one end, then multiply this by the length of the prism
- add these two measurements together.

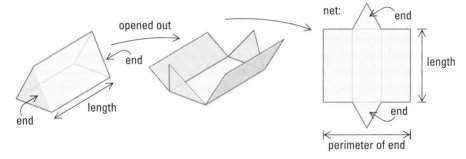

| | |
|---|---|
| **Example** | Find the surface area of this right-angled triangular prism. |
| **Working** | Surface area |

= area of ends + perimeter of end × length.

Area of the two ends of the prism

= 2($\frac{1}{2}$ × base × height)

= 2($\frac{1}{2}$ × 3 × 4)

= 12 cm$^2$

perimeter of end
= 3 + 4 + 5
= 12 cm

Perimeter × length

= 11 × 12

= 132 cm$^2$

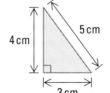

Surface area = area of ends + perimeter of end × length

= 12 + 132

**Answer** 144 cm$^2$

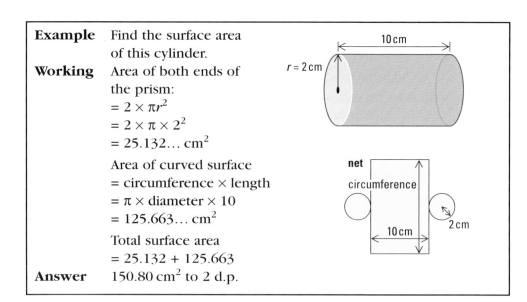

**Example** Find the surface area of this cylinder.

**Working** Area of both ends of the prism:
$$= 2 \times \pi r^2$$
$$= 2 \times \pi \times 2^2$$
$$= 25.132\ldots \text{ cm}^2$$

Area of curved surface
= circumference × length
= π × diameter × 10
= 125.663… cm$^2$

Total surface area
= 25.132 + 125.663

**Answer** 150.80 cm$^2$ to 2 d.p.

## Try It Out

Find the surface areas of the following prisms.

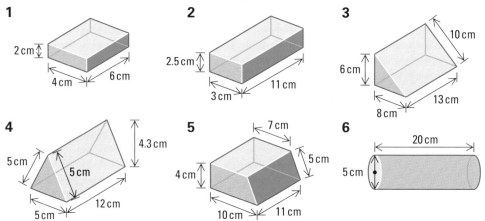

# Practice

 Calculate the surface areas of the following prisms.

**1** a metal bar 2 m × 4.5 cm × 12.6 cm

Be careful with the units!

**2** the triangular prism chocolate bar shown in the diagram

**3** a small paperback book 11.5 cm × 18 cm × 2 cm

**4** a large paperback book 21 cm × 29.5 cm × 1.8 cm

**5** a cylindrical tin can of diameter 4 cm and height 10 cm

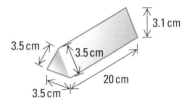
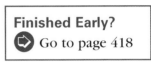

**Finished Early?**
➡ Go to page 418

# Further Practice

**1** Calculate the surface areas of these cuboids.
   **(a)** 3 cm × 4 cm × 212 cm     **(b)** 3 m × 2.4 m × 9.7 m
   **(c)** 6 mm × 5 mm × 100 mm     **(d)** 5 cm × 4.5 cm × 2.6 cm

**2** A cylindrical tin has a diameter of 7 cm and is 4.5 cm high. Work out the total area of metal required to make the tin.

**3** Calculate the surface areas of these prisms.

**(a)**

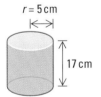

**(b)**

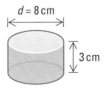

**(c)**

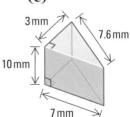

**Finished Early?**
➡ Go to page 418

# Unit 12 *Mensuration*
## Summary of Chapters 22, 23 and 24

### Area

- The **perimeter** of a shape is the distance all the way around the outside.

- **Area** is the amount of surface something occupies.

  Area is measured in square units, for example square centimetres ($cm^2$).

  There are $100\,mm^2$ in $1\,cm^2$. There are $10\,000\,cm^2$ in $1\,m^2$.

- To work out the area ($A$) of a rectangle, multiply length ($l$) by width ($w$).

  The formula is $A = lw$.

  A square's edges ($e$) are all the same length. So $A = e \times e$ or $A = e^2$.

- If you know the area of a rectangle and the length of one side, you can work out the length of the other side. Divide the area by the length of the side you know.

  To find the side of a square, find the square root of the area.

- The area of a parallelogram = base × height.

  You can find unknown lengths in a parallelogram by dividing, just as for a rectangle.

- The area of a triangle is base × height ÷ 2.

  The formula is $A = \dfrac{bh}{2}$ or $A = bh \div 2$ or $A = \frac{1}{2}bh$.

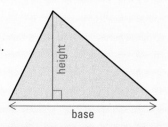

  You can find unknown measurements from $b = \dfrac{2A}{h}$ or $h = \dfrac{2A}{b}$.

- **Compound shapes** are made by putting shapes together or taking one shape out of another.

## Circles

- Two **radii** make one diameter. $2r = d$.

- $\pi$ (*pi* pronounced 'pie') is the number of times the diameter of a circle fits into its circumference.

- **Circumference** of a circle = $\pi \times$ diameter. The formula is $C = \pi d$.

  You can use the $\boxed{\pi}$ key on your calculator. If you do not have one, use 3.142 for $\pi$.

- When a wheel turns through one **revolution**, the distance it moves is its circumference.

- Area of a circle = $\pi \times$ radius$^2$. The formula is $A = \pi r^2$.

## Volume

- **Volume** is the amount of space a 3D object occupies.
  Volume is measured in **cubic** units, such as $mm^3$, $cm^3$, $m^3$ or $km^3$.
  $1000\ mm^3 = 1\ cm^3$   $1\,000\,000\ cm^3 = 1\ m^3$   $1\,000\,000\,000\ mm^3 = 1\ m^3$

- Volume of a cuboid = length $\times$ width $\times$ height. The formula is $V = lwh$.

- **Compound** solid shapes can be made by adding cuboids together, or taking one cuboid away from another.

- When you are talking about liquids, volume is called **capacity**.

  Capacity is measured in litres ($l$), centilitres (cl) and millilitres (ml).

  $100\ cl = 1\,l$       $1000\ ml = 1\,l$       $10\ ml = 1\ cl$

  $1\ cm^3 = 1\ ml$      $1000\ cm^3 = 1\,l$      $1000\,l = 1\ m^3$

- Volume of a **prism** = area of end $\times$ length (height).

## Pythagoras' Theorem

- Pythagoras' theorem says that in every right-angled triangle, $a^2 + b^2 = c^2$, where $c$ is the **hypotenuse** of the triangle.

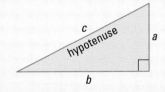

## Surface Area

- The **surface area** of a solid shape is the total area of all its faces. For a prism, the surface area is ($2 \times$ area of end) + (length $\times$ perimeter of end).

# Brush Up Your Number 13

## Fraction Calculations

### Learn About It

To work out $\frac{1}{*}$ of something, divide it by $*$.

| | |
|---|---|
| **Example** | What is $\frac{1}{10}$ of £360? |
| **Working** | $\frac{1}{10}$ of £360 = £360 ÷ 10 = £36 |
| **Answer** | £36 |

To work out a fraction of something when the numerator is not 1:
- divide the number by the denominator of the fraction
- multiply the answer by the numerator.

| | |
|---|---|
| **Example** | What is $\frac{2}{3}$ of 48 kg? |
| **Working** | $\frac{2}{3}$ of 48 kg = 48 ÷ 3 × 2 |
| | = 16 × 2 = 32 kg |
| **Answer** | 32 kg |

### Try It Out

**A** In each of the following calculations two of the answers are the same. Write down which is the odd one out.

| | |
|---|---|
| **Example** | **(a)** $\frac{1}{3}$ of 24  **(b)** $\frac{1}{4}$ of 36  **(c)** $\frac{1}{2}$ of 16 |
| **Working** | **(a)** $\frac{1}{3}$ of 24 = 24 ÷ 3 = 8 |
| | **(b)** $\frac{1}{4}$ of 36 = 36 ÷ 4 = 9 |
| | **(c)** $\frac{1}{2}$ of 16 = 16 ÷ 2 = 8 |
| **Answer** | **(b)** is the odd one out. |

**1 (a)** $\frac{1}{2}$ of 24p     **(b)** $\frac{1}{5}$ of 60p     **(c)** $\frac{1}{4}$ of 64p

**2 (a)** $\frac{2}{3}$ of 42 kg     **(b)** $\frac{1}{4}$ of 120 kg     **(c)** $\frac{1}{3}$ of 90 kg

**3 (a)** $\frac{3}{10}$ of 150 books     **(b)** $\frac{2}{5}$ of 125 books     **(c)** $\frac{1}{2}$ of 100 books

**4 (a)** $\frac{9}{20}$ of 240 km     **(b)** $\frac{1}{4}$ of 420 km     **(c)** $\frac{7}{10}$ of 150 km

### Learn More About It

To add or subtract fractions, they must have the same **denominator**. You **don't** add or subtract the denominators.

| Example | $\frac{2}{7} + \frac{3}{7}$ |
|---|---|
| Working | $2 + 3 = 5$ |
| Answer | $\frac{5}{7}$ |

Sometimes you need to change one of the fractions to match the other.

| Example | $\frac{1}{5} + \frac{3}{10}$ |
|---|---|
| Working | Change $\frac{1}{5}$ to $\frac{2}{10}$. |
| | $\frac{2}{10} + \frac{3}{10} = \frac{5}{10} = \frac{1}{2}$   (*Cancel to lowest terms.*) |
| Answer | $\frac{1}{2}$ |

Sometimes you need to change both fractions.

| Example | $\frac{5}{12} - \frac{3}{8}$ |
|---|---|
| Working | $\frac{5}{12} = \frac{10}{24}, \frac{3}{8} = \frac{9}{24}$ |
| | $\frac{10}{24} - \frac{9}{24} = \frac{1}{24}$ |
| Answer | $\frac{1}{24}$ |

## Try It Out

Calculate the following. Cancel to lowest terms if necessary.

**1** (a) $\frac{3}{10} + \frac{3}{10}$   (b) $\frac{6}{7} - \frac{2}{7}$   (c) $\frac{11}{24} + \frac{5}{24}$   (d) $\frac{13}{18} - \frac{5}{18}$

**2** (a) $\frac{1}{2} + \frac{3}{8}$   (b) $\frac{3}{5} + \frac{3}{10}$   (c) $\frac{7}{12} - \frac{1}{4}$   (d) $\frac{1}{6} - \frac{1}{24}$

**3** (a) $1 - \frac{1}{4}$   (b) $1 - \frac{1}{7}$   (c) $1 - \frac{7}{8}$   (d) $1 - \frac{2}{11}$   (e) $1 - \frac{11}{15}$

## Practice

Use the fraction strips on the right for the following calculations.

**1** Write down the fraction each strip shows.

**2** Calculate the following.

| Example | $A + C$ |
|---|---|
| Working | $\frac{1}{2} + \frac{1}{4} = \frac{2}{4} + \frac{1}{4}$ |
| Answer | $\frac{3}{4}$ |

(a) $C + D$   (b) $D + E$   (c) $D - A$   (d) $E + G$
(e) $G - E$   (f) $B - D$   (g) $F + C$   (h) $F - G$

**3** If the **whole** strip is 12 cm long, find the length of each fraction strip.

**Finished Early?**
➡ Go to page 418

# 25 Chance

In this chapter you will learn about ...
1. theoretical probability
2. experiments
3. possibility spaces

## 1 Theoretical Probability

### Remember?

Anything that happens by chance has a **probability** that describes how likely it is.

A probability is a **number** from 0 to 1.

You can write it as a **fraction**, a **decimal** or a **percentage**.

You can put any probability on a **probability scale**.

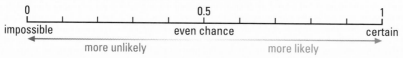

When you say 'there is an even chance of getting a head or a tail when you flip a coin', you mean that the probability is $\frac{1}{2}$ or 0.5.

 In mathematics, it is *not* correct to say 'two to one', 'one in two', 'one out of two', 'fifty-fifty', etc. Probabilities are **fractions**, **decimals** or **percentages**. But you can use words to say roughly what the probability is.

## Try It Out

 **1** Match each of the following statements with one of the words below:
**IMPOSSIBLE, UNLIKELY, EVEN, LIKELY, CERTAIN.**
(a) Somewhere in the world today, a baby will be born.
(b) $1 + 2 = 4$
(c) Someone in your family will win £1 000 000 on the lottery.
(d) You will have some homework to do tonight.
(e) The sun will rise tomorrow morning.
(f) Your teacher will walk into the room wearing a funny hat.
(g) You will have chips to eat today.
(h) The school fire alarm will sound this week.

**2** Which of these are correctly written probabilities?
Copy each one and give it a ✔ or ✘. If you put ✘, give a reason.

(a) $\frac{1}{3}$        (b) 1 chance in 2        (c) $\frac{5}{8}$

(d) 3:1        (e) 17%        (f) 1

(g) 0.25        (h) 50–50        (i) $\frac{10}{15}$

(j) 61%        (k) 6 to 1        (l) 6.1

# Learn About It

In mathematics, anything that is controlled by chance is called an **event**.
The results of an event are called **outcomes**. Outcomes have probabilities,
for example:

| Event | Flip a coin | |
|---|---|---|
| **Outcome** | Head | Tail |
| **Probability** | $\frac{1}{2}$ | $\frac{1}{2}$ |

| Event | Roll a dice | | | | | |
|---|---|---|---|---|---|---|
| **Outcome** | 1 | 2 | 3 | 4 | 5 | 6 |
| **Probability** | $\frac{1}{6}$ | $\frac{1}{6}$ | $\frac{1}{6}$ | $\frac{1}{6}$ | $\frac{1}{6}$ | $\frac{1}{6}$ |

These events have something in common. For each event, all the outcomes
have the same probability. Outcomes like this are called **equally likely**.

There are six different outcomes for rolling a fair, six-sided dice. That's why the
probabilities are all $\frac{1}{6}$.

---

## Key Fact

If all the outcomes are equally likely, the probability is

$$\frac{1}{\text{number of possible outcomes}}.$$

---

There is a mathematical way of writing down probabilities.

Instead of writing 'The probability of getting a head is $\frac{1}{2}$', you write:
$P(\text{head}) = \frac{1}{2}$.

**1** Draw a sketch of this spinner. Just write the names of the colours if you do not have coloured pens or pencils. Copy and complete the list of probabilities for the spinner.

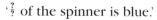

$P$(red) =

$P$(white) =

$P$(yellow) =

$P$(black) =

**2** Sometimes the outcomes are **not** all equally likely.

Draw a sketch of this spinner.
Copy and complete these statements.

'$\frac{?}{?}$ of the spinner is blue.'

'$\frac{?}{?}$ of the spinner is green.'

Now copy and complete these probabilities.

$P$(blue) =

$P$(green) =

**3** Copy and complete this calculation.

$P$(blue) + $P$(green) =

Simplify your answer as much as possible.

You should get 1. It is **certain** you will get either blue or green, so their probabilities must add up to 1.

On this spinner, $P$(red) = $\frac{3}{10}$ or 0.3. You know that $P$(red) + $P$(white) = 1, so $P$(white) must be 1 − 0.3 = 0.7.

> ## Key Fact
>
> The sum of the probabilities of **all** the outcomes **always** equals 1.

**4** Use this idea to answer the following question.

The probability that Dayna catches the early bus in the morning is $\frac{1}{5}$. What is the probability that she misses the early bus? Use $P$(catch) and $P$(miss) in your answer.

## Word Check

**event** something that is controlled by chance

**outcome** a possible result of an event

**probability** the likelihood of a given outcome occurring

**equally likely** having the same probability

**$P$(outcome)** the probability that a particular outcome will happen

# Try It Out

**1** Work out *P*(red) and *P*(yellow) for each spinner.

(a)   (b)   (c)   (d)

**2** Robin has a bag of letter tiles. There are 4 B tiles, 3 A tiles and 5 G tiles.
If he picks a tile at random, what is:

**(a)** *P*(B)?  **(b)** *P*(A)?  **(c)** *P*(G)?

**3** Miriam drives to work.

**(a)** The probability that she will be held up at the railway crossing is 0.2.
What is the probability that she will be able to drive straight over the crossing?

**(b)** The probability she will get a space in the free car park is 0.55.
What is the probability that she will have to use the other car park?

**4** There is a 2% probability that a new Luxibrite light bulb will not work.
What is the probability that it will work?

# Learn More About It

You can use probability to **estimate** how many times something will happen.

On this spinner, the probability of landing on black is $\frac{1}{3}$.

Suppose you spin the pointer 60 times. How many times
would you expect it to land on black?

*P*(black) = $\frac{1}{3}$, so you would expect it to come up $\frac{1}{3}$ of the time.

$\frac{1}{3}$ of 60 = 60 ÷ 3 = 20 times.

This is called the **expected number** of times, or **expected frequency**.

The expected number of times the spinner will land on orange is

$\frac{2}{3}$ of 60 = 60 ÷ 3 × 2 = 40 times.

When you are testing probability, each 'go' is called a **trial**.

Imagine you do 100 trials with this spinner.

Copy and complete these statements.

*P*(grey) = ____.  Expected number of grey  = ____ of 100 = ____ times.

*P*(blue) = ____.  Expected number of blue  = ____ of 100 = ____ times.

*P*(mauve) = ____.  Expected number of mauve = ____ of 100 = ____ times.

## Key Fact

Expected number =
probability × number of trials.

## Word Check

**expected number** an estimate of how
many times an outcome will happen

**expected frequency** expected number

**trial** an event

## Try It Out

**1** When you press a robot's nose, it does one of the things written on its body.
The probability it will do each thing is written there too.

**(a)** Imagine you press each robot's nose 100 times. Write down the
expected number for each outcome.

---

**Example**

**Working**   $P(\text{beep}) = 0.4$
$0.4 \times 100 = 40$
$P(\text{hoot}) = 0.6$
$0.6 \times 100 = 60$

**Answer**    Expected number of beeps = 40.
Expected number of hoots = 60.

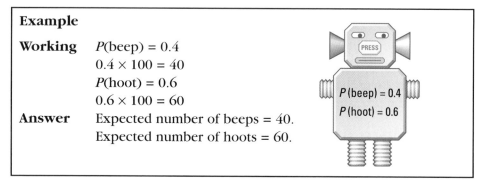

$P(\text{beep}) = 0.4$
$P(\text{hoot}) = 0.6$

---

**(i)**                **(ii)**                **(iii)**

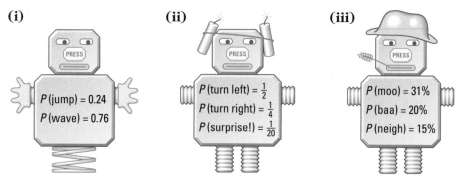

(i) $P(\text{jump}) = 0.24$
$P(\text{wave}) = 0.76$

(ii) $P(\text{turn left}) = \frac{1}{2}$
$P(\text{turn right}) = \frac{1}{4}$
$P(\text{surprise!}) = \frac{1}{20}$

(iii) $P(\text{moo}) = 31\%$
$P(\text{baa}) = 20\%$
$P(\text{neigh}) = 15\%$

**(b)** Some of the robots sometimes do nothing. This is the case if the
probabilities do not add up to 1. If this is true, write down $P(\text{do}$
nothing) as well, and calculate the expected probability.

**2** When Jim goes out in the evening, there is a $\frac{1}{3}$ probability he will see his
friend Farukh. One month, he went out 18 times. How many times do you
expect he saw Farukh?

# Practice

**1** There are 52 playing cards in a normal pack.

There are four **suits** – hearts ♥, spades ♠, diamonds ♦ and clubs ♣.

The **number** cards are the 1–10 of each suit.

The **court** cards are the Jack (11), Queen (12) and King (13).

When a pack has been shuffled, what is the probability of taking:

**(a)** the ace of spades?

**(b)** a King?

**(c)** a number card?

**(d)** an even-numbered club (the Queen counts as even)?

**(e)** a red card?

**(f)** a black 3?

**(g)** an odd-numbered card (the Jacks and Kings count as odd)?

**(h)** a red card that is worth 4 or less?

**2** At Dairy Dream they make yoghurt. A machine fills the pots with yoghurt. Most of the time, the amount of yoghurt in a pot is just right. Sometimes there is too much (an **overweight** pot) or too little (an **underweight** pot). The probabilities vary, depending on the mass of the pot.

| Mass of pot (g) | P (overweight) | P (correct) | P (underweight) |
|---|---|---|---|
| 125 | 2% | | 3% |
| 250 | 1.5% | | 2.5% |
| 500 | 1% | | 1.2% |

**(a)** Copy and complete the table above.

**(b)** They need to estimate how many pots will be overweight, underweight or just right.

Copy and complete this table for a day's work.

| Mass of pot (g) | Number of pots filled | Number of pots expected to be ... overweight | correct | underweight |
|---|---|---|---|---|
| 125 | 1000 | | | |
| 250 | 600 | | | |
| 500 | 500 | | | |

> **Finished Early?**
> ➡ Go to page 419

# Further Practice

**E** **1** Work out *P*(green) and *P*(blue) for each spinner.

(a)

(b)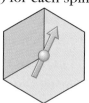

(c)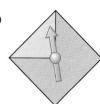

(d)

(e)

(f)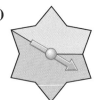

**2** Suppose each of the spinners from question 1 is given 120 spins. Work out the expected totals for scoring green and blue.

**F** In Zorah's game at a charity fair, you pay 20p and throw a dart at this board.

There's an equal chance of landing on each square. You win whatever you land on:

| LOSE ☹ | WIN 20p | LOSE ☹ | WIN 10p | LOSE ☹ |
|---|---|---|---|---|
| WIN 10p | LOSE ☹ | WIN 50p | LOSE ☹ | WIN 20p |
| WIN 20p | LOSE ☹ | WIN 50p | LOSE ☹ | WIN 10p |
| LOSE ☹ | WIN 10p | LOSE ☹ | WIN 20p | LOSE ☹ |

**1** What is the probability that you will land on:
   (a) LOSE?
   (b) WIN 10p?
   (c) WIN 20p?
   (d) WIN 50p?

**2** In 100 trials, what are the expected frequencies for each kind of square?

**3** Imagine you are running Zorah's game and that 100 people have a go.
   (a) How much money would you take in?

   Suppose that the numbers come up as expected.
   (b) How much would you have to pay out to winners who landed on the 10p squares?
   (c) How much would you have to pay out on the 20p squares?
   (d) How much would you have to pay out on the 50p squares?
   (e) How much would you pay out altogether?
   (f) How much profit would you make for charity?

**4** Do you think this game is fair?

**Finished Early?**
 Go to page 419

# Experiments

## Learn About It

**Experimental probability** is about using an experiment to **estimate** probability. It is different from **theoretical probability**, in which you think mathematically about an event and predict what will happen.

Suppose you flipped a coin 100 times and this happened.

| Outcome | Tally | Frequency |
|---------|-------|-----------|
| Heads | ⅃﹢ ﹢⅃ ⅃﹢ ﹢⅃ ﹢⅃ ||| | 28 |
| Tails | ﹢⅃ ⅃﹢ ﹢⅃ ﹢⅃ ⅃﹢ ﹢⅃ ﹢⅃ ﹢⅃ ⅃﹢ ﹢⅃ ﹢⅃ ﹢⅃ ﹢⅃ ﹢⅃ || | 72 |

You would probably think something was wrong with the coin. You expect to get about the same number of heads and tails. It looks as if this coin is more likely to land on tails than heads. The coin is **unfair** or **biased**.

Out of 100 trials, 28 were heads.

So the experimental probability is $P(\text{head}) = \frac{28}{100} = 0.28$.

Tails came up 72 times out of 100, so $P(\text{tail}) = \frac{72}{100} = 0.72$.

If the coin were fair, these probabilities should both be 0.5.

You can show this clearly on a probability scale.

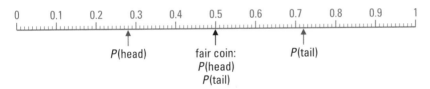

> ## Key Fact
>
> Experimental probability = frequency ÷ number of trials.

## Word Check

**experimental probability** an estimate of probability, made by doing trials or experiments

**theoretical probability** probability calculated by taking into account the mathematics affecting the events

**biased** when the outcomes are not equally likely

# Try It Out

**1** **(a)** Copy and complete the table, working out the experimental
probabilities for these rolls of an unusual dice.

| Outcome | 1 | 2 | 3 | 4 | 5 | 6 | Total |
|---|---|---|---|---|---|---|---|
| Frequency | 15 | 18 | 35 | 0 | 15 | 17 | |
| Probability | | | | | | | 1 |

**(b)** Illustrate the probabilities on a probability scale.

**(c)** There is something unusual about this dice. What do you think it is?

**2** Dominic has an old car. He uses it every
day. Every day during June he writes down
whether the car starts on the first try or
not. He puts a ✔ on his calendar if it
does, and a ✘ if it doesn't.

**(a)** Copy and complete this table.

| | 6 MON ✘ | 13 MON ✘ | 20 MON ✔ | 27 MON ✘ |
|---|---|---|---|---|
| **June** | 7 TUE ✘ | 14 TUE ✔ | 21 TUE ✘ | 28 TUE ✘ |
| 1 WED ✔ | 8 WED ✘ | 15 WED ✘ | 22 WED ✘ | 29 WED ✘ |
| 2 THU ✘ | 9 THU ✘ | 16 THU ✔ | 23 THU ✘ | 30 THU ✔ |
| 3 FRI ✘ | 10 FRI ✔ | 17 FRI ✘ | 24 FRI ✘ | |
| 4 SAT ✔ | 11 SAT ✘ | 18 SAT ✔ | 25 SAT ✘ | |
| 5 SUN ✘ | 12 SUN ✘ | 19 SUN ✘ | 26 SUN ✔ | |

| Outcome | Frequency | Probability |
|---|---|---|
| Started first try | | $P(✔) =$ |
| Didn't start first try | | $P(✘) =$ |
| Total | | 1 |

**(b)** Illustrate the probabilities on a probability scale.

# Practice

For each of the following experiments:

**(a)** draw a tally table

**(b)** carry out 100 trials and tally the results (except question 4 - 50 trials)

**(c)** count your tally marks to get the frequency

**(d)** work out the probabilities

**(e)** illustrate them on a probability scale.

**1** **Point Up?**

Drawing pin

Drop a drawing pin onto your desk from a height of about 30 cm. Record
whether it lands point up or point down.

| Outcome | Tally | Frequency | Probability |
|---|---|---|---|
| Point up | | | $P(\text{up}) =$ |
| Point down | | | $P(\text{down}) =$ |
| Total | | 100 | 1 |

## 2 Biased Dice

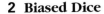

Squared paper, scissors, glue or sticky tape, scrap paper

Draw the net of a dice. Make each square 4 cm wide.

Before you fold up the net and stick the flaps, tape or glue a small wad of paper to the inside of one of the faces. This weights the dice so it will favour one number.

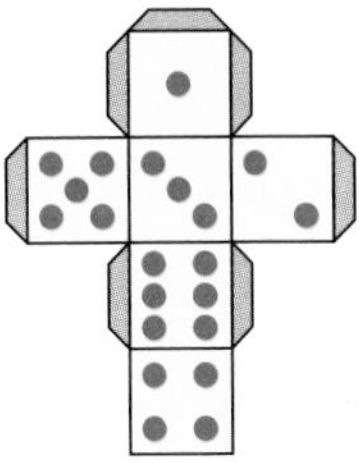

| Outcome | Tally | Frequency | Probability |
|---|---|---|---|
| 1 | | | $P(1) =$ |
| 2 | | | $P(2) =$ |
| 3 | | | $P(3) =$ |
| 4 | | | $P(4) =$ |
| 5 | | | $P(5) =$ |
| 6 | | | $P(6) =$ |
| | Total | 100 | 1 |

## 3 Improbable Protractor

Drawing pin, pointer, card, compasses, protractor

You can use probability to estimate an angle!

Make a spinner with two unequal sectors. Label them **A** and **B**. You can choose the angles, but do not measure them!

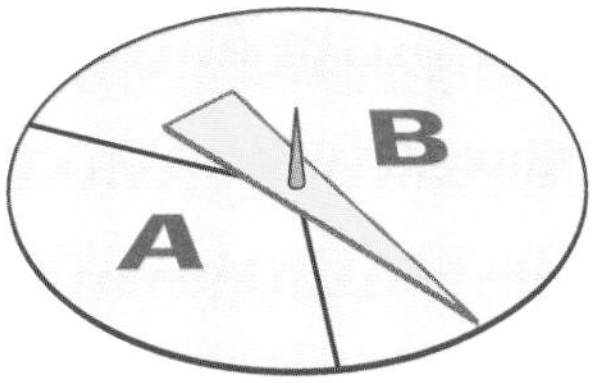


| Outcome | Tally | Frequency | Probability |
|---|---|---|---|
| A | | | $P(A) =$ |
| B | | | $P(B) =$ |
| | Total | 100 | 1 |

When you have worked out the probabilities, multiply them by 360°. This gives an estimate of the angles. Copy and complete this table.

| Angle | Estimated | Measured |
|---|---|---|
| A | $\times 360° =$ | |
| B | $\times 360° =$ | |

Now measure the angles with a protractor and complete the table. How good were your estimates?

## 4 Quadruple Flip

A4 paper, coin, small counter or token

In the game below one 'trial' means working from **Start** to one of the letters by flipping a coin four times. Use a counter or other small object to mark your place on the board.

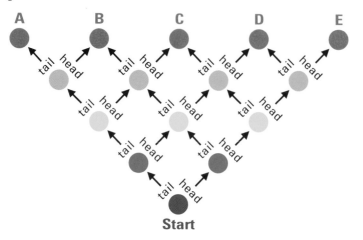

Do 50 trials and record the letter you end up on after each trial. Make a probability table and work out $P(A)$, $P(B)$, etc.

> **Finished Early?**
> Go to page 420

## Further Practice

**1** Michael did an experiment. He repeatedly flipped three coins. Each time, he wrote down whether all three coins showed the same or showed a mixture of heads and tails. Copy and complete the table of his results.

| Outcome | Frequency | Probability |
|---|---|---|
| Mixed | 27 | $P(\text{mixed}) =$ |
| Same | 73 | $P(\text{same}) =$ |
| Total | | 1 |

**2** Kirsty's watch isn't very accurate. She always sets it in the morning and checks it at night. One month, she decides to write down what her watch does. She writes 'F' for fast, 'S' for slow and 'R' for right. This is what her calendar looks like at the end of the month.

| April | | | | | |
|-------|---|---|---|---|---|
| MON | | 4 S | 11 F | 18 F | 25 F |
| TUE | | 5 F | 12 F | 19 F | 26 S |
| WED | | 6 S | 13 F | 20 F | 27 F |
| THU | | 7 F | 14 F | 21 R | 28 R |
| FRI | 1 S | 8 F | 15 S | 22 F | 29 F |
| SUN | 2 F | 9 S | 16 R | 23 S | 30 S |
| SUN | 3 F | 10 F | 17 S | 24 F | |

**(a)** Copy and complete this table.

| Outcome | Frequency | Probability |
|---------|-----------|-------------|
| Fast | | $P(F) =$ |
| Slow | | $P(S) =$ |
| Right | | $P(R) =$ |
| Total | 30 | 1 |

**(b)** Illustrate Kirsty's data on a probability scale.

**3** In 60 spins of a spinner, 15 landed on the green sector and 45 landed on the yellow sector. Draw the spinner.

**Finished Early?**
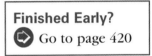 Go to page 420

# ❸ Possibility Spaces

## Learn About It

Sometimes a chance event depends on two things, not just one. This makes it harder to calculate the probabilities. For example, suppose you flip two coins. What is the probability they will both land the same way up?

You can use a **possibility space diagram** to help. Put the outcomes for the first coin along the top. Put the outcomes for the second coin at the side.

| | | 1ˢᵗ coin | |
|---|---|---|---|
| | | **Head** | **Tail** |
| **2ⁿᵈ coin** | **Head** | same | different |
| | **Tail** | different | same |

There are four ways the coins can land. Two of these show the same side. So $P(\text{same}) = \frac{2}{4} = \frac{1}{2}$.

A toy slot machine has two reels with four sections on each reel. Each time you pull the handle, the reels rotate and stop with one picture from each reel showing in the window.

Reel 1 has

Reel 2 has

You 'win' the amount of money shown in the windows. What are the probabilities of the various wins?

There are 16 possible combinations of pictures that can appear in the windows.

| | Reel 1 | | | |
|---|---|---|---|---|
| **Reel 2** | no win | 10p | no win | 5p |
| | 5p | 15p | 5p | 10p |
| | 10p | 20p | 10p | 15p |
| | no win | 10p | no win | 5p |

There are 4 ways to win 5p, so $P$(win 5p) $= \frac{4}{16} = \frac{1}{4}$.

There are 5 ways to win 10p, so $P$(win 10p) $= \frac{5}{16}$.

There are 2 ways to win 15p, so $P$(win 15p) $= \frac{1}{8}$.

There is 1 way to win 20p, so $P$(win 20p) $= \frac{1}{16}$.

You can only use these diagrams when each possibility is **equally likely**.

**Word Check**

**possibility space diagram** a table showing all the possible outcomes of two events

## Try It Out

Two dice

**1** Suppose you roll two dice and add the two numbers.
Copy and complete the possibility space diagram, showing the possible totals.

| | | 1st dice | | | | | |
|---|---|---|---|---|---|---|---|
| | | 1 | 2 | 3 | 4 | 5 | 6 |
| **2nd dice** | 1 | | 3 | | | | |
| | 2 | 3 | | | | | |
| | 3 | | | | | | |
| | 4 | | | | 9 | | |
| | 5 | | | | | | |
| | 6 | | | 10 | | | |

**2** Now calculate the probability of each possible score. Round off your answers to 2 d.p.

> **Example** $P(3) = \frac{2}{36} = 0.06$ to 2 d.p.

**3** Work out the expected frequency of each score for 100 trials.

> *Remember: expected frequency = probability × number of trials.*

> **Example** Expected number of 3s = $0.06 \times 100 = 6$ times.

**4** Roll two dice 100 times and record the results in a table like the one below. If you have only one dice, you can roll it twice instead.

| Score | Tally | Frequency | Expected frequency |
|-------|-------|-----------|--------------------|
| 2 | | | |
| 3 | | | |
| 4 | | | |

**5** Were the results similar to what you predicted?

## Practice

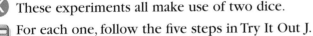

Two dice

**K** These experiments all make use of two dice.

For each one, follow the five steps in Try It Out J.

**1** The score is the **difference** between the numbers on the two dice.

> **Example** 2 and 5 score **3** because 5 - 2 = 3.

**2** The score is the **bigger** number on the dice.

> **Example** 2 and 5 score **5** because 5 > 2.

**3** If both dice show even numbers, **add** the scores.
If one dice shows an odd number, that number **is** the score.
If both dice show an odd number, score **0**.

**4** If both dice show the same number, score **1**.
If the dice show different numbers, score **0**.

**L** **Twin spin**

If both spinners land on **WIN**, add the amounts of money together.

If either spinner lands on a , you lose.

Spinner 1        Spinner 2

**1** Draw a possibility space diagram.

**2** Work out the probability of each win. Round your answers to 2 d.p.

**3** Work out the expected frequency of each win for 100 trials.

**4** **(a)** Imagine you are running the game. You have decided to charge £1 a go. How much money would you take from 100 goes?

　**(b)** If the £1 win came up as many times as you expected, how much would you have to pay out?

　**(c)** Repeat (b) for the other winning amounts.

　**(d)** Add all the amounts from (b) and (c) together. This is the total amount you would have to pay out.

　**(e)** Would you make a profit or lose money? How much?

**5** Make the spinners. Carry out 100 trials. Record your results.

**6** Repeat question 4 using the actual results of your trials.

**7** Do you think this game is fair? Give reasons for your answer.

> **Finished Early?**
> ➡ Go to page 420

## Further Practice

 **1** Use the possibility space diagram from Try It Out J to answer these questions. What is the probability that the score on two dice is:

**(a)** even?　　　　　　　　**(b)** odd?

**(c)** 3 or less?　　　　　　 **(d)** more than 7?

**(e)** a prime number?　　　 **(f)** a double (1 and 1, 2 and 2 etc.)?

**(g)** a multiple of 3?

> **Finished Early?**
> ➡ Go to page 420

# Unit 13 *Probability*

## Summary of Chapter 25

- A probability is a **number** from 0 to 1, written as a **fraction**, **decimal** or **percentage**. You can put any probability onto a **probability scale**.

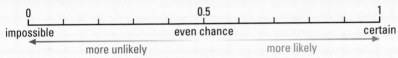

- In mathematics, anything that is controlled by chance is called an **event**. The results of an event are called **outcomes**. Outcomes have probabilities.

| Event | Outcome | Probability |
|---|---|---|
| Flip a coin | head | $\frac{1}{2}$ |
| | tail | $\frac{1}{2}$ |

Instead of writing 'The probability of getting a head is $\frac{1}{2}$', you can write $P(\text{head}) = \frac{1}{2}$.

- Outcomes that have the same probability are called **equally likely**.

  The probability of an outcome is $\dfrac{1}{\text{number of possible outcomes}}$.

  **Fair** dice and coins have equally likely outcomes.

  In a biased or unfair event, the outcomes are **not** equally likely.

- If you add the probabilities of **all** the outcomes of an event together, you **always** get 1.

- You can use probability to **estimate** how many times something will happen. This is called the **expected number** of times, or **expected frequency**. Expected frequency = probability × number of trials.

- **Experimental** probability is about using an experiment to **estimate** probability. Experimental probability = frequency ÷ number of trials.

- Sometimes a chance event depends on two things, not just one. Use a **possibility space diagram** to list all the outcomes.

| | | 1ˢᵗ coin | |
|---|---|---|---|
| | | **Head** | **Tail** |
| **2ⁿᵈ coin** | **Head** | same | different |
| | **Tail** | different | same |

# Brush Up Your Number 14

## Ratios and Scale Factors

### Learn About It

The red **ratio** shows there
are twice as many white as
brown sandwiches.

white : brown

$= 2 : 1$ ⎫
⎬ equivalent
$= 4 : 2$ ⎭ ratios

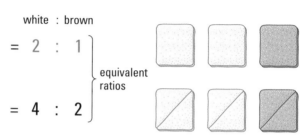

You can change a ratio into an **equivalent
ratio** by multiplying or dividing the ratio
numbers by the *same* number.

$$\overset{\times 2}{2{:}1 = 4{:}2} \qquad \overset{\div 2}{4{:}2 = 2{:}1}$$

White and brown sandwiches weigh 50 g each.

So    white:brown
=      100 g:50 g
=       100:50    (*You can leave out the units if they are the same.*)
=        2:1

If you divide both numbers in the ratio by one of the numbers, the ratio will
contain a 1. For instance, if you have three white sandwiches and two brown
sandwiches:

white:brown
=   3:2
=   $1\frac{1}{2}$:1   (divide by 2)
So there are $1\frac{1}{2}$ times as many
white sandwiches as brown.

white:brown
=   3:2
=   $1$:$\frac{2}{3}$   (divide by 3)
So there are $\frac{2}{3}$ as many brown
sandwiches as white.

### A Try It Out

**1** Copy these equivalent ratios and fill in the missing numbers.
    **(a)** 2:5 = 6:?     2:5 = ?:50     2:5 = 14:?     2:5 = 1:?     2:5 = ?:75
    **(b)** 3:4 = 15:? = ?:44 = 24:? = ?:400 = 0.3:?
    **(c)** 7:10 = 70:? = ?:70 = ?:1 = 3.5:? = ?:1 000 000

**2** In the following ratios, change the quantities so the units match, if
    necessary. Then cancel the ratios to their lowest terms.
    **(a)** 9 g:6 g           **(b)** 16 cm:12 cm        **(c)** 30 m:8 m
    **(d)** 2 t:300 kg       **(e)** 125 m:4 km       **(f)** 0.4 m:60 cm
    **(g)** 1.2 km:800 m   **(h)** 650 g:1.6 kg     **(i)** 6 cm:42 mm
    **(j)** 45 minutes:$1\frac{1}{2}$ hours

**3** Change the red ratio number to 1 by dividing. Write the ratios using decimals.

(**a**) 20:4  (**b**) 6:48  (**c**) 2:5  (**d**) 18:8

(**e**) 200:120  (**f**) 275:1000  (**g**) 0.8:0.2  (**h**) 10:5.2

(**i**) 1.8:8  (**j**) 0.5:3

## Learn More About It

A photocopier is used to **enlarge** a picture. You can describe the enlargement using a ratio.

Enlargement length:Original length

$$10 \text{ cm}:4 \text{ cm}$$
$$= \quad 10:4$$
$$= \quad \tfrac{10:4}{4:4} \text{ (divide by 4)}$$
$$= \quad 2.5:1$$

The photocopy enlargement is 2.5 times the size of the original picture. The **scale factor** of enlargement is 2.5.

## Try It Out

**B** **1** A photocopier was used to enlarge these pictures. Find the scale factor of each enlargement.

(**a**) original  enlargement  (**b**)

7 cm

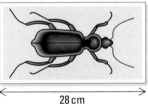

28 cm

8 cm

12 cm

(**c**)

5 cm

17.5 cm

(**d**)

6 cm

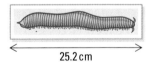

25.2 cm

**2** Write the length of each picture from question 1 if it was enlarged by the following scale factors.

(**a**) 2  (**b**) 3.5  (**c**) 1.2  (**d**) 10

## Practice

**C** Change the following ratios to equivalent ratios with whole numbers. Cancel them to their lowest terms.

**1** 0.6:0.4  **2** 1.5:2  **3** 0.4:1  **4** 2.4:1.6

**5** 0.02:0.12  **6** $\tfrac{1}{3}$:2  **7** $\tfrac{3}{4}$:$\tfrac{1}{4}$

**8** $\tfrac{7}{10}$:$\tfrac{3}{20}$  **9** $\tfrac{2}{3}$:$\tfrac{1}{5}$  **10** $1\tfrac{3}{5}$:2

**Finished Early?**

⇨ Go to page 421

# 26 Transformations

In this chapter you will learn about …
1. reflection
2. rotation
3. translations and vectors
4. enlargements

## T 1 Reflection

 Squared paper

### Learn About It

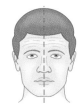

A shape has **symmetry** if you can fold one half exactly on to the other. The fold is called the **line of symmetry**. One half is a **mirror image** or **reflection** of the other.

A point below the line matches a point the **same distance** above the line.

points the same distance above and below

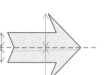

The original shape before reflection is called the **object**. The new shape made by the reflection is called the **image**.

This object triangle is drawn on axes.

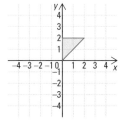

This image is the reflection in the *x*-axis.

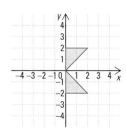

This is the reflection in the *y*-axis.

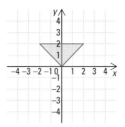

This is the reflection in the line *y* = *x*.

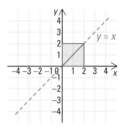

## Word Check

**reflect** make a symmetrical design by adding a mirror image to an object

**object** the original shape before reflection

**image** the new shape made by the reflection

**line of reflection** the mirror line in a reflection

# Try It Out

**A** Copy these shapes on squared paper and draw in their reflections in the lines of symmetry shown.

**1** 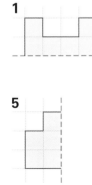 **2**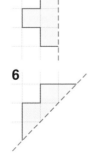

**3** 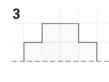 **4**

**5** **6**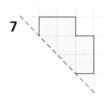

**7** 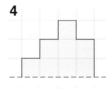 **8**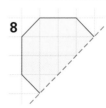

**B** Copy these diagrams on squared paper and put in their lines of symmetry.
They may have more than one line of symmetry.

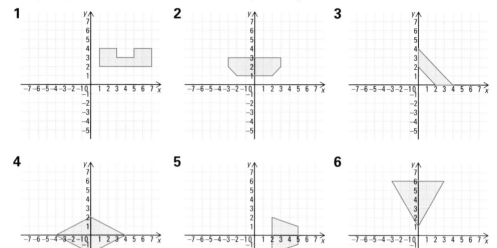

## Practice

**C** Copy the diagrams below and put in the lines of symmetry. Write down the
equations of the lines of symmetry.

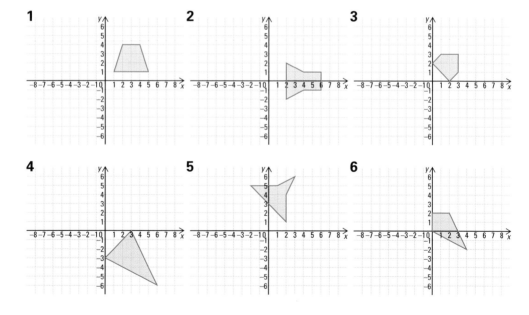

Copy these shapes and reflect them in the lines you are given. If there is more than one line, reflect them in both lines.

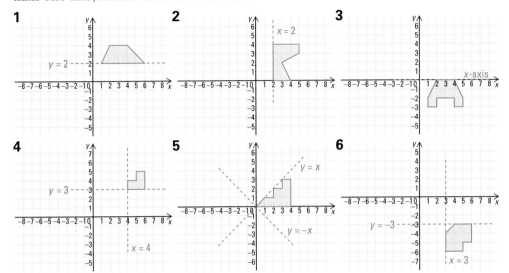

## Further Practice

Copy these shapes on to squared paper and draw their lines of symmetry, if any.

1    2   3    4

5    6   7   8

**F** Copy these diagrams and reflect the shapes in both the *x*- and *y*-axes.

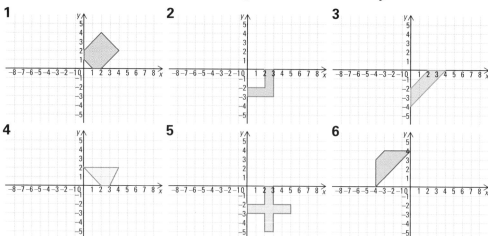

**Finished Early?**
➡ Go to page 422

**T ❷ Rotation**

 Squared paper, tracing paper, protractor

## Remember?

A shape that looks the same in different positions when it is **rotated** about a point has **rotational symmetry**.

The letter S has rotational symmetry.

S has rotational symmetry of **order 2** because it is the same in two different positions. The order must be 2 or more for a shape to have rotational symmetry.

The point around which a shape is rotated is called the **centre of the rotation**.

centre of rotation

top rotates to the bottom

## Try It Out

**G** Write down whether each shape has rotational symmetry and, if so, give the order of symmetry.

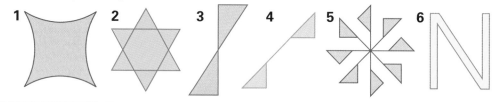

# Learn About It

To rotate an object about a given centre, use tracing paper. Trace the object, then turn the tracing paper round, keeping the centre fixed by pressing on it with your pencil point, until you find where the image should be. Then draw the image.

**Example** Rotate this triangle 90° clockwise about the origin (0, 0).

**Working** You can mark an 'L' shape on your tracing paper to help you (shown in red).

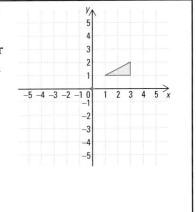

**Answer**

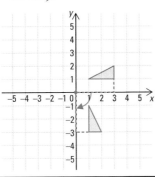

Here are the rotations through 90° anticlockwise and through 180°.

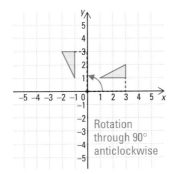

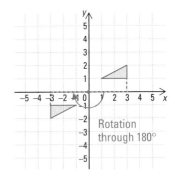

If you put all these images and the object together, you see a pattern with rotational symmetry of order 4.

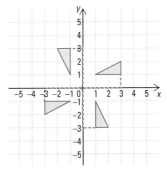

## Word Check

**rotate** turn about a point

**centre of rotation** the point about which the shape is turned

**object** the original shape before rotation

**image** the rotated shape

You can use any point as a centre of
rotation. This diagram shows a 90°
clockwise rotation about (2, 1).

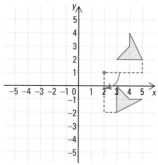

# Try It Out

**H** Draw these shapes on squared paper
and rotate them through the angles shown,
about the red spot .

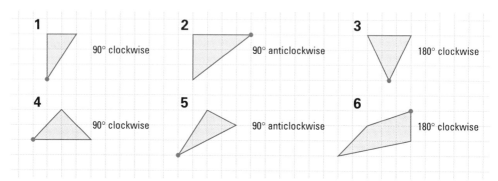

**1** 90° clockwise

**2** 90° anticlockwise

**3** 180° clockwise

**4** 90° clockwise

**5** 90° anticlockwise

**6** 180° clockwise

**I** Draw these shapes and rotate them as shown. Write down the coordinates of
the corners of the images.

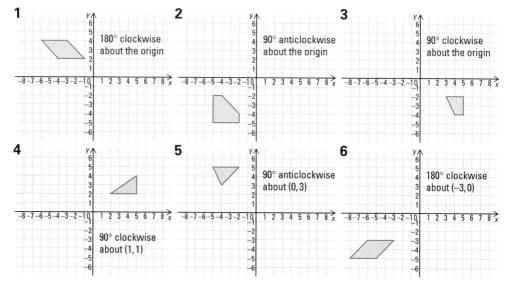

**1** 180° clockwise about the origin

**2** 90° anticlockwise about the origin

**3** 90° clockwise about the origin

**4** 90° clockwise about (1,1)

**5** 90° anticlockwise about (0,3)

**6** 180° clockwise about (−3,0)

# Practice

**J** Draw these objects and rotate them so that they have the rotational symmetry shown.

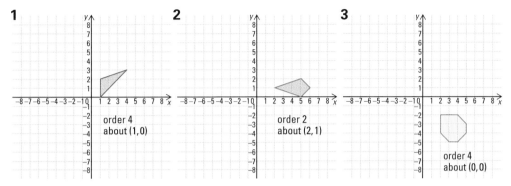

**Finished Early?**
➡ Go to page 422

# Further Practice

Draw these shapes and rotate them by 90° clockwise about the origin.
Mark in the coordinates of the corners of the rotated figures.

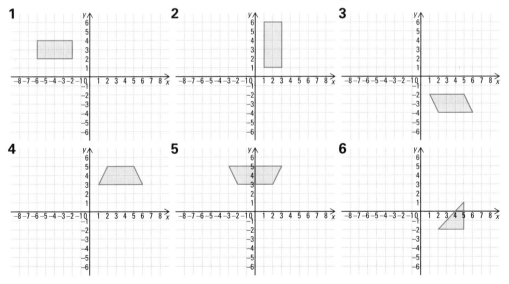

**Finished Early?**
➡ Go to page 422

**353**

# T ❸ Translations and Vectors

## Learn About It

A **translation** is a movement without any enlargement, rotation or reflection.

The pencil has been translated.

A translation is described by how far an object moves horizontally and by how far it moves vertically.

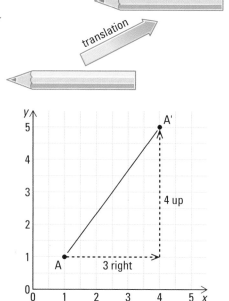

The object of this translation is A(1, 1). The image after the translation is A'(4, 5). The translation moves objects 3 units to the right and 4 units up. This is written using the **column vector** $\begin{pmatrix} 3 \\ 4 \end{pmatrix}$.

The top number gives the horizontal ($x$) movement. The bottom number gives the vertical ($y$) movement.

$\begin{pmatrix} -1 \\ -2 \end{pmatrix}$ means 1 unit left and 2 units down.

### Word Check

**translation** a sliding movement

**column vector** a way of writing down instructions for a translation

## Try It Out

**L**

**1** Write these translations using vectors.

    **(a)** 2 right, 3 up     **(b)** 3 left, 5 up     **(c)** 2 right, 1 down

    **(d)** 2 left, 3 down     **(e)** 4 right, 3 up     **(f)** 2 left, 1 up

**2** Describe the translations these column vectors represent. Use 'left', 'right', 'up' and 'down'.

| **Example** | $\begin{pmatrix} 4 \\ 2 \end{pmatrix}$ |
|---|---|
| **Answer** | 4 right and 2 up |

    **(a)** $\begin{pmatrix} 1 \\ 1 \end{pmatrix}$     **(b)** $\begin{pmatrix} 2 \\ 1 \end{pmatrix}$     **(c)** $\begin{pmatrix} -5 \\ 6 \end{pmatrix}$     **(d)** $\begin{pmatrix} 6 \\ -2 \end{pmatrix}$

    **(e)** $\begin{pmatrix} -3 \\ -1 \end{pmatrix}$     **(f)** $\begin{pmatrix} 0 \\ 3 \end{pmatrix}$     **(g)** $\begin{pmatrix} -2 \\ 0 \end{pmatrix}$     **(h)** $\begin{pmatrix} 0 \\ 0 \end{pmatrix}$

**3** Use column vectors to describe the following translations.

**(a)**  **(b)**  **(c)**  **(d)**

  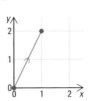 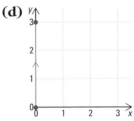

**(e)**  **(f)**  **(g)**

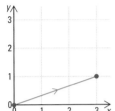 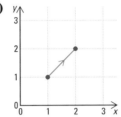 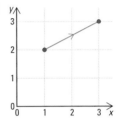

## Practice

Squared paper

For each question, draw $x$- and $y$-axes and label them from 0 to 6. Plot the point A at $(0, 1)$, then translate point A by the following column vectors. Write down the coordinates of each image point A'.

**1** $\begin{pmatrix} 1 \\ 1 \end{pmatrix}$  **2** $\begin{pmatrix} 2 \\ 1 \end{pmatrix}$  **3** $\begin{pmatrix} 4 \\ 6 \end{pmatrix}$  **4** $\begin{pmatrix} \frac{1}{2} \\ 1 \end{pmatrix}$

**5** $\begin{pmatrix} 0.5 \\ 1.5 \end{pmatrix}$  **6** $\begin{pmatrix} \frac{1}{4} \\ \frac{1}{2} \end{pmatrix}$  **7** $\begin{pmatrix} 0 \\ 0 \end{pmatrix}$

**1** Use column vectors to describe the translations of the following triangles.

**(a)**  **(b)**  **(c)**  **(d)**

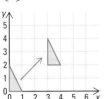 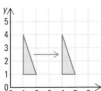 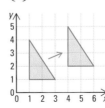 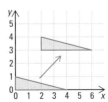

**2** Draw the triangle ABC with A at $(0, 0)$, B at $(3, 1)$ and C at $(1, 1)$.

**(a)** Translate the triangle ABC by $\begin{pmatrix} 2 \\ 1 \end{pmatrix}$ and label this triangle X.

**(b)** Translate the triangle ABC by $\begin{pmatrix} 4 \\ 3 \end{pmatrix}$ and label this triangle Y.

**(c)** Translate the triangle ABC by $\begin{pmatrix} 2 \\ 4 \end{pmatrix}$ and label this triangle Z.

**Finished Early?**
➡ Go to page 423

## Further Practice

Copy and complete this table.

| Original point | Translation in vector form | New position |
|---|---|---|
| $(0, 0)$ | $\begin{pmatrix} 1 \\ 2 \end{pmatrix}$ | $(1, 2)$ |
| $(1, 0)$ | $\begin{pmatrix} 1 \\ 3 \end{pmatrix}$ | |
| $(2, -3)$ | $\begin{pmatrix} 1 \\ 6 \end{pmatrix}$ | |
| $(5, 6)$ | $\begin{pmatrix} 2 \\ -5 \end{pmatrix}$ | |
| $(6, 8)$ | $\begin{pmatrix} -3 \\ -4 \end{pmatrix}$ | |
| $(1, 3)$ | $\begin{pmatrix} 2 \\ 2 \end{pmatrix}$ | |
| $(5, 3)$ | | $(4, 2)$ |
| $(6, 4)$ | | $(6, 2)$ |
| $(3, 7)$ | | $(4, 7)$ |
| | $\begin{pmatrix} 1 \\ 1 \end{pmatrix}$ | $(1, 1)$ |
| | $\begin{pmatrix} 3 \\ 4 \end{pmatrix}$ | $(2, 3)$ |
| | $\begin{pmatrix} 1 \\ 2 \end{pmatrix}$ | $(4, 5)$ |

**Finished Early?**
➡ Go to page 423

# Enlargements

1 cm squared paper

## Learn About It

1 Draw these axes on squared paper and plot the triangle ABC. The corners of the triangle are A (2, 4), B (2, 1), C (4, 1).

2 Multiply each coordinate by two. Draw A'B'C'.

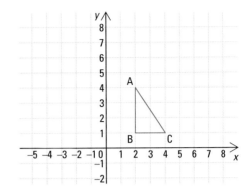

$$A\ (2,4) \xrightarrow[\times 2]{\text{moved to}} A'\ (4,8)$$

$$B\ (2,1) \xrightarrow[\times 2]{} B'\ (4,2)$$

$$C\ (4,1) \xrightarrow[\times 2]{} C'\ (8,2)$$

3 Measure and record the lengths of the sides of triangle ABC and triangle A'B'C'. Copy and complete this table.

| Length of sides | |
|---|---|
| AB = | A'B' = |
| BC = | B'C' = |
| AC = | A'C' = |

4 What can you say about the lengths of the sides of these triangles?

5 Draw in the lines AA', BB', CC' and extend them until they meet. They should meet at the origin (O).

6 Measure and record OA, OA', OB, OB', OC, OC'. What can you say about the lengths of these lines?

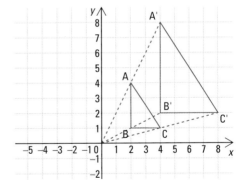

A'B'C' is an **enlargement** of ABC of **scale factor** 2. The origin is the centre of the enlargement. Distances from the centre are doubled.

## Word Check

enlargement a shape changed in size

scale factor the change in size

object the original shape before enlargement

image the enlarged shape

# Try It Out

Squared paper

**P** For each question:
**(a)** copy the diagram onto squared paper with axes from −8 to 8
**(b)** multiply the coordinates of ABC by 2 to find A'B'C'
**(c)** draw A'B'C', an enlargement of ABC by scale factor 2.

**1**

**2**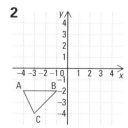

**3**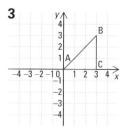

## Key Fact

To enlarge by scale factor 2 with centre at the origin, multiply both coordinates by 2.

# Practice

Squared paper

**Q** In each question below, draw a set of axes from −10 to 10 on squared paper, then draw the object and its enlargement, with centre at the origin.

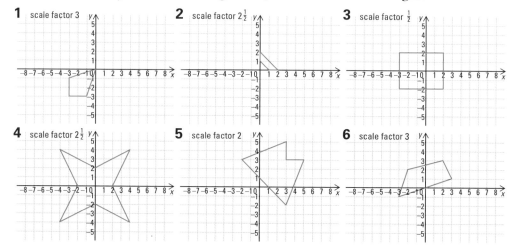

**1** scale factor 3

**2** scale factor 2½

**3** scale factor ½

**4** scale factor 2½

**5** scale factor 2

**6** scale factor 3

The blue shapes are enlargements of the red shapes. What is the scale factor of these enlargements? Write down the coordinates of the object and image, and compare them.

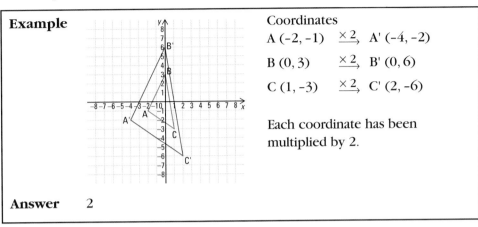

**Example**

Coordinates

A (−2, −1)  $\xrightarrow{\times 2}$  A' (−4, −2)

B (0, 3)  $\xrightarrow{\times 2}$  B' (0, 6)

C (1, −3)  $\xrightarrow{\times 2}$  C' (2, −6)

Each coordinate has been multiplied by 2.

**Answer**  2

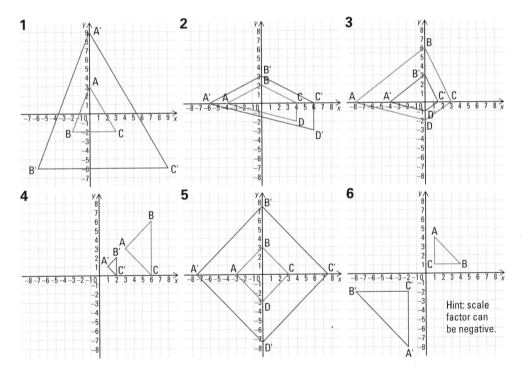

Hint: scale factor can be negative.

**Finished Early?**
➡ Go to page 423

# Further Practice

Squared paper

**S** For each of the following questions, draw a set of axes labelled from –10 to 10. Mark in the object and then draw the enlargement.

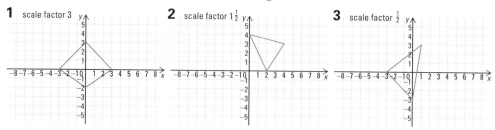

**1** scale factor 3

**2** scale factor $1\frac{1}{2}$

**3** scale factor $\frac{1}{2}$

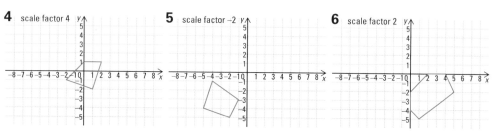

**4** scale factor 4

**5** scale factor –2

**6** scale factor 2

**Finished Early?**
➡ Go to page 423

# 27 Loci and Constructions

In this chapter you will learn about ...
1. single points and lines
2. triangles
3. constructions
4. double points and lines

## Single Points and Lines

Compasses, protractor, squared paper

### Learn About It

The path of any object that travels a fixed distance from a point is a circle. We say that its **locus** is a circle.

#### Word Check

**locus** (plural **loci**) the path traced by an object when it moves according to a set pattern or rule

### Try It Out

1 Sketch the loci of the following.
   (a) a satellite as it moves in orbit around the Earth

   (b) the tip of a rotor blade of a helicopter as it hovers above the ground

**2** Draw to scale the loci of the following:

**(a)** a point X travelling 3 cm from a fixed point Y

**(b)** the tip of a 2 m aeroplane propeller as it starts up (scale: 2 cm to 1 m)

**(c)** the locus of a donkey pulling tightly on a 3 m rope tethered to a stake in a field (scale: 2 cm to 1 m).

## Learn More About It

The locus of points at a fixed distance from a straight line is a pair of parallel lines.

locus

line

locus

If the line is short, the locus of points moving a fixed distance from the line is a 'sausage' or 'race track' shape. The locus is made up of two parallel lines with two semicircles.

## Try It Out

**B** **1** Sketch the loci of the following:

**(a)** the head of a boy sliding down a hill on a sledge

**(b)** the head of the pilot in an aeroplane as it taxis along a runway.

**2** Draw to scale the loci of the following:

(a) the head of a woman 1.5 m high as she skateboards along a straight road (scale: 4 cm to 1 m)

(b) the path of a guard dog on a 2 m chain which can slide along a 5-m rail (scale: 1 cm to 1 m).

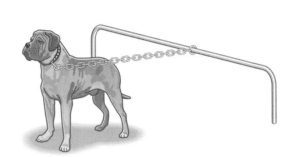

**3** Draw to scale the loci of points:

(a) 5 m away from the corner of a wall (scale: 1 cm to 1 m)

(b) 1 m away from a desk measuring 2 m × 1 m  (scale: 2 cm to 1 m).

Watch out for the corners!

# Practice

**1** A line, XY, is 12 cm long.

(a) Draw the locus of points which are 6 cm from X.

(b) Draw the locus of points which are 7 cm from Y.

(c) Shade the area where the two loci cross.

(d) Draw the locus of points which are 5 cm from the line XY.

**2** Two goats are tethered in a field on 3-m ropes. They are tethered 5.5 m apart. Draw the loci of the two goats, and shade the area where the loci cross. Use a scale of 2 cm to 1 m.

**3** A horse trainer is sitting on the fence in the corner of a square corral with perimeter of 60 m. He can lasso any horse within 12 m. Draw a diagram to show the area where a horse can stand without being caught. Use a scale of 1 cm to 1 m.

**Finished Early?**
Go to page 423

# Further Practice

**(D)** **1** Copy the diagrams and accurately construct the locus of points 1 cm from the lines.

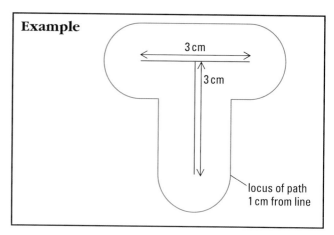

**Example**

3 cm

3 cm

locus of path
1 cm from line

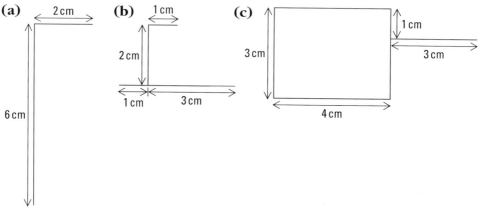

**(a)**  2 cm

6 cm

**(b)**  1 cm

2 cm

1 cm  3 cm

**(c)**  1 cm

3 cm  3 cm

4 cm

**2** A school has a security light in the corner of a fenced playing field. The light is triggered by any movement within 5 m of it. Draw, to a scale of 1 cm to 1 m, the area in which movement will trigger the light.

**3** Mr Green is watering his garden. He has a sprinkler which sprinkles water to a range of 6 m. There is a 1 m wide path 5 m from the sprinkler.

Draw, to a scale of 1 cm to 1 m, the garden, the path and the area which the sprinkler reaches. Indicate on the path the place where walkers are likely to get wet.

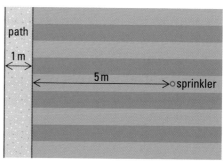

path

1 m

5 m  sprinkler

**Finished Early?**
➡ Go to page 423

# Triangles

Compasses

## Learn About It

Follow these steps to draw a triangle with sides of 6 cm, 8 cm and 10 cm.

**1** Select a side to draw first (e.g. 10 cm).

Draw a horizontal line a bit longer than you need. This is the **base line**. Mark two points on it 10 cm apart. These are two vertices of the triangle.

**2** Open out the compasses to the same length as another of the sides (6 cm).

Place the point of the compasses at one end of the base line and draw an **arc**.

**3** Open out the compasses to the length of the third side (8 cm). With the point of the compasses on the other base line mark, draw another arc that crosses the first arc. The first arc may need extending.

**4** Join the marks on the base line to the point where the arcs **intersect**.

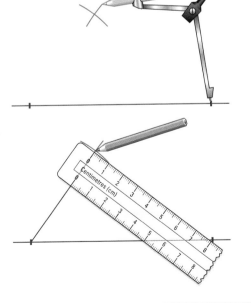

### Word Check

**arc** part of the circumference of a circle

**intersect** cross or meet

It is impossible to make a triangle with some combinations of lengths.

| | |
|---|---|
| **Example** | Draw a triangle with sides of 10 cm, 6 cm and 2 cm. |
| **Working** | Draw a base of 10 cm. |
| | Open the compasses to 2 cm. Mark an arc from one end of the line. |
| | Open the compasses to 6 cm. Mark an arc from the other end. The two arcs do not intersect. This triangle is impossible. |
| **Answer** | It is not possible to construct a 2 cm, 6 cm, 10 cm triangle. |

If the sum of the two shortest sides is less than the longest side, then it is impossible to draw the triangle.

## Try It Out

**E** **1** Construct the following triangles. Measure their angles.

   (a) 4 cm, 5 cm, 6 cm                 (b) 4 cm, 6 cm, 8 cm

   (c) 7 cm, 8 cm, 12 cm                (d) 6 cm, 7 cm, 9 cm

**2** Which of the following sets can't be sides of triangles?

   (a) 12 cm, 13 cm, 14 cm             (b) 10 cm, 4 cm, 5 cm

   (c) 5 cm, 5 cm, 5 cm                (d) 6 cm, 8 cm, 10 cm

   (e) 3 cm, 7 cm, 7 cm                (f) 3 cm, 5 cm, 12 cm

## Learn More About It

Follow these steps to draw a triangle with a base of 10 cm and angles of 40° and 50°.

base

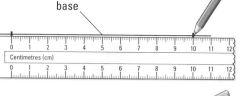

**1** Draw the base.

**2** Place the protractor at one end of the base and mark off 40°.

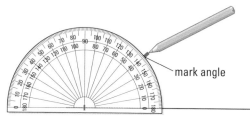

mark angle

**3** Draw a line from the end of the base through the protractor mark.

mark angle

**4** Using the protractor, mark off 50° at the other end of the base.

**5** Draw a line from that end of the base through the protractor mark until it intersects the other line.

Check your construction by measuring the third angle. It should be 180° − 40° − 50° = 90°.

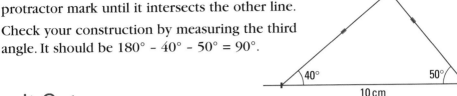

## Try It Out

**F** Construct the following triangles. Measure and record the new sides.

| Triangle | Base | Angle 1 | Angle 2 |
|---|---|---|---|
| 1 | 6 cm | 90° | 50° |
| 2 | 8 cm | 80° | 45° |
| 3 | 7 cm | 60° | 70° |

## Practice

**G** Copy the table below. Construct the triangles and complete the missing information.

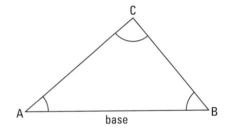

| Triangle | AB (base) | AC | BC | Angle A | Angle B | Angle C | Is it possible? |
|---|---|---|---|---|---|---|---|
| 1 | 6 cm | | | 60° | 80° | | |
| 2 | 6 cm | 7 cm | 7 cm | | | | |
| 3 | 6 cm | | 7 cm | | | 90° | |
| 4 | 7 cm | 7 cm | | 110° | | | |
| 5 | 6 cm | 2 cm | 3 cm | | | | |

> **Finished Early?**
> ➡ Go to page 424

## Further Practice

**H 1** Construct triangles with the following sides. Measure the angles.
  **(a)** 3 cm, 4 cm, 5 cm  **(b)** 5 cm, 12 cm, 13 cm
  **(c)** 7 cm, 4 cm, 4 cm  **(d)** 9 cm, 12 cm, 11 cm
  **(e)** 8 cm, 8 cm, 8 cm  **(f)** 16 cm, 8 cm, 10 cm

**2** Using a base line of 10 cm each time, construct triangles with these base angles. Measure the new sides.
  **(a)** 20°, 60°   **(b)** 35°, 85°   **(c)** 17°, 109°

> **Finished Early?**
> ➡ Go to page 424

#  Constructions

 Compasses, protractor, squared paper

## Learn About It

A pencil, ruler and compasses are used to **construct** accurate drawings.

To draw the **perpendicular bisector** of the line between two points A and B:

- Open the compasses to a little more than half of the distance between the two points. Place the point of the compasses on A and draw an arc above and below the area between the points.

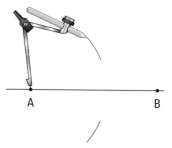

- Keeping the compasses set to the same radius, place the point on B and draw arcs above and below. Make sure that the two sets of arcs cross. Join the two places where the arcs cross with a straight line.

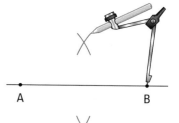

The line you have drawn bisects the straight line that joins two points and is perpendicular (at right angles) to that line.

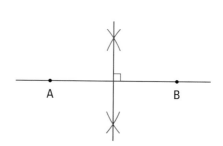

### Word Check

**bisect** cut into two halves
**perpendicular** at right angles

## Try It Out

Draw the perpendicular bisector of the line between two points …

**(a)** 5 cm apart **(b)** 10 cm apart **(c)** 12 cm apart.

## Learn More About It

To construct a 60° angle without using a protractor:

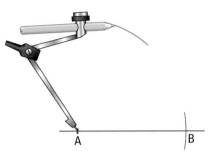

- Draw a base line and mark a point (A) on it.
- Open your compasses to any radius. Place the point of your compasses on A and draw two arcs as shown. One of the arcs should cross the base line.

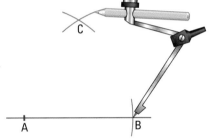

- With the compasses at the same radius, put the point of the compasses on B and mark an arc so that it crosses the first arc. This is point C.

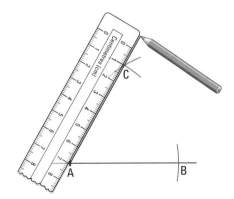

- Join AC. Angle CAB = 60°.

To bisect an angle:

- Open your compasses and put the point on the vertex of the angle to be bisected (A).
- Draw a faint arc with the compasses to cut both arms of the angle (B and C).

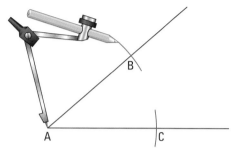

- Put the point of the compasses on intersection point B and make another arc near the middle of the angle.

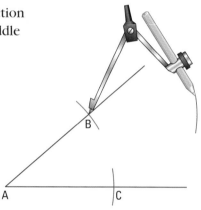

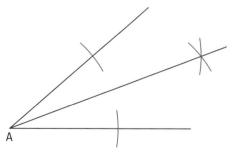

- Using the same radius, put the point of the compasses on C and draw another arc that intersects the first.

- Draw a line from the vertex of the angle through the intersection of the arcs. You have bisected the angle.

These techniques can be combined to construct other angles.

## Try It Out

**J** **1** Construct a 60° angle and bisect it.

**2** Construct a right angle using a perpendicular bisector. Bisect the angle.

## Practice

**K** **1** Construct an equilateral triangle with sides 6 cm without using a protractor.

**2** Sophie discovers an old pirate map of Triangularland. The island is a triangle, with one angle 45° and another 60°.

(a) Draw the island to a scale of 1 cm to 10 km.

(b) A chest of treasure is located where the bisectors of the two angles meet. On your map, indicate with a small cross where the treasure is.

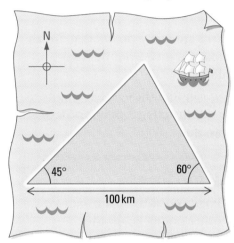

> **Finished Early?**
> ➡ Go to page 424

## Further Practice

**L** **1** The map shows a house and a garden. Draw it using a scale of 1 cm to 5 m.

A path is laid from the back door (which is in the middle of the rear of the house), at right angles to the house, to a gate at the back of the garden. Construct the path and draw the garden gate on the map.

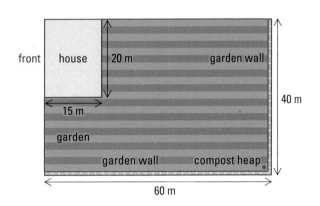

**2** A second path is laid from the compost heap at the corner of the garden. The path bisects the angle made by the two garden walls and stops when it meets the other path. Construct the path.

> **Finished Early?**
> ➡ Go to page 424

# T ❹ Double Points and Lines

 Compasses, protractor, squared paper

## Learn About It

Each ship in the diagram is the same distance from Buoy A as from Buoy B.

There are many points that are an equal distance from the two buoys.

You can find these other points by constructing a **perpendicular bisector**.

> ### Key Fact
> Points **equidistant** from two other points lie on the perpendicular bisector of the line between the two points.

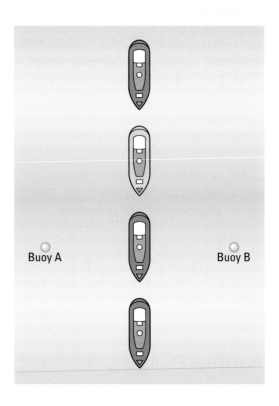

Buoy A          Buoy B

## Try It Out

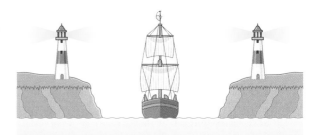

Using a scale of 2 cm to 1 km, draw the path a ship must take if it is to remain equidistant from two lighthouses that are:

**(a)** 5 km apart

**(b)** 10 km apart.

### Word Check
equidistant the same distance

## Learn More About It

Any point on the red line is equidistant from the **blue** lines.
You can find the position of the red line by bisecting the
angle made by the blue lines.

> ### Key Fact
> A line that bisects an angle is equidistant
> from the lines that form the angle.

## Try It Out

Draw a line equidistant from two lines that form an angle of:
**(a)** 90° **(b)** 60° **(c)** 45°.

## Practice

**1** Draw the island, Mathematica, using a
scale of 1 cm to 5 km.

A ship leaves the port, A, on a course
that is equidistant from the two sides
of the river mouth. Draw its path.

**2** There is a small airport situated 30 km
from A and 40 km from B. Show its
location on the map.

**3** A lake is equidistant from the
airport and B and 25 km from A.
Indicate on the map the location of the lake.

> **Finished Early?**
> Go to page 424

## Further Practice

An island, Equilatria, is in the shape of an equilateral triangle of sides 20 km.
There are two lighthouses, A and B, on two points of the island.

**(a)** Draw the island using a scale of 1 cm to 2 km.

**(b)** Draw the locus of a ship that sails around the island 2 km from the shore.

**(c)** A port is situated on the shore equidistant from the two lighthouses.
Indicate on the map the position of the port.

**(d)** A ship sails from the port on a course that is equidistant from the two
lighthouses. Draw its locus.

**(e)** A volcano is situated 10 km from A and 15 km from B. Show its position.

**(f)** When the volcano is active it can throw out lava a distance of 6 km. Shade
the area of the map that the lava would reach.

**(g)** Indicate on the map the area where the ship in
part (b) is in danger from the volcano.

> **Finished Early?**
> Go to page 424

**373**

# Unit 14 *Transformations and Loci*

## Summary of Chapters 26 and 27

- A shape has **line symmetry** if you can fold one half exactly on to the other.

  To **reflect** a shape in a line, draw a mirror image.

- A shape has **rotational symmetry** if it looks the same in different positions when it is rotated.

  To rotate a shape about a point, work out the positions of the corners.

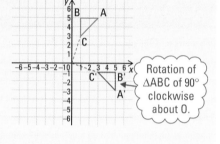

Rotation of △ABC of 90° clockwise about O.

- An **enlargement** changes the size of a shape. The **scale factor** shows how much bigger (or smaller) the new shape is.

- A **translation** is a sliding movement. The object translated does not change its shape or rotate.

  A translation can be described using a **column vector**.

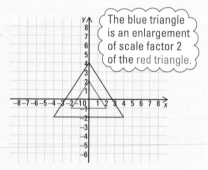

The blue triangle is an enlargement of scale factor 2 of the red triangle.

$\begin{pmatrix} 3 \\ -2 \end{pmatrix}$ means moving 3 units right and 2 units down.

- The **locus** of an object moving at a fixed distance from a point is the circumference of a circle.

- The locus of points the same distance from a straight line is a pair of parallel lines.

  The locus of an object that is equidistant from two fixed points is the perpendicular bisector of the line between the points.

  The locus of an object that is equidistant from two fixed lines is the bisector of the angle between the lines.

- To draw a triangle:
  **1** given 3 sides                  **2** given a side and 2 angles

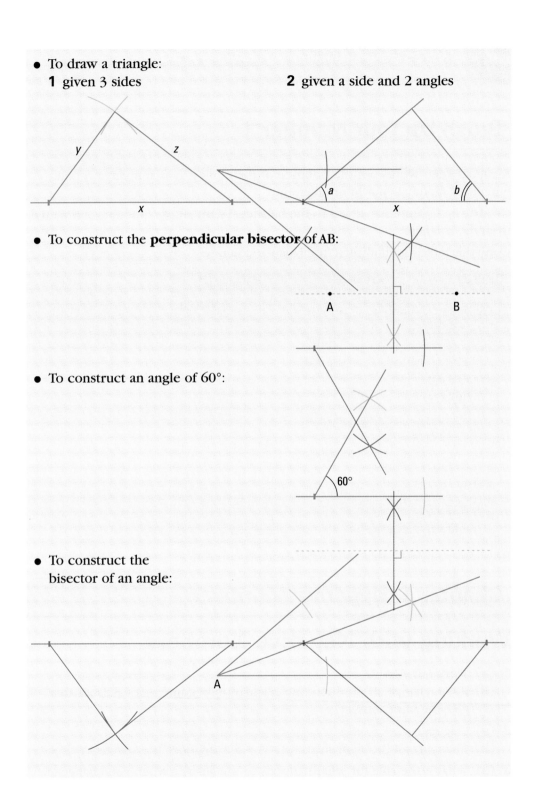

- To construct the **perpendicular bisector** of AB:

- To construct an angle of 60°:

- To construct the
  bisector of an angle:

## Brush Up Your Number 1

An accountant works out the **balance** of the money in a company account whenever money is put in or taken out.

**Credit** shows amounts added to the balance. **Debit** shows amounts subtracted from the balance.

Copy this table and complete the balance column.

| Debit (£) | Credit (£) | Balance (£) |
|---|---|---|
| ——— | ——— | 2 500 000 |
| 650 000 | | |
| | 125 000 | |
| | 1 225 500 | |
| 565 400 | | |
| 624 430 | | |
| | 345 725 | |
| 1 112 345 | | |
| | 3 435 000 | |
| 1 125 250 | | |
| | 120 050 | |
| 133 465 | | |
| 540 385 | | |

How can you check that the final balance is correct?

## Chapter 1 *Negative Numbers*

# ❶ Working with Negative Numbers

**1** **(a)** Work out –2 + 3.
   **(b)** If you change all the signs, the calculation becomes +2 – 3. Does this give the same answer?

**2** **(a)** Calculate –2 + 3 – 4.
   **(b)** Changing all the signs gives +2 – 3 + 4. How does the answer change?

**3** **(a)** What is the rule for what happens to the answer when you change all the signs?
   **(b)** Test the rule with some longer calculations.

**4** Work out 3 – 5 + 2.

**5** **(a)** Write down five calculations that give the answer 0. Each calculation must be longer than the one before.

    **(b)** If you change all the signs in your calculations from part (a), what would the answers be? Try it and see.

# ❷ Adding and Subtracting Negative Numbers

**1** Russell calculates –3 + 2 – 4 + 7 – 1 + 5 like this.

First he adds the numbers that come after a plus sign: 2 + 7 + 5 = 14.

Then he adds the numbers that come after a minus sign: 3 + 4 + 1 = 8.

To get the answer he subtracts the second total from the first: 14 – 8 = 6.

So –3 + 2 – 4 + 7 – 1 + 5 = 6. Check his answer.

Use Russell's method to do the following calculations. Check your answers using another method.

    **(a)** –4 + 2 – 3 + 5 – 1

    **(b)** 4 – 2 – 3 – 4 + 5 + 6

    **(c)** –2 + 5 + 3 – 4 – 6 – 2 + 1

    **(d)** –1 + 2 – 3 + 4 – 5 + 6 – 7 + 8 – 9 + 10

**2** **(a)** Work out –3 + 2 – 5 + 4.

    **(b)** Imagine that each sign is stuck in front of the number that follows it, like this: –3 +2 –5 +4.

    Rearrange the numbers: –5 +2 –3 +4 (keep the signs stuck to the same numbers).

    Work out the new calculation: –5 + 2 – 3 + 4. Do you get the same answer?

    **(c)** Rearrange the numbers in different ways. Do you always get the same answer?

    **(d)** Investigate using other calculations, e.g. 3 – 5 – 1 + 2 – 8.

# ❸ Multiplying and Dividing Negative Numbers

**1** **(a)** What happens to the number 5 when you multiply it by –1?

    **(b)** What happens to the number –5 when you multiply it by –1?

    **(c)** What effect does multiplying a number by –1 have on it?

**2** **(a)** $5 \times (-1) =$

    **(b)** $5 \times (-1) \times (-1) =$

    **(c)** $5 \times (-1) \times (-1) \times (-1) =$

    **(d)** $5 \times (-1) \times (-1) \times (-1) \times (-1) =$

    **(e)** What happens when you multiply a number by –1 again and again?

    **(f)** Write down a rule that tells you whether the answer is positive or negative.

**3** **(a)** Can you tell the sign of the answer to $(-2) \times (-3) \times (-4) \times (-5)$ without
working out the answer?
**(b)** Write down a rule for when you multiply several numbers together,
including negative ones.
**(c)** Test your rule with other calculations.

---

## **Chapter 2** *Line Graphs*

---

# ❶ Reading Graphs

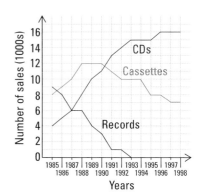

A shop sells records, cassettes and CDs.
Their yearly sales from 1985 to 1998 are
shown on the graph.

**1** For which product did sales drop the
most?

**2** For which product did sales increase the
most?

**3** What was the difference between record
and cassette sales in 1990?

**4** What was the difference between cassette and CD sales in 1988?

**5** When did CD sales first become larger than cassette sales?

**6** Describe each line in words and explain, without giving figures, what
happened to the sales.

# ❷ Drawing Graphs

Graph paper

£1 = 12 Norwegian kroner. £1 = 2.5 Australian dollars.

**1** Draw two conversion graphs to convert up to £20 to kroner and to
Australian dollars.

**2** What is £14 in kroner?

**3** What is £18 in Australian dollars?

**4** What is 100 kroner in pounds?

**5** What is 100 kroner in Australian dollars?

**6** What is 40 Australian dollars in pounds?

**7** What is 40 Australian dollars in kroner?

**8** What is 23 Australian dollars in kroner?

## Brush Up Your Number 2

For each total below, write down six calculations – three multiplication and three division – which give that answer.

**1**  1200  **2**  800  **3**  1500  **4**  1 200 000
**5**  1 800 000  **6**  240 000  **7**  800  **8**  2 500 000
**9**  140 000  **10**  3 600 000

## Chapter 3 *Angles*

# ① Angle Facts

Protractor

Extending one of the sides of a triangle forms an **exterior** angle.

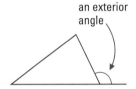
an exterior angle

**1** Draw ten triangles of different sizes and shapes.
**2** Extend one of the sides of each triangle to make an exterior angle.
**3** Measure all the interior angles of each triangle and the exterior angle. Mark the angles on your diagrams.
**4** Make a table like this listing the exterior angle and interior angles of each triangle.

| Triangle | Exterior angle | Angle 1 (next to exterior angle) | Angle 2 | Angle 3 |
|---|---|---|---|---|
| 1 | | | | |
| 2 | | | | |
| 3 | | | | |

**5** Look at the numbers in your table and write down a connection between the exterior angles and the two interior angles farthest away from it.
**6** Draw three more triangles, extend one side of each and, without measuring the exterior angle, predict what it will be by measuring the two interior angles farthest from it. Test your prediction by measuring the exterior angle.

## ❷ Parallel Lines

Copy these diagrams and write on your copies the sizes of all the angles you
can work out.

**1**

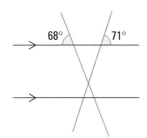

**2**

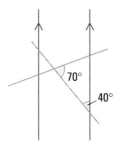

**3**

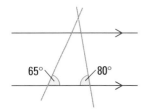

**4**

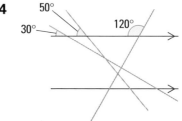

---

## Chapter 4 *Quadrilaterals and Polygons*

## ❶ Quadrilaterals

 Protractor

**1 (a)** Draw five different parallelograms.

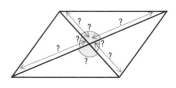

Mark the diagonals – the lines joining the
corners – and measure the angles at the
centre and the lengths to where the
diagonals cross.

**(b)** Describe how the diagonals of a parallelogram cross.

**2 (a)** Draw five rhombi (plural of rhombus) and measure the lengths and
angles as you did in question 1.

**(b)** Can you say anything about how the diagonals of a rhombus cross?

**3** Repeat the same activity with rectangles.

**4** Repeat the same activity with squares.

# 2 Angle Sums of Polygons

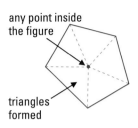

any point inside the figure

triangles formed

**1** Draw a pentagon and, choosing any point inside it, draw lines from each corner to this point, making triangles.

Count the triangles and, using their angles and the angles at a point, find the sum of the interior angles of the pentagon.

**2** Repeat question 1 with a hexagon.

**3** Repeat question 1 with a heptagon.

**4** Explain how you can find a formula for the sum of the angles of any polygon.

# 3 Interior and Exterior Angles

Sketch the following diagrams and fill in the values of all the exterior and interior angles.

**1**
2x, 3x, 2x, 3x, 2x, 2x

**2**
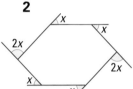
x, x, 2x, 2x, x, x

**3**
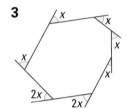
x, x, x, x, 2x, 2x

**4**
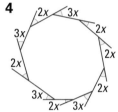
2x, 3x, 2x, 3x, 2x, 2x, 2x, 3x, 2x, 3x

# 4 Regular Polygons

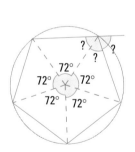

Compasses, protractor

**1** You can draw regular polygons using a circle as a guide.

To draw a regular pentagon you need five angles at the centre. 360 ÷ 5 = 72 so each angle is 72°.

Draw a regular pentagon and mark the sizes of the interior and exterior angles.

**2** Repeat this for a regular: **(a)** hexagon **(b)** heptagon **(c)** octagon.

**3** Write down a connection between the angles at the centre and the exterior angles of the polygons.

# Chapter 5 *Three Dimensions*

## ❶ Drawing Solids

Isometric paper, cubes

Make a shape from cubes and draw it in three different positions, shading in the same side on each drawing.

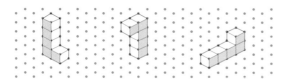

Make five more shapes and draw each one in three different ways.

## ❷ Nets

Cubes, card, scissors

Use about six cubes to make a solid of any shape. Draw the net of your solid.

Swap your net with another pupil and make each other's solids. Compare the solid made from each net with the original shape.

Repeat this with other shapes made from different numbers of cubes.

## ❸ Plans

Squared paper

Design your own house. First design a plan of the ground floor of a single-storey house. Make it a reasonable size; think of the dimensions of the rooms where you live.

Then decide where the windows and doors would be and draw plans of the outside of the house. You should include elevations for the front, back and sides of the house. Make your diagrams as clear and neat as possible.

## Brush Up Your Number 3

Numbers are usually rounded to 10, 100, 1000, etc. but they can be rounded to other numbers.

Round these numbers to the nearest: **(a)** 25 **(b)** 50 **(c)** 250 **(d)** 500 **(e)** 2500.

| | | | |
|---|---|---|---|
| **1** 3224 | **2** 5176 | **3** 12 480 | **4** 13 204 |
| **5** 18 775 | **6** 4312 | **7** 7894 | **8** 6213 |
| **9** 9562 | **10** 39 422 | **11** 321 183 | **12** 21 325 |

## Chapter 6 *Decimals*

# Decimals

Add together the numbers and fractions in each of the circles below. Write your answers as decimals.

**Example**

$\frac{3}{10}$  2  $\frac{7}{1000}$  400  $\frac{5}{100}$

**Working**  $400 + 2 + \frac{3}{10} + \frac{5}{100} + \frac{7}{1000} = 400 + 2 + 0.3 + 0.05 + 0.007$

**Answer**  402.357

**1**

50  7  200  $\frac{3}{100}$

**2**
$\frac{1}{10}$  3  $\frac{2}{100}$  20  100

**3**

$\frac{5}{1000}$  4  2000  50  $\frac{3}{10}$

**4**

5  300  $\frac{4}{100}$  $\frac{6}{1000}$

**5**
4  $\frac{3}{10}$  $\frac{5}{1000}$  70  $\frac{3}{10\,000}$

**6**
$\frac{2}{10}$  20  $\frac{3}{1000}$  500

**7**
$\frac{7}{10}$  40  5  $\frac{3}{1000}$  300

**8**

8  10  $\frac{4}{10\,000}$  $\frac{1}{10}$  $\frac{3}{100}$

**9** Make up a number circle like the ones above by splitting up a decimal number into four or five parts. Swap with another pupil and work out each other's totals.

# ❷ Rounding

Below are six statements and six comments. Match each statement with the correct comment.

## Statements

**A** | After adding the interest I should have £125.3472 in my account at the end of the year.

**B** | The winner of the 200-m race took 23.62 seconds and the runner-up took 23.64 seconds.

**C** | The recipe calls for 12.4951 g of flour.

**D** | The length of a car is 5.333333 m.

**E** | Jane timed her journey to school at 25 minutes 48.25 seconds.

**F** | A bee can collect 0.002 g of nectar from a flower.

## Comments

**1** | There are too many decimal places. Round it to the nearest whole number or to 2 d.p.

**2** | This should probably be rounded to the nearest minute.

**3** | You need all three decimal places. If you rounded, the statement would be nonsense.

**4** | You need to use both decimal places.

**5** | This should be rounded to 2 d.p.

**6** | You cannot measure that amount. Round to the nearest whole number.

# ❸ Calculations

For each of the following calculations:

**(a)** work out the answer and then round it to 1 d.p.

**(b)** round each number to 1 d.p. first, then work out the answer and round it to 1 d.p.

**(c)** find the difference between your answers for parts (a) and (b).

**1** $2.35 \times 15.76$

**2** $7.85 \times 0.05$

**3** $15.36 \times 2.07$

**4** $3.424 + 31.249 + 43.64$

**5** $25.743 + 18.64 - 32.34$

**6** $54.25 + 13.36 \times 0.254$

**7** $36.25 \times 0.025 + 14.662$

**8** $2.354 \times 3.45 \times 0.06$

## Brush Up Your Number 4

To calculate $3 \times (7 - 2)$, work out the brackets first: $3 \times 5 = 15$.

**1** Some calculations have brackets within brackets: $3 \times (7 - [5 - 3])$. Which part do you do first? Work out the answer then check using your calculator.

**2** Calculate the following.
    **(a)** $2 \times (4 \times [3 + 5])$      **(b)** $(20 - [7 - 3]) \times 4$      **(c)** $10 + (7 - [2 + 3])$
    **(d)** $(12 - [2 \times 5]) - 1$      **(e)** $15 - (4 \times [5 - 2])$

**3** Work out the answer then check using your calculator.
    **(a)** $2 \times (6 - 1) + 3 \times (2 + 4)$          **(b)** $4 + (3 \times [8 - 6])$
    **(c)** $10 - (6 - [5 - 3])$      **(d)** $2 + 2 \times (2 + 2 \times [2 + 2])$      **(e)** $7 - (5 - [3 - 8] - 3)$

**4** Replace each of the numbers in questions 2 and 3 with your own numbers. Work out the answer then check using your calculator.

**5** What is the rule for working out brackets within brackets?

## Chapter 7 *Formulae and Expressions*

# 1 Substitution

Graph paper

**1** $x^2$ means $x \times x$. $3x^2$ means $3 \times x \times x$.
Find the value of $3x^2$ when: **(a)** $x = 2$ **(b)** $x = -2$.

**2 (a)** Find the value of $y = 1 + 2x + 3x^2$ when $x$ has values from $-4$ to $4$ by copying and completing this table.

| $x$ | $-4$ | $-3$ | $-2$ | $-1$ | $0$ | $1$ | $2$ | $3$ | $4$ |
|---|---|---|---|---|---|---|---|---|---|
| 1 | 1 | 1 | 1 | 1 | 1 | 1 | 1 | 1 | 1 |
| $+ 2x$ | | | | | | | $+ 4$ | | |
| $+ 3x^2$ | | | | | | | $+ 12$ | | |
| $y$ | | | | | | | $17$ | | |

    **(b)** Plot the data from the table on a graph. Use these scales:
         $x$-axis: 2 cm to 1 unit. $y$-axis: 1 cm to 5 units.
    **(c)** Join the points using a smooth curved line.

**3** Repeat for **one** of these equations.
    $y = 3x^2 + 10$
    $y = x^2 - 4x - 10$   (*Draw the y-axis from $-15$ to $25$.*)
    $y = 10 + 4x - 3x^2$ (*Draw the y-axis from $-55$ to $15$.*)

# ❷ Making Formulae

**1 (a)** Make as many formulae as you can that start with $a =$, using the letters $b, c$, the sign + and the number 2. Here are a few examples: $a = b + 2$, $a = b + c + 2$, $a = b^2$.

**(b)** Find the value of $a$ by substituting $b = 2$ and $c = 5$ in each formula.

**2 (a)** Make as many formulae as you can that start with $p =$, using the letters $q, r$, the sign $\times$ and the number 3. For example, $p = 3 \times q$, which you can write as $p = 3q$.

**(b)** Find the value of $p$ by substituting $q = 5$ and $r = -2$ in each formula.

**3 (a)** Choose three letters of your own, an operation (+, -, $\times$ or $\div$) and a number and use them to make as many formulae as you can.

**(b)** Choose your own numbers to substitute in each formula.

**4** Repeat question 3 using two operations. For example, using + and $\times$ might give the formula: $M = 2n + k$.

# ❸ Simplifying Expressions

Look at this expression: $5x^2 + 3x^2 + 6x - 2x$.

$5x^2$ and $3x^2$ are like terms because they have exactly the same letters: $x^2$ and $x^2$.

$6x$ and $-2x$ are like terms because they have exactly the same letters.

So $5x^2 + 3x^2 + 6x - 2x$ can be simplified to $8x^2 + 4x$.

$8x^2$ and $4x$ are **not** like terms, because they do not have **exactly** the same letters: $x^2$ and $x$. They cannot be simplified.

**1** Simplify these expressions.

**(a)** $4a^2 + 3a + 5a^2 - a$

**(b)** $2y^2 - 3y - 2y + 7y^2$

**(c)** $6t + 8t^2 - t^2 - 3t + 5t^2 + 2t$

**2 (a)** Write down three terms at a time from the strip below to make an expression. Simplify each expression.

| $3m^2 - 2m + 2m^2$ | $-5m + 7m^2 - m + n^2 - 3n - 10n + 7n^2 + 10n - 3n^2$ |

**(b)** Now cut off four terms at a time and simplify the expressions.

**(c)** Repeat for six terms at a time.

**(d)** Simplify the whole strip.

# ⓓ Brackets

**1** Expand and simplify the following expressions.

| | |
|---|---|
| **Example** | $3(a + 2) + 2(a + 5)$ |
| **Working** | $= 3a + 6 + 2a + 10$ |
| | $= 3a + 2a + 6 + 10$   *(Rearrange terms.)* |
| | $= 5a + 16$   *(Simplify by adding like terms.)* |
| **Answer** | $5a + 16$ |

    **(a)** $4(p + 5) + 3(p + 2)$         **(b)** $3(x + 4) + 7(x - 1)$
    **(c)** $3(f + 2) + 5(f - 1)$         **(d)** $10(a - 2) + 5(a - 1)$
    **(e)** $2(m + 5) + 3(m - 1) + 4(m + 6)$   **(f)** $5(n - 1) + 4(n - 1) + 3(n + 3)$

**2 (a)** Choose any two of the following expressions. Add them to make a
      longer expression and simplify it. Do this three times.

        $4(a - 2)$   $2(a + 3)$   $5(a + 2)$   $7(a + 1)$   $4(a - 1)$

   **(b)** Now add and simplify any three expressions in part (a). Do this three times.
   **(c)** Now add and simplify all the expressions in part (a).

# ⓔ Factorising

**1** Combine any two terms using + or –.
   Factorise the expression you have made,
   if possible. Do the same with four
   more pairs.

**2** Combine any three terms using + or
   – signs and factorise them, if
   possible. Do the same for three
   more groups of three.

**3** Combine five or more terms. See if
   your partner can factorise them.

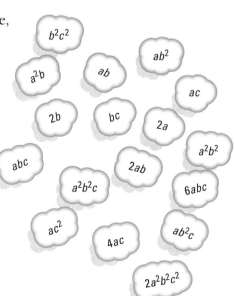

> # Chapter 8 *Equations and Inequalities*

## ❶ Solving Equations

**1** This is an equation generator.
Using the equation generator,
choose your own numbers and
operations to make five equations.
Choose from these:

**2** Solve your equations. The answers
may be negative, fractions or decimals.

**3** Now repeat Steps 1 and 2,
choosing from these numbers:

| Example | $x \times 2 - 4 = 8$ |
|---|---|
| Working | $2x - 4 = 8$ |
| | $2x = 8 + 4$ |
| | $2x = 12$ |
| Answer | $x = 6$ |

## ❷ Simplifying Equations

**1** Choose any three of the terms on
the right, make them into an
equation and solve it. Your answer
may be a fraction or a decimal.

| Example | $3a + 10 = 9a$ |
|---|---|
| Working | $10 = 9a - 3a$ |
| | $10 = 6a$ |
| Answer | $a = 1\frac{2}{3}$ |

**2** Make three more equations like this and solve them.

**3** Choose any four of the terms, make an equation and solve it. Make and solve
three more equations like this, using brackets in one of them.

**4** Make equations with five, six and seven terms and solve them.

**5** Make an equation with all the terms and solve it.

# ❸ Trial and Improvement

$5^3$ means $5 \times 5 \times 5$. So $a^3$ means $a \times a \times a$.

**1** Solve $a^3 = 50$. Copy and complete the table. Continue guessing until you have found $a$ to 2 d.p.

| Guess, $a$ | $a^3$ | Comment |
|---|---|---|
| 2 | $2^3 = 2 \times 2 \times 2 = 8$ | Too low. $a$ is bigger than 2 |
| 3 | $3^3 = 3 \times 3 \times 3 =$ | |

**2** Solve these equations, correct to 1 d.p.
   **(a)** $a^3 = 20$    **(b)** $a^3 + 5 = 30$    **(c)** $a^3 + a = 100$

**3** Choose a number, $p$, between 100 and 1000.
   **(a)** Solve the equation: $a^3 = p$, correct to 1 d.p.
   **(b)** Solve the equation: $a^3 + a = p$, correct to 1 d.p.

# ❹ Inequalities

**1** Inequalities can sometimes be combined to make new inequalities.

Suppose that $x > 5$ and $x \leqslant 10$ are true at the same time. Represent them on a number line.

Now combine them.

This inequality is $5 < x \leqslant 10$.

**2** Write down your own inequality (it can be one to solve if you like). Get together with a neighbour and see if it's possible to combine your inequalities. If you can, write down both of them with the combined answer, and illustrate them on number lines.

**3** Try this a few times. See if you can find a pair of inequalities that **don't** combine.

## Brush Up Your Number 5

**1** Find a shortcut for each calculation. Show your working.

    **(a)** 9 + 9 + 99 + 99     **(b)** 19 + 29 + 39     **(c)** 75 – 9 – 9 – 9

    **(d)** 580 – 99 – 99 – 99     **(e)** 400 × 30 × 5000     **(f)** 28 + 57 + 39

**2** Make up five similar calculations of your own, and find shortcuts for them.

## Chapter 9 *Calculating with Confidence*

# ❶ Using Your Calculator

 This calculation does not make sense: 6 + × 2. You do not know whether to add 6 and 2 or to multiply them together.

Try working out the calculation using your calculator. It will probably tell you there is an error.

**1** Which of these make sense? Try them on your calculator.

    **(a)** 6 – × 2         **(b)** 6 + –2         **(c)** 6 + ÷ 2

    **(d)** 6 – ÷ 2         **(e)** 6 – –2

**2** Write down five different impossible calculations. Does your calculator show an error?

**3** **(a)** Work out this calculation: **6** **×** **(** **3** **+** **2** **)** **=**.

    **(b)** Now leave out **×**. Do you get the same answer?

    **(c)** Now leave out the closing bracket **)**. Do you get the same answer?

**4** Work out the following calculations. Then work them out using as few keys as possible. You should get the same answer each time.

    **(a)** 52 – 4 × (7 – 2)

    **(b)** (25 + 17) × (74 ÷ 2)

    **(c)** $\dfrac{3 \times (12 + 4)}{17 + 23}$

**5** Work out 3 + +2 on your calculator. Some calculators will do it. Some won't!

## ❷ Checking Your Answer

**1** Calculate $4.5 \times 4.5$ exactly.

**2** Estimate $4.5 \times 4.5$ by rounding to 1 s.f.

**3** Calculate the **error** by subtracting the smaller from the bigger answer.

**4** Do the same with these calculations.
  **(a)** $4.5 \times 4.5 \times 4.5$
  **(b)** $4.5 \times 4.5 \times 4.5 \times 4.5$
  **(c)** $4.5 \times 4.5 \times 4.5 \times 4.5 \times 4.5$

> ### Word Check
> **error** difference between exact
>   answer and estimated answer

**5** What do you notice about the errors?

**6** Continue multiplying by $4.5$. Stop
  when the exact answer is more than twice the estimate.

**7** Multiply each number below by itself, again and again. Stop when the exact
  answer is more than twice the estimate, or vice versa.
  **(a)** $2.4$      **(b)** $9.6$

---

## Chapter 10 *Powers and Roots*

## ❶ Powers

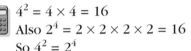

$4^2 = 4 \times 4 = 16$
Also $2^4 = 2 \times 2 \times 2 \times 2 = 16$
So $4^2 = 2^4$

**1** Work out the following powers and write down those that are the same.
  $9^2$   $4^4$   $5^4$   $16^2$   $3^4$   $25^2$

**2** What do you notice about powers that are the same? Write down a rule.

**3** Use your rule to find two more powers that are the same. Check that your
  rule works.

**4** Work out the following powers and write down those that are the same.
  $27^3$   $2^9$   $64^3$   $3^9$   $4^9$   $8^3$

**5** What do you notice about the powers that are the same? Write down a rule.

**6** Use your rule to find two more powers that are the same. Check that your
  rule works.

## ❷ Square Roots and Cube Roots

The fourth power of $2 = 2^4 = 2 \times 2 \times 2 \times 2 = 16$.

The fourth root of 16 is 2.

Finding the fourth root is the inverse of finding the fourth power.

You write it like this $\sqrt[4]{\phantom{x}}$ .

The fourth root of $16 = \sqrt[4]{16} = 2$.

**1** Fill in the missing numbers.

   (a) $3^4 = ?$      (b) $2^5 = ?$      (c) $4^4 = ?$      (d) $10^6 = ?$

     $\sqrt[4]{?} = 3$        $\sqrt[5]{?} = 2$        $\sqrt[4]{?} = 4$        $\sqrt[6]{?} = 10$

**2** Match each red root with a blue number.

$\sqrt[4]{10\,000}$   6      $\sqrt[6]{64}$   3

$\sqrt[5]{243}$   2      $\sqrt[3]{216}$   10

**3** Use your calculator to find $\sqrt[4]{20}$.

   Press ▢**4** ▢$^x\!\sqrt{\phantom{}}$ ▢**2** ▢**0** ▢**=**    `2.114 742 527`

   $\sqrt[4]{20} = 2.11$, correct to 2 d.p.

   Check your answer by calculating the fourth power of 2.11.

**4** Calculate these roots, correct to 2 d.p. Check your answers by calculating the correct power.

   (a) $\sqrt[4]{30}$      (b) $\sqrt[5]{30}$      (c) $\sqrt[6]{30}$

**5** (a) Choose a number between 100 and 1000.

   (b) Calculate the third to the tenth roots of the number, correct to 2 d.p.

   (c) Check your answers by calculating the correct power.

## ❸ Powers of 10

This large number has lots of significant figures: 295 842 613.

You can approximate it using 3 s.f.: 296 000 000.

Now you can write this approximation using standard form: $2.96 \times 10^8$.

So $295\,842\,613 \approx 2.96 \times 10^8$ (to 3 s.f.).

**1** Write these numbers in standard form, correct to 3 s.f.

   (a) 34 659          (b) 2565          (c) 923 435 561

   (d) 40 562 300    (e) 9 155 294 756    (f) 88 888 888 888 888

   (g) 75 976 107    (h) 438 505 100 452 193 723

**2** Write the numbers in question 1 in standard form, correct to 2 s.f.

**3** Write the numbers in question 1 in standard form, correct to 1 s.f.

**4** (a) Write down ten different large numbers, e.g. 2 345 678 999.

   (b) Write these numbers in standard form, correct to 3 s.f.

Brush Up Your Number 6

Work out the 11 and 12 times tables. Practise them. Get a friend to test you.

Chapter 11 *Coordinates*

# Straight Lines

Draw axes for each question below and plot the coordinates. Draw horizontal and vertical lines through the point given and write their equations on them. Write down the coordinates of the points where the lines cross.

**1** $(2, 3), (4, 2)$ **2** $(3, 1), (5, -1)$ **3** $(4, -4), (1, -1)$ **4** $(6, 4), (-6, -4)$

**5** $(-3, -4), (0, 1)$ **6** $(-2, 0), (3, -3)$

**7** Write down four pairs of coordinates of your own, then plot them on a graph, draw horizontal and vertical lines through them and write down the equations.

# More Straight-Line Graphs

The diagram shows the lines
$y = 2x, y = -2x, y = 2x - 3, y = -2x + 3$.

Between the points where the lines cross a rhombus is formed.

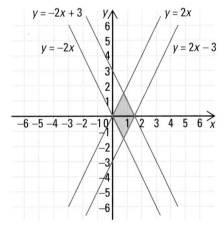

**1** For each set of equations below, draw a graph and plot the lines. Write down the name of the shape that is formed.

(a) $y = 2x, y = -2x, y = 2x - 5$,
$y = -2x + 5$

(b) $y = 3x, y = -3x, y = 3x + 7$,
$y = -3x - 7$

(c) $y = x, y = -x, y = x + 5, y = -x - 5$

(d) $y = x, y = -x, y = x - 5, y = -x + 7$

**2** Make up two more sets of equations using different numbers and draw the diagrams. Write down rules on how to make different shapes using four lines.

# ❸ Regions

**1** Draw the graph of $y = x$.

Below the line, all the $y$ values are less than the $x$ values.

Above the line, all the $y$ values are greater than the $x$ values.

**(a)** Look at some points and check that the above is true.

**(b)** Shade the region $y > x$.

**(c)** Shade the region $y < x$ a different colour.

**2** Draw the lines $y = -x$, $y = 4$ and $x = 4$ to make a triangle. Write down the coordinates of the triangle's vertices and the inequalities that define it.

**3** Using the line $y = x$ and two other lines, make more triangles and write down the inequalities that define them.

# ❹ Curved Graphs

**1 (a)** Plot the following curves on the same axes.

**(i)** $y = \dfrac{1}{x} + 1$    **(ii)** $y = \dfrac{2}{x} + 1$    **(iii)** $y = \dfrac{3}{x} + 1$    **(iv)** $y = \dfrac{4}{x} + 1$

**(b)** What do you notice?

**2 (a)** Plot the following curves on the same axes.

**(i)** $y = \dfrac{1}{x} + 1$    **(ii)** $y = \dfrac{1}{x} + 2$    **(iii)** $y = \dfrac{1}{x} + 3$    **(iv)** $y = \dfrac{1}{x} + 4$

**(b)** What do you notice?

**3** Can you predict what shape you will get for $y = \dfrac{1}{x} + 5$? Test your prediction. What about other curves?

---

## Chapter 12 *Simultaneous Equations*

---

# ❶ Changing the Subject

**1 (a)** Invent a formula based on the word *Year* with the first letter as the subject, keeping the other letters in order (for instance, $Y = \dfrac{e + a}{r}$).

**(b)** Choose one of the other letters and rearrange the formula to make this letter the subject.

**(c)** Write the new formula on a scrap of paper. Give it to a neighbour.

**2** When you've got a formula from your neighbour, rearrange the formula so that the capital letter is the subject.

**3** Repeat steps 1–2 with the words *Note*, *Light* and *Answer*. Think of a different formula each time.

# ❷ Simultaneous Equations and Graphs

Make up your own simultaneous equations:
- Choose values for $x$ and $y$.
- Make up two expressions using $x$ and $y$.
- Work out the value of the expressions.

| | | |
|---|---|---|
| **Example** | Let $x = 2$ and $y = 1$ | (*Choose values.*) |
| | $x + y$ and $x - y$ | (*Make up expressions.*) |
| | $x + y = 3$ and $x - y = 1$ | (*Evaluate the expressions.*) |

You now have a pair of equations.
Write down the two equations and give them to a partner to solve by drawing a graph.

# Brush Up Your Number 7

**1 (a)** Think of a 2-digit number, for example, 26. Square it.
  **(b)** Now multiply one less than the number by one more than the number.
    If you started with 26, you would work out $25 \times 27$.
  **(c)** Write down anything you notice about the two answers.

**2** Repeat question 1 three times with different starting numbers.
  Write down what you notice about the answers.
  Is there a pattern?

**3 (a)** Pick another two-digit number, for example, 32. Cube it.
  **(b)** Now multiply one less than the number by the number.
    Multiply the answer by one more than the number.
    If you started with 32, you would work out $31 \times 32 \times 33$.
  **(c)** Write down anything you notice about the two answers.

**4** Repeat question 3 three times with different starting numbers.
  Write down what you notice about the answers.
  Is there a pattern?

# Chapter 13 *Fractions*

## ❶ Decimals and Fractions

**1** Convert $\frac{1}{3}$ to a decimal using your calculator. What do you notice about the answer?

**2** Convert $\frac{1}{99}$ to a decimal using your calculator. What do you notice about the answer?

**3** 0.3434343434… is called a **recurring decimal**. The digits 34 repeat themselves (recur) and make a pattern.

Which of these fractions do you think give recurring decimals?

> **Word Check**
>
> **recur** repeat
>
> **recurring decimal** decimal with a pattern of one or more digits repeated endlessly

   **(a)** $\frac{20}{99}$    **(b)** $\frac{7}{8}$    **(c)** $\frac{80}{333}$

   **(d)** $\frac{7}{11}$    **(e)** $\frac{15}{32}$    **(f)** $\frac{1}{7}$

Convert the fractions to decimals. Were you right?

**4** Make five fractions that do *not* give recurring decimals.

**5** **(a)** Make up your own recurring decimal using two digits, e.g. 0.3636363636.
   **(b)** Make a fraction out of 99 using your two digits, e.g. $\frac{36}{99}$.
   **(c)** Convert your fraction to a decimal using your calculator. What do you notice?

**6** Make five fractions that give recurring decimals.

## ❷ Mixed Numbers

**1** Look at this sequence of numbers: $1\frac{2}{3}, 2\frac{3}{4}, 3\frac{4}{5}$ …
   Write down the next two numbers.

**2** Choose a pair of numbers that are next to each other in the sequence. For example, $1\frac{2}{3}$ and $2\frac{3}{4}$. Calculate their difference, e.g. $2\frac{3}{4} - 1\frac{2}{3}$.

**3** Do this for other pairs of numbers from the sequence. What do you notice about the answers? Write a rule about this.

**4** Use your rule to write down the following differences without calculating them.
   **(a)** $7\frac{8}{9} - 6\frac{7}{8}$    **(b)** $9\frac{10}{11} - 8\frac{9}{10}$    **(c)** $19\frac{20}{21} - 18\frac{19}{20}$    **(d)** $98\frac{99}{100} - 97\frac{98}{99}$

# Fraction Calculations

You can find two different fractions that add up to 1 like this:
- choose a whole number, e.g. 10
- create a fraction which has this number for numerator and denominator and so equals 1, e.g. $\frac{10}{10} = 1$
- split the numerator, 10, into the sum of two numbers, e.g. 3 + 7
- then $\frac{3}{10} + \frac{7}{10} = \frac{10}{10} = 1$.

**1** Find two different fractions that add up to 1.

**2** Find three different fractions that add up to 1.

**3** Find seven different fractions that add up to 1.

**4** Find two different fractions that add up to 2.

**5** Find three different fractions that add up to 2.

**6** Find two different fractions that multiply to give 1.

**7** Find three different fractions that multiply to give 1.

**8** Find six different fractions that multiply to give 1.

> *Hint: what would you have to multiply $\frac{2}{3}$ by to give an answer of 1?*

# Fractions of an Amount

**1** Make three fractions that add up to 1. Write them in their lowest terms.

**2** Make your own fruit cocktail. Choose three fruits and give each fruit one of your fractions, e.g. $\frac{1}{4}$ apple juice, $\frac{1}{3}$ pear juice, $\frac{5}{12}$ grape juice.

**3** Copy and complete the table to show how much of each type of fruit juice you need to mix each quantity of cocktail. Use your own types of fruit and fractions from question 2.

| Amount of cocktail (cl) | Fruit juice | | |
|---|---|---|---|
| | Apple $\frac{1}{4}$ | Pear $\frac{1}{3}$ | Grape $\frac{5}{12}$ |
| 120 | | | |
| 30 | | | |
| 1500 | | | |

**4 (a)** Make up a new cocktail using four fruits.
   **(b)** Draw a new table. Add an extra column for the fourth type of fruit juice.

**5** Make up a new cocktail using five fruits.

## Chapter 14 *Percentages*

# ❶ Percentages of an Amount

 Compasses, protractor

**1** Lindsay asked 10 of her friends what they drink most: fruit juice, fizzy drink or water. She made a table of her results and calculated the percentage of people that chose each drink.

**(a)** Copy and complete Lindsay's table.

| Drink | Number of people | Percentage |
|---|---|---|
| Fruit juice | 3 | $\frac{3}{10} = 30\%$ |
| Fizzy drink | 2 | |
| Water | 5 | |

**(b)** She wanted to draw a pie chart to show her results. She calculated the percentages of 360° for each drink. Copy and complete the table.

| Drink | Number of people | Percentage | Angle of pie chart |
|---|---|---|---|
| Fruit juice | 3 | $\frac{3}{10} = 30\%$ | 30% of 360° = 0.3 × 360° = 108° |
| Fizzy drink | 2 | | |
| Water | 5 | | |

**(c)** Draw a pie chart for Lindsay's results. Write the percentages on the pie chart.

**2 (a)** Choose five percentages that add up to 100%.
  **(b)** Draw a pie chart using these percentages.

# ❷ Percentage Increase and Decrease

Laurence invests £60 in his bank for a year. His bank pays 5% interest each year. At the end of the year, he has the £60 plus 5% interest, which is 105% of £60 = 1.05 × £60 = £63.

**1 (a)** Laurence keeps all his money in the bank for another year. How much does he have in the bank at the end of the second year?
  **(b)** How much will he have in the bank at the end of the third year?

So far, you have multiplied £60 by 1.05 three times (once for each year): £60 × 1.05 × 1.05 × 1.05. You can write this using powers: £60 × 1.05³.

You can calculate $60 \times 1.05^3$ using the power key $\boxed{x^y}$ or $\boxed{y^x}$ of your calculator:

$\boxed{6}\,\boxed{0}\,\boxed{\times}\,\boxed{1}\,\boxed{.}\,\boxed{0}\,\boxed{5}\,\boxed{x^y}\,\boxed{3}$ $\boxed{\text{69.4575}}$

After three years, Laurence has £69.46 (to the nearest penny).

**2** Use the method above to calculate how much Laurence would have after:
   **(a)** 4 years    **(b)** 5 years    **(c)** 10 years.

**3** Find how many years he needs to keep his money in the bank for it to double.

**4** **(a)** Choose an amount of money to invest at 5% per annum.
   **(b)** Calculate how long it would take to double. Is your answer the same as in question 3?

**5** Choose any sum of money and calculate how long it takes to double at three different interest rates, e.g. 4%, 10%, 11%.

# Reverse Calculations

| | Population in 1998 (millions) | % increase from 1997 |
|---|---|---|
| World | 5901 | 1.33 |
| More developed regions | 1182 | 0.28 |
| Less developed regions | 4719 | 1.59 |
| Africa | 749 | 2.37 |
| Asia | 3585 | 1.38 |
| Europe | 729 | 0.03 |
| North America | 305 | 0.85 |

The table shows data for the population of a number of regions in 1998.
**(a)** Find the population of each region in 1997.
**(b)** Find similar data from an atlas or the Internet for countries and calculate the population in previous years.

# Brush Up Your Number 8

**1** Look at this pattern.

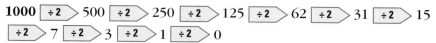

The remainders have been ignored (e.g. 125 ÷ 2 = 62 r 1, not 62).

After 1000, **ten** numbers were written down altogether.

Work out what will happen if you divide repeatedly by 3, ignoring remainders. Stop when you reach 0.

1000 ÷3 > ? ÷3 > ? ÷3 > ? ...

How many numbers did you write down after 1000?

**2** Repeat this for 1000 ÷4 > ? ... 1000 ÷5 > ? ... etc. up to ÷10 > .

**3** Use your results to complete this table from 2 to 10.

| Dividing number | How many numbers after 1000? |
|---|---|
| 2 | 10 |
| 10 | |

**4** Draw a graph like this to illustrate your results.

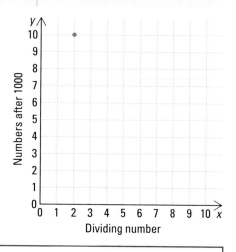

# Chapter 15 *Averages*

## ❶ Mode and Median

**1 (a)** Jai has a list of numbers. Find the mode of these numbers.

| 50 | 80 | 70 | 50 | 40 | 50 | 30 | 70 | 20 | 20 |
|---|---|---|---|---|---|---|---|---|---|

**(b)** Madeleine adds 1 to each of Jai's numbers. Find the mode of Madeleine's numbers. What has happened to the mode?

| 51 | 81 | 71 | 51 | 41 | 51 | 31 | 71 | 21 | 21 |
|----|----|----|----|----|----|----|----|----|----|

**(c)** Prakash takes 3 away from Jai's numbers. Find the mode of Prakash's numbers. What has happened to the mode?

| 47 | 77 | 67 | 47 | 37 | 47 | 27 | 67 | 17 | 17 |
|----|----|----|----|----|----|----|----|----|----|

**(d)** Trudi adds 10 to Jai's numbers. What is the mode of Trudi's numbers?
**(e)** Trudi didn't have to count the frequencies to find the mode of her numbers. Describe the rule you think she used.

**2** Repeat question 1, but find the median each time.

**3** Anthony doubles Jai's numbers. What happens to the mode and median?

**4** Sasha halves Jai's numbers. What happens to the mode and median?

**5** Think up some other rules you could use on the numbers. Test them out.

# ❷ Mean and Range

**1 (a)** Madeleine has a list of numbers. Find the mean of these numbers.

| 500 | 400 | 700 | 500 | 800 | 300 | 500 | 200 | 700 | 200 |
|-----|-----|-----|-----|-----|-----|-----|-----|-----|-----|

**(b)** Jai adds 5 to each of Madeleine's numbers. Find the mean of Jai's numbers. What has happened to the mean?

| 505 | 405 | 705 | 505 | 805 | 305 | 505 | 205 | 705 | 205 |
|-----|-----|-----|-----|-----|-----|-----|-----|-----|-----|

**(c)** Sasha takes 12 away from Madeleine's numbers. Find the mean of Sasha's numbers. What has happened to the mean?

| 488 | 388 | 688 | 488 | 788 | 288 | 488 | 188 | 688 | 188 |
|-----|-----|-----|-----|-----|-----|-----|-----|-----|-----|

**(d)** Anthony adds 57 to Madeleine's numbers. What is the mean of Anthony's numbers?
**(e)** Anthony didn't have to add up his numbers to find the mean. Describe the rule you think he used.

**2** Repeat question 1, but find the range each time.

**3** Trudi doubles Madeleine's numbers. What happens to the mean and range?

**4** Prakash halves Madeleine's numbers. What happens to the mean and range?

**5** Think up some other rules you could use on the numbers. Test them out.

# ❸ Grouped Data

This data shows the heights of the pupils in 8K.

| 157 | 174 | 160 | 172 | 158 | 144 | 152 | 147 | 150 | 169 | 153 | 148 | 170 | 163 | 161 |
|-----|-----|-----|-----|-----|-----|-----|-----|-----|-----|-----|-----|-----|-----|-----|
| 166 | 156 | 153 | 155 | 159 | 149 | 148 | 146 | 158 | 143 | 159 | 159 | 148 | 151 | 155 |

**1 (a)** Copy and complete this frequency table using the data above. The classes are 10 cm apart.

| Height (cm) | Frequency | Middle value | MV × frequency |
|-------------|-----------|--------------|----------------|
| 141–150 | | | |
| 151–160 | | | |
| 161–170 | | | |
| 171–180 | | | |
| **Total** | | | |

**(b)** Calculate the estimated mean height.

**(c)** Calculate the estimated range.

**2 (a)** Copy and complete a frequency table using the same data, with classes 5 cm apart.

| Height (cm) | Frequency | Middle value | MV × frequency |
|-------------|-----------|--------------|----------------|
| 141–145 | | | |
| 146–150 | | | |
| | | | |
| 171–175 | | | |
| **Total** | | | |

**(b)** Calculate the estimated mean height.

**(c)** Calculate the estimated range.

**3 (a)** Calculate the actual mean height.

**(b)** Calculate the actual range.

**4 (a)** Copy and complete the table below.
The **error** is the difference between the estimated mean and the actual one.

| Calculation type | Mean | Error |
|---|---|---|
| 10 cm classes (q. 1) | | |
| 5 cm classes (q. 2) | | |
| actual (q. 3) | | 0 |

**(b)** Comment on the error figures.

# ❹ Comparing Sets of Data

Here is the comparison table for the shot putters from **Learn About It** on page 194.

| | Mean | Best | Worst | Range |
|---|---|---|---|---|
| A. Putter | 14.5 | 18 | 11 | 7 |
| B. Chucker | 16 | 22 | 9 | 13 |

**1** You are going to draw a **mean/range diagram** to compare the sets of data. You need a scale on which all the numbers will fit, so it needs to go from 9 to 22.

Copy this mean/range diagram.

Above the number line, draw a line going from Putter's worst to best distances. This illustrates the **range**. Place a dot on this line to show the **mean**. Label this line 'Putter'.

**2** Now draw another line representing Chucker. Use different colours for the two lines.

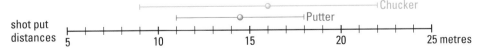

**3** Work through the other questions from Further Practice **S**, drawing mean/range diagrams.

You will have to think carefully about what scale to use.

# Chapter 16 *Statistical Diagrams*

## ❶ Scatter Diagrams

 A coin

**1** Flip a coin 10 times. Record the number of heads.

Next, flip it 12 times, then 14, etc. Carry on until you reach 30 flips. Record your results each time.

Draw a scatter diagram. The axes should be labelled 'Number of flips' and 'Number of heads'. Is there a relationship between number of flips and number of heads? If so, what is it?

**2** Now prepare a table to record the number of heads and tails scored.

Work out the number of tails for each set of flips. Draw a scatter diagram. The axes should be labelled 'Number of heads' and 'Number of tails'. What is the relationship between number of heads and number of tails?

**3** If you have time, think of another coin experiment. Make a scatter diagram of its results.

## ❷ Correlation

For each question, decide whether you think there is a link between the two amounts. Write down what kind of correlation you think there is. You do **not** need to draw any diagrams.

| | | |
|---|---|---|
| **1** | Number of people in a lift | Weight of the lift |
| **2** | Number of chocolate bars sold at break-time | Number of pupils in the school |
| **3** | Shoe size of pupils | Number of pets pupils own |
| **4** | Marks in a maths test | Marks in a science test |
| **5** | Speed of a car | Time taken to travel 1 km |
| **6** | Number of crisps eaten from a packet | Number of crisps left in the packet |
| **7** | Time taken to build a wall | Number of builders |
| **8** | Months people were born in | Number of the house they live at |
| **9** | Speed of a car | Time taken to stop |
| **10** | Temperature in the room | Time an ice cube takes to melt |

## Brush Up Your Number 9

The formula for a temperature in degrees Fahrenheit (°F) in terms of the temperature in degrees Celsius (°C) is $F = \frac{9}{5}C + 32$.

Find the temperature in degrees Celsius when the temperature is:

**1** 122 °F  **2** 97 °F  **3** 75 °F  **4** 145 °F  **5** 63 °F

**6** 144 °F  **7** 32 °F  **8** 212 °F  **9** 318 °F  **10** 23 °F

## Chapter 17 *Multiples and Factors*

# ❶ Multiples

The lowest common multiple of 1 and 2 is 2.

The lowest common multiple of 1, 2 and 3 is 6.

The lowest common multiple of 1, 2, 3 and 4 is 12.

Continue this pattern to find the lowest common multiple of the numbers 1 to 10.

# ❷ Factors

**1** Complete this table to list the factors of the numbers 1 to 20.

| Number | Factors | Number of factors |
|--------|---------|-------------------|
| 1 | 1 | 1 |
| 2 | 1, 2 | 2 |
| 3 | 1, 3 | 2 |
| 4 | 1, 2, 4 | 3 |

**2** Write down a list of all the numbers with only two factors. What is special about these numbers? What do we call these numbers?

**3** Write down a list of numbers with an odd number of factors. What is special about these numbers? What do we call these numbers?

# Chapter 18 *Patterns and Sequences*

## ❶ What's Next?

Make up five sequences of numbers. Write down the first six terms of each. Write down the rule that describes how each sequence is made.

 Swap the rules, but not the sequences, with another pupil and write down the first six terms of each other's sequences.

## ❷ Finding the Formula

Find the equation of each graph.

**1**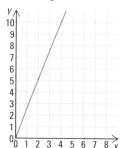

**2**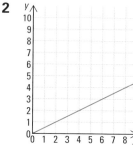

**3**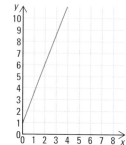

**4**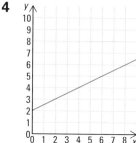

## ❸ Quadratic Sequences

**1** If the formula for a term is $n^3$, you get the sequence $1, 8, 27, 64 \dots$ Copy this sequence and write down the next three terms. Find the differences between the terms and then find the differences between the differences. Write down a method to decide if a formula starts with $n^3$.

**2** Repeat question 1 for $2n^3$.

**3** Repeat question 1 for $3n^3$.

**4** Investigate sequences with formulae that start with $n^4$, $2n^4$, etc.

# Brush Up Your Number 10

**1** There are lots of ways to multiply two numbers to get the same answer.

$0.1 \times 0.2 = 0.02$

$0.4 \times 0.05 = 0.02$

$2 \times 0.01 = 0.02$, etc.

Work out $0.9 \times 0.4$. Find as many other pairs of numbers as you can that give the same answer when you multiply them.

**2** There are lots of ways to divide two numbers to get the same answer.

$0.1 \div 0.2 = 0.5$

$0.5 \div 1 = 0.5$

$2 \div 4 = 0.5$, etc.

Work out $0.4 \div 0.05$. Find as many other pairs of numbers as you can that give the same answer when you multiply them.

# Chapter 19 *Length, Mass and Capacity*

# ❶ Metric Units

Suppose you have a balance and some weights: $2 \times 1$ g, 5 g, $2 \times 10$ g, 50 g, $2 \times 100$ g, 500 g. Investigate how you could balance different things.

| **Example** | a sweet weighing 3 g. | |
|---|---|---|
| **Answer** | You could put the two 1 g weights with the sweet and the 5 g weight on the other pan. |  |

Work up from objects weighing 4 g until you find a pattern. Write down the pattern.

# ❷ Accuracy of Measurements

**1** Remember that to find the volume of a cuboid, you multiply length × width × height. The measurements for the following cuboids are given to the nearest whole number. Find the lower and upper bounds of the volume of each.

**(a)**  **(b)**  **(c)**

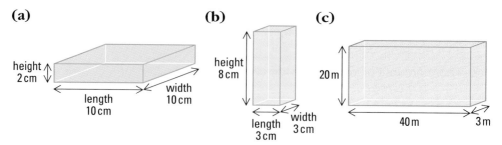

**2** If the measurements in question 1 are accurate to 1 d.p., what would be the lower and upper bounds of volume of each cuboid?

**3** $n = 5$ to the nearest whole number. Investigate the lower and upper bounds of $n^2, n^3, n^4, n^5$, etc.

**4** Repeat question 3 with different accuracies for $n$.

# ❸ Calculations

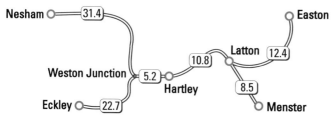

This is a diagram of a railway. The numbers in the boxes tell you the distances between places, in kilometres.

New signals are being built along the tracks.
There must be a signal 500 m from any station or junction.
All other signals on a section of track must be equally spaced.
The minimum spacing allowed is 1250 m.
The maximum spacing allowed is 1600 m.

**1** For each section of track, work out:
   **(a)** how many signals there will be; if there is a choice, use the smallest number of signals to save money
   **(b)** the distance between signals.

| **Example** | Hartley to Weston Junction. |
| --- | --- |
| **Working** | There must be a signal 500 m from Hartley and one 500 m from Weston Junction. |
| | This leaves 4.2 km to be covered. |
| | If the signals are 1.25 km apart, there is room for $4.2 \div 1.25 = 3.36$ gaps between signals. |
| | If the signals are 1.6 km apart, there is room for $4.2 \div 1.6 = 2.625$ gaps between signals. |
| | So there must be 3 equal gaps. Each gap must be $4.2 \div 3 = 1.4$ km. |
| | If there are 3 gaps, there must be 4 signals. |

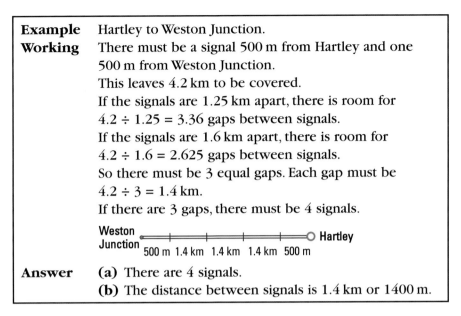

| **Answer** | **(a)** There are 4 signals. |
| --- | --- |
| | **(b)** The distance between signals is 1.4 km or 1400 m. |

**2** How many signals does the railway need altogether?

# Chapter 20 *Time*

## ❶ Time Calculations

**1** Copy and complete this table. Write your working underneath. Assume you will live to be 80.

| Number of | 1 hour | 1 day | 1 week | 1 month | 1 year | Life so far | Whole life |
| --- | --- | --- | --- | --- | --- | --- | --- |
| seconds in … | | | | | | | |
| minutes in … | | | | | | | |
| hours in … | | | | | | | |
| days in … | | | | | | | |
| weeks in … | | | | | | | |
| months in … | | | | | | | |
| years in … | | | | | | | |

**2** Why is the **Life so far** column difficult to fill in?

# ❷ Timetables

Use the information below to draw up a timetable for this bus service.

The route name is **Central Station to Brigham**.

The information is for **Mondays to Fridays**.

The first bus leaves Central Station at 7.30am.

5 minutes later it arrives at the Shopping Centre.

8 minutes after that, it arrives at Warren Grove.

10 minutes later, it arrives at Brigham Marina.

6 minutes after that it arrives at the centre of Brigham. It sets off on the return journey immediately.

The journey back to Central Station takes the same time as the journey out.

The second bus leaves Central Station at 7.50am. After that, there is a bus every half hour until 6pm.

Then there is one more bus, leaving at 6.30pm, but this does not stop at Warren Grove.

# ❸ Speed

These are the results of a 400-metre race.

**1** Work out the average speed, in m/s, of each runner.

**2** Work out how far each of them had still to run when Tindall crossed the line.

**3** Draw a diagram of the finishing positions.

You will need to think carefully about the scale to use.

| Position | Name | Time (sec) |
|---|---|---|
| 1 | R. Tindall | 61.4 |
| 2 | S. Akhmed | 65.0 |
| 3 | P. Manson | 66.2 |
| 4 | L. Lister | 66.7 |
| 5 | D. Holley | 66.9 |
| 6 | N. Ramprakash | 69.1 |
| 7 | A. Anderson | 70.6 |
| 8 | E. Wellings | 75.3 |

# Brush Up Your Number 11

**1** Start with a simple fraction, e.g. $\frac{2}{3}$.

**2** Make an equivalent fraction, e.g. $\frac{10}{15}$.

**3** Make a fraction that is *not* equivalent, e.g. $\frac{10}{21}$ (multiply the numerator of $\frac{2}{3}$ by one number and the denominator by another).

**4** Mix up the three fractions on a piece of paper and give them to your partner. They have to find which two fractions are equivalent and explain why.

**5** Repeat the activity, starting with improper fractions, e.g. $\frac{9}{2}$ and writing one as a mixed number. For example, which of these fractions are equivalent: $4\frac{1}{2}, \frac{27}{10}, \frac{18}{4}$?

# Chapter 21 *Ratio and Proportion*

## ① Ratios

Gary, Stephen and Maria have divided ten marbles among them in the ratio:

Gary:Stephen:Maria = 2:3:5

You could use fractions, decimals or percentages to show this information.

**1** Make a table like the one on the right for these people:
  **(a)** Jane:Toni:Shelley = 1:6:3
  **(b)** Emma:Atul:Naomi = 1:2:1
  **(c)** Yuk Sin:Peter:Mervyn = 3:9:8

| Gary | : | Stephen | : | Maria |
|------|---|---------|---|-------|
| 2 | : | 3 | : | 5 |
| $\frac{2}{10}$ | : | $\frac{3}{10}$ | : | $\frac{5}{10}$ |
| 0.2 | : | 0.3 | : | 0.5 |
| 20% | : | 30% | : | 50% |

**2** Choose any three percentages that add up to 100%. Draw a table like the one above, starting with percentages and working through decimals and fractions to whole numbers.

*Hint: there are 100 parts altogether.*

**3** Choose any three decimals that add up to 1. Draw a table like the one above.

**4** Choose any three fractions that add up to 1. Draw a table like the one above.

## ❷ Using Ratios

**1** The recipe for 50 cl of Summer Cup fruit cocktail is: 15 cl apple juice, 30 cl orange juice and 5 cl lime juice. Write this recipe using a ratio (see page 272).

**2** Calculate the amounts of each juice required to make 120 cl of Summer Cup.

**3** How much Summer Cup could you make if you had these amounts of juice: 150 cl apple juice, 400 cl orange juice, 50 cl lime juice?

**4** Make your own recipe for 50 cl of Summer Cup using different ratios of apple, orange and lime juice. Repeat questions 1–3 for your own recipe.

## ❸ Proportional Quantities

 Graph paper

20 cm of gold chain has a mass of 5 g.
12 g of gold cost £96.

**1** **(a)** Find the mass of 1 cm of gold chain.
  **(b)** Write a formula to find the mass ($M$ g) of a gold chain from its length ($L$ cm).
  **(c)** Draw a graph relating $M$ and $L$.
  **(d)** Find the mass of 7 cm of gold chain.
  **(e)** What length of gold chain has a mass of 18.5 g?

**2** **(a)** Write a formula to find the cost (£$C$) of a mass ($M$ g) of gold.
  **(b)** Draw a graph relating $C$ and $M$.
  **(c)** Find the cost of 25 g of gold chain.
  **(d)** What mass of gold chain can you buy for £105?

**3** **(a)** Find how much 1 cm of gold chain costs.
  **(b)** Write a formula to find the cost (£$C$) of a length ($L$ cm) of gold chain.
  **(c)** Draw a graph relating $C$ and $L$.
  **(d)** Find the cost of 10 cm gold chain.
  **(e)** What length of gold chain costs £45?

# Brush Up Your Number 12

Scientists use the **body mass index** (BMI) to tell if people are a healthy weight for their height.

First, square the height in metres. Then divide the weight in kilograms by the result.

| | |
|---|---|
| **Example** | Monica weighs 47.38 kg and is 150 cm tall. What is her body mass index? |
| **Working** | Her height in metres is 1.5 m. |
| | $1.5 \times 1.5 = 2.25$    (*Square the height.*) |
| | BMI = $47.38 \div 2.25$. |
| **Answer** | 21.1 (to 1 d.p.) |

**1** Copy the table below. Work out the BMI for each person. Put your working underneath.

| Name | Height (m) | Weight (kg) | BMI | Weight range |
|---|---|---|---|---|
| Abel | 1.6 | 63.18 | | |
| Brenda | 1.3 | 47.94 | | |
| Carl | 1.9 | 99 | | |
| Davinder | 1.5 | 58.42 | | |
| Edwin | 1.9 | 64.8 | | |

**2** Use this guide to fill in the last column.

| BMI | Weight range |
|---|---|
| 19 or less | underweight |
| 20 to 26 | medium weight |
| 27 or over | overweight |

---

## Chapter 22 *Area and Perimeter*

---

# ❶ Parallelograms and Triangles

 A4 squared or dotted paper (long side horizontal)

**1** Draw the following shapes on a coordinate grid with the *x*-axis numbered from 0 to 20 and the *y*-axis numbered from 0 to 15.

The shapes made by the coordinates are **rhombi** (the plural of rhombus).
**(a)** $(1, 6) \rightarrow (6, 6) \rightarrow (9, 2) \rightarrow (4, 2) \rightarrow (1, 6)$
**(b)** $(2, 9) \rightarrow (10, 15) \rightarrow (20, 15) \rightarrow (12, 9) \rightarrow (2, 9)$
**(c)** $(11, 7) \rightarrow (17\frac{1}{2}, 7) \rightarrow (20, 1) \rightarrow (13\frac{1}{2}, 1) \rightarrow (11, 7)$

You will need another set of axes for this one.
**(d)** $(1, 2) \rightarrow (14, 2) \rightarrow (19, 14) \rightarrow (6, 14) \rightarrow (1, 2)$

**2** Measure the base and height of each rhombus. Record the measurements in a table like this, and work out the area of each.

**3** Make up coordinates for six more rhombi of your own. Draw them and add them to the table.

| Rhombus | Base (cm) | Height (cm) | Area (cm²) |
|---|---|---|---|
| **(a)** | | | |
| **(b)** | | | |
| **(c)** | | | |
| **(d)** | | | |

# ❷ Compound Shapes

**1** Work out the areas of these trapezia (the plural of trapezium).

**(a)**  **(b)**  **(c)**  **(d)**

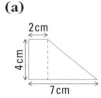 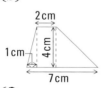 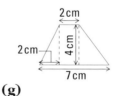 

**(e)**  **(f)**  **(g)**  **(h)**

**2** What do you notice about the answers to question 1?

**3** **(a)** Pick three more measurements (base, top and height). Draw **one**
   trapezium using your measurements.

   **(b)** Pick three more measurements. Draw **one** trapezium.

**4** Copy and complete this table.

| Question | Base (*b*) | Top (*t*) | *b* + *t* | Height (*h*) | *h* × (*b* + *t*) | Area |
|---|---|---|---|---|---|---|
| 1 | 7 | 2 | 9 | 4 | 36 | 18 |
| 3(a) | | | | | | |
| 3(b) | | | | | | |

**5** What do you notice about the last two columns?
   Can you think of a rule that will find the area of **any** trapezium?

**6** Test your rule.

# ③ Pythagoras' Theorem

A rectangle has a perimeter of 80 cm. Find five possible diagonal lengths. Find
the shortest possible and longest possible diagonal length.

## Chapter 23 *Circles*

# ① Measuring Circumferences

Some long (30 cm or more), thin (about 1 cm) strips of paper
Here is another way to measure circumferences.

**1** Measure the diameter of a round object.

**2** Wrap the strip around it as many times as possible.
   Remember how many times this is. Make a mark on the part
   of the outside of the strip that is above the other end. This
   mark is a whole number of circumferences away from the other end.

**3** Write down the number of times you wrapped the strip around the object
   (*w*), then measure and record the distance from your mark to the other end
   of the strip (*m*). The circumference is $\frac{w}{m}$.

**4** Try this with other objects. Can you estimate π any better this way?

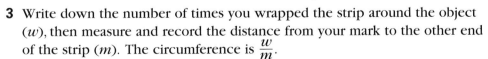

# ❷ Circumference Calculations

1 Work out the **perimeters** of these shapes. They are made from semicircles and quarter circles. Remember to include the straight lines as well.

(a)

10 cm

(b)

6 cm

(c)

16 cm

(d)

8 cm

2 This pattern uses squares and semicircles. Each square has sides of 1 cm.

(a) (b) (c) (d) (e)

(i) Work out the perimeter of each pattern. Copy and complete this table up to pattern (e).

| Pattern number | (a) | (b) | (c) | (d) | (e) | (f) | (g) | (h) | (i) | (j) |
|---|---|---|---|---|---|---|---|---|---|---|
| Perimeter | | | | | | | | | | |

(ii) Predict the perimeters of the patterns from (f) to (j). Draw them if you have to, but try not to.

3 Repeat 2 (i) and (ii) with this pattern.

(a) (b) (c)

(d) (e) (f)

# ❸ Areas of Circles

 Compasses, squared paper

**1** You can work out the area of a circle if you know its radius.
So how do you work out the radius if you know its area? Write the answer
as a formula.

**2** Find the radius and diameter of circles with these areas.

(a) 3 m²

(b) 24 cm²

(c) 150 cm²

**3** This diagram shows a square and circle with the same
area. This is called the **equivalent circle**.

Use your answer from question 1 to find the radius of
the circle.

Draw an **accurate**, full-size diagram of the square and
circle.

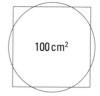

100 cm²

**4** Draw diagrams like the last one to show these rectangles with their
equivalent circles.

(a) 3 cm × 9 cm      (b) 4 cm × 6 cm      (c) 10 cm × 6 cm
(d) 12 cm × 5 cm     (e) 15 cm × 1 cm

---

## Chapter 24 *Volume and Surface Area*

# ❶ Volume of Cuboids

**1** Cuboids with these dimensions have a volume of 60 cm³.

| Length | Width | Height | Volume |
|--------|-------|--------|--------|
| 10 cm | 3 cm | 2 cm | 60 cm³ |
| 10 cm | 6 cm | 1 cm | 60 cm³ |

Copy the table and add the measurements of three more cuboids with
the same volume.

**2** Pick your own volume for a cuboid. Find as many dimensions as possible
that make this volume.

## ❷ Volume of Prisms

**1** A wooden shed, which has an end section
with the dimensions shown, is for sale at a
DIY shop.

    **(a)** Calculate its volume if the shed is
1.5 m long.

    **(b)** Another shed with the same end
dimensions is also sold. It has a volume
of 5.25 m³. Calculate its length.

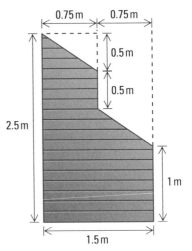

**2** A water container is to be designed so that it has a maximum volume of
2 m³. Its length is 1 m. Find possible dimensions of the container if it is:

    **(a)** a cuboid                  **(b)** a triangular prism

    **(c)** a cylinder               **(d)** a composite shape.

## ❸ Surface Area

**1** Find five different cuboids each with a volume of 120 cm³.

**2** Find the surface area of each of your cuboids from question 1. Which is
the smallest?

**3** Try to design a 120-cm³ cuboid with a smaller surface area.

---

## Brush Up Your Number 13

Remember that to multiply fractions, you multiply the top numbers and multiply
the bottom numbers.

$$\frac{2}{3} \times \frac{4}{5} = \frac{8}{15}$$

You can also cross-cancel.

$$\frac{\overset{1}{\cancel{2}}}{\underset{1}{\cancel{3}}} \times \frac{\overset{1}{\cancel{3}}}{\underset{4}{\cancel{8}}} = \frac{1}{4}$$

To divide one fraction by another, turn the **second** fraction upside down and
change the × to ÷.

$$\frac{5}{8} \div \frac{4}{5} = \frac{5}{8} \times \frac{5}{4} = \frac{25}{32}$$

**1** Using the fractions from Practice C on page 327, copy and complete this multiplication square. Write your working underneath.

| × | A | B | C | D | E | F | G |
|---|---|---|---|---|---|---|---|
| A | $\frac{1}{4}$ | | | | | | |
| B | | | | | | | |
| C | | | | | | | |
| D | | | | | | | |
| E | | | | | | | |
| F | | | | | | | |
| G | | | | | | | |

**2** Draw a division square for the same fractions from Practice C on page 327.

---

## Chapter 25 *Chance*

# ❶ Theoretical Probability

This diagram shows another one of Zorah's charity games. It's a dartboard. The probability of hitting a square on the dartboard depends on its area.

Here are the sizes of each type of square on the dartboard, and what you win.

**1** Work out the total area of each colour.

| Region | Length of side | Outcome |
|---|---|---|
| Whole board | 25 cm | |
| Red | 15 cm | Win 10p |
| Yellow | 5 cm | Win 20p |
| White | 2 cm | Win 50p |
| Black | What's left of the board | Lose |

**2** Work out the probability of hitting each colour.

**3** It costs 20p for one throw. Work out what profit Zorah makes on 100 throws.

**4** If you have time, design your own dartboard. Work through the steps above to see if it will make a profit.

# ❷ Experiments

### Buffon's Needle

A matchstick or a piece of straw or dowel no longer than 4 cm,
A3 or A4 paper

If you thought measuring angles with probability was weird, how about calculating the value of π? Georges Louis Leclerc, Comte de Buffon, first did this experiment in 1777 by tossing French bread sticks over his shoulder onto a tiled floor!

**1** Measure the length of your matchstick **accurately**. Call this length $x$ cm.

**2** On paper, rule as many parallel lines as you can. They must all be **exactly** $x$ cm apart.

**3** Do 100 trials of this experiment: throw the matchstick onto the paper. If it crosses or touches one of the lines, call it a hit. Otherwise, call it a miss. Put your results into a table.

**4** Calculate the probabilities $P$(hit) and $P$(miss).

**5** Work out $2 \div P$(hit). This is your first approximation to π. How close is it? (See page 296 for the value of π.)

**6** If you have time, carry on with more trials. The more you do, the closer to π you should get.

# ❸ Possibility Spaces

Compasses, protractor, two pointers, two drawing pins, card

Possibility space diagrams only work when the outcomes are **equally likely**.

Suppose you flipped two coins that had been altered so that $P$(head) = 0.4 and $P$(tail) = 0.6.

You could not work out the probabilities of $P$(2 heads), $P$(2 tails) or $P$(1 head, 1 tail) using a possibility space diagram.

You can **simulate** the coin-flipping by using two identical spinners like the one on the right.

**1** Make the spinners.

Do 100 trials. Copy and complete this table. (HT means head on spinner 1 and tail on spinner 2).

| Outcome | Tally | Frequency |
|---|---|---|
| HH | | |
| HT | | |
| TH | | |
| TT | | |

**2** Now draw this table.

| | | 1ˢᵗ spin | |
|---|---|---|---|
| | | Head | Tail |
| 2ⁿᵈ spin | Head | | |
| | Tail | | |

Write the **frequencies** in it.

**3** Now work out the following probabilities.

    **(a)** $P$(2 heads)         **(b)** $P$(1 head, 1 tail)     **(c)** $P$(2 tails)

**4** If you have time, try simulating the effect of two coins with $P$(head) = 0.25 and $P$(tail) = 0.75.

## Brush Up Your Number 14

**1** Naomi photocopied a 30 cm ruler using a scale factor of 0.5.

    **(a)** How long is the ruler in the photocopy?

    **(b)** Has the ruler been enlarged or reduced?

**2** Calculate the length of the ruler when photocopied using each of these scale factors. Has the ruler been enlarged or reduced in each case?

    **(a)** 1.5      **(b)** $\frac{1}{4}$      **(c)** 0.8      **(d)** 1.2      **(e)** 1

**3** The photocopier scale factor has got stuck on 0.5. Naomi wants to reduce the ruler to 5 cm long. She photocopies the ruler. Then she photocopies the photocopy, and so on. How many times does she need to use the photocopier until the ruler is 5 cm or less?

**4** Find the scale factor that reduces the ruler to about 10 cm after five photocopies. Give your answer correct to 1 d.p.

**5** Find the scale factor that enlarges the ruler to about 100 cm after five photocopies. Give your answer correct to 2 d.p.

## Chapter 26 *Transformations*

 Squared paper

# ❶ Reflection

Using the *x*- and *y*-axes and the lines $y = x$ and $y = -x$ as lines of symmetry, you can make a complicated pattern.

Start with this shape.

**(a)**

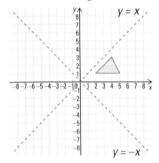

If you keep reflecting your drawings in the lines, you end up with this shape.

**(b)**

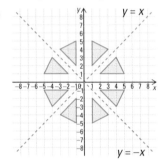

Draw a simple shape of your own and keep reflecting it until you have completed the pattern.

Repeat with other shapes and make different patterns.

# ❷ Rotation

 Squared paper

To draw a shape with rotational symmetry of order 3:

**(a)** Start with lines meeting at angles of 120°.

**(b)** Draw a shape in one angle.

**(c)** Now rotate the shape through 120° to complete the diagram.

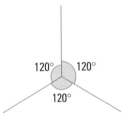

Draw shapes of your own with rotational symmetry of order:

**1** 4          **2** 6          **3** 8          **4** 9          **5** 10.

# ❸ Translations and Vectors

Graph paper

1 On graph paper draw the triangle ABC with A at (1,1), B at (1,4) and
   C at (2,1).

   **(a)** Translate the triangle by $\begin{pmatrix} 2 \\ 1 \end{pmatrix}$. Label this triangle X.

   **(b)** Translate triangle X by $\begin{pmatrix} 1 \\ 1 \end{pmatrix}$. Label it Y.

   **(c)** Translate triangle Y by $\begin{pmatrix} 2 \\ 0 \end{pmatrix}$. Label it Z.

   **(d)** What translation would translate the original triangle ABC onto:
      **(i)** Y?   **(ii)** Z?

2 Draw a triangle on graph paper and translate it three times by the same
   vector translation. Describe the single translation to map your original
   triangle onto each of the other triangles.

# ❹ Enlargements

Squared paper

Copy each diagram on squared paper and draw the enlargements with scale
factors 2, 3 and 4.

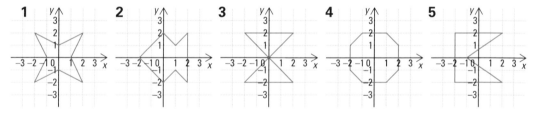

# Chapter 27 *Loci and Constructions*

# ❶ Single Points and Lines

A goat is tethered to the middle of the shortest side of a barn. The barn is
20 m × 10 m.

**(a)** Using a scale of 1 cm:5 m, draw the area the goat can graze if his tether is:
   **(i)** 10 m   **(ii)** 15 m   **(iii)** 20 m.

**(b)** Change the size of the barn. Now draw the possible areas the goat
   can graze.

# ❷ Triangles

Quadrilaterals can be constructed by placing two triangles with a common (same length) side together. Construct as many different types of quadrilateral as you can by placing two triangles together.

# ❸ Constructions

**1** Construct an angle of 75°. (*Hint: 75 = 45 + 30.*)

**2** Construct an angle of $22\frac{1}{2}°$.

**3** Choose angles of other sizes and see if you can construct them.

# ❹ Double Points and Lines

**1** Construct a triangle with sides of 9 cm, 12 cm and 15 cm. Bisect each of the three angles. What do you notice?

**2** Draw another copy of the triangle. Bisect the three sides of the triangle. What do you notice?

**3** Construct triangles of other sizes to see if this always happens.